SCIENCE *of* CERAMICS

Volume 2

SCIENCE *of* CERAMICS

*Proceedings of the second Conference held under the auspices of
the British Ceramic Society and the Nederlandse Keramische
Vereniging, at Noordwijk aan Zee, 13—17 May 1963*

Edited by

G. H. STEWART
The British Ceramic Society

Volume 2

Published by
ACADEMIC PRESS
LONDON and NEW YORK
for the
BRITISH CERAMIC SOCIETY
1965

ACADEMIC PRESS INC. (LONDON) LTD.

Berkeley Square House

Berkeley Square

London, W.1

666
St49s
V. 2

U.S. Edition published by

ACADEMIC PRESS INC.

111 Fifth Avenue

New York, New York 10003

Library of Congress Catalog Card Number: 62–19884

Papers classified according to the D.E.C. system
of the European Ceramic Association

PRINTED IN GREAT BRITAIN BY
WILLMER BROTHERS & HARAM LIMITED
BIRKENHEAD

Contents

CONTENTS

Part One

PROPERTIES OF RAW MATERIALS

1—Characteristics of Fine Oxide Powders

By J. WILLIAMS

Head of Ceramics Branch, Metallurgy Division, Atomic Energy Research Establishment, Harwell

ABSTRACT   D421—C525

With the increasing interest in sintered oxide bodies having low and controlled porosity, attention is being paid to the use of very fine powders as starting materials; the intention is usually to obtain the required properties with modest sintering-temperatures. The characteristics of such powders are discussed in terms of the physical and physico-chemical properties of the crystallites, the behaviour and properties of crystallite aggregates, and the effect of minor amounts of impurities. Emphasis is laid on the importance of the physical and chemical properties of the compound from which the oxide powders are derived.

Charactéristics des poudres d'oxyde fines

En raison de l'intérêt croissant que soulèvent les pâtes d'oxyde frittés à porosité faible et contrôlée, l'attention se porte sur l'emploi, comme substances de départ, de poudres très fines; on cherche généralement à obtenir les propriétés nécessaires à l'aide de températures de frittage peu élevées. Les caractéristiques de telles poudres sont étudiées en fonction des propriétés physiques et physico-chimiques des cristallites, du comportement et des propriétés des agrégats de cristallites et de l'influence de quantités mineures d'impurities. L'accent est mis sur l'importance des propriétés physiques et chimiques du composé dont dérivent les poudres d'oxyde.

Charakterisierung von feinen Oxidpulvern

Mit zunehmendem Interesse für oxidkeramische Körper mit niedriger oder kontrollierter Porosität wird einem sehr feinen Ausgangspulver erhöhte Aufmerksamkeit gewidmet. Die Absicht dabei ist, die geforderten Eigenschaften mit mässiger Sintertemperatur zu erreichen. Die Charakterisierung solcher Pulver wird im Hinblick auf die physikalischen und physikochemischen Eigenschaften der Kristallite, das Verhalten und die Eigenschaften der Kristallitaggregate und den Einfluss kleiner Anteile von Verunreinigungen besprochen. Dabei wird die Wichtigkeit der physikalischen und chemischen Eigenschaften der Verbindung, aus der das Oxidpulver hergestellt wird, hervorgehoben.

1. INTRODUCTION

The characteristics desired in a powder are largely dictated by the properties required of the product. There is an increasing demand for dense impermeable oxide bodies in several fields of application. The property of impermeability imposes a fairly severe limitation on the amount and nature of porosity that can be tolerated. One of the more important features which has emerged from studies of the sintering process over the past 10 years is that densifi-

3

cation proceeds primarily by the elimination of inter-connected or open porosity, the proportion of closed porosity remaining at a constant low level. As defined by techniques involving liquid displacement or even surface-area measurement, it has been shown for the sintering of single-phase solids—both metal and ceramics—that closed porosity persists at ~5% from a very early stage in densification up to the point at which the open porosity is eliminated, i.e. about 95% theoretical density, before it in turn begins to be eliminated. However, recent studies of the permeability of low-porosity oxide bodies has shown that open porosity, as measured by gas permeability, can persist to densities as high as 98% theoretical.[1] The demand for impermeability therefore makes severe calls on the control of the sintering process and hence on the nature of the powder to be used.

What leads can sintering theories give to the characteristics of a powder that will sinter to give these properties? The driving force in sintering is generally assumed to be the excess of surface free energy of a powder over that of the same material in densified form, and this should increase with decrease of particle size. All the detailed mechanisms of sintering predict that sintering-rates will increase with decreasing particle-size, other things being equal, although the rates of variation are likely to change with the mechanism invoked. For a given pore volume, the overall permeability will diminish with decrease in size of pores. Thus from a naive viewpoint, all factors argue in favour of the use of the finest possible particles. For metal powders the lower practical limit of particle size is usually about one micron, because of difficulties in handling as well as in preparation. With oxides there is basically no reason for the existence of a lower limit of particle size, certainly down to the " tens of angstroms " level.

Under these circumstances, what practical limitations exist in densities attainable by sintering? What oversimplifications have been used in the arguments so far advanced? With this in mind, the first question that has to be answered is whether the properties of the individual crystallites differ from that of the bulk material.

2. PROPERTIES OF THE INDIVIDUAL PARTICLES

The assumption that the driving force behind the sintering of powders is the excess surface free energy is true only if the free energy associated with the volume of the material is independent of particle size, i.e. the relevant physical properties of these fine powders are the same as those of the bulk material. Data on such properties is not readily obtained.[2]

X-ray diffraction can give information on the size, shape and state of strain of crystallites by studies of line-broadening, and can also measure lattice parameters. With the more recent refinements in techniques, accurate data can be obtained for particle sizes as low as 40Å. Using a diffractometer, proportional counters and automatic point-counting equipment, very broad lines, undetectable by photographic techniques, can be delineated precisely. Thus the [422] reflection for thoria of 10μ particle size shows a spread of $\sim 0.2°$, but for a 50Å crystallite size the reflection is spread over $\sim 10°$. Measurements of this type are only possible for materials with a simple structure where overlapping of such broad lines will be minimized. Using these techniques, measurement of the shifts of the diffraction peaks and centres of gravity of the broadened line profiles has shown that the lattice parameter of thoria increases by 0.3% at 40Å crystallite size and 0.18% at 50Å. For magnesia of similar particle sizes the increase of lattice parameter was $\sim 1\%$.[3] The volume free energy contribution for such material would seem unlikely to be as high as for material of larger particle size having the normal lattice parameter, suggesting that the total free energy may reach a maximum beyond which it will remain sensibly constant with decreasing particle size.

Broadening of diffraction lines can result from lattice distortions as well as from diminution of crystallite size. Strains of this description will add to the total energy content of the powder, so it is important to know the magnitude of the contribution as well as its variation with particle size. This problem has been examined both for magnesia[4] and thoria.[5]

The particle size broadening β_p is given by

$$\beta_p = K\lambda / \varepsilon \cos \theta$$

and the strain broadening β_s by

$$\beta_s = \eta \tan \theta$$

where K is the shape factor, ε the crystallite size, η the strain function, θ the Bragg angle, and λ the wavelength.

If $\beta \cos \theta$, where β is the true line broadening, is plotted against sine θ, a straight line should be obtained whose intercept on the abscissae is $K\lambda / \varepsilon$ and whose slope is the strain function (Hall plot).

The studies of THOMAS and BAKER[4] for magnesia of mean particle size between 144Å and 2,350Å led to the conclusion that line broadening for this material was predominantly due to small crystallite size, although a small strain contribution could be masked by the scatter of experimental results. Recent more accurate work has extended the range of particle size to which this statement would apply down to $\sim$40Å.[3] However, using magnesia of particle size $\sim$200Å, this work also indicated that the Hall plot showed a slight positive slope which, depending on the method used to measure the true broadening (Scherrer or Warren and Biscoe correction) and whether half breadth, integral breadth or Fourier analysis were used, indicated strains of 10^{-4} to 10^{-3} in the particles.

This agrees partially with the findings of FERGUSON for thoria[5] where, using a photographic technique and a range of particle size 320–3,600Å, strains of 2–8×10^{-4} were measured, decreasing with increasing particle size. In this case again the main contribution to line broadening stemmed from particle size broadening. In both cases the maximum contribution of measured strain to the energy content is about 10^{-2} kcal/mol which is a small fraction of that due to surface free energy.

Direct measurements of this latter property are not easily made and the major corrections which have to be made to experimental observations can lead to considerable inaccuracy. LIVEY et al.[6] have obtained data on the variation of surface free energy with particle size for a hydroxide-derived MgO and it has been shown for this particular powder, using Weissenbach's relationship between particle size and surface-energy content, that the variation in X-ray crystallite size quantitatively accounts for the variation in heat of solution.[4] Correlations with surface area measured by adsorption were less good at the lowest particle size used, the B.E.T. areas here, most unusually, giving a lower particle size than that derived by X-ray methods (144Å).[6]

Information on the shape of the crystallite for magnesia,[3] beryllia[7] and thoria,[5] obtained by X-ray diffraction techniques, suggests that in no case did the crystallite shape deviate markedly from an equi-axed form.

Probably the most important chemical property of these powders relates to their composition. Chemical adsorption of gases and vapours must certainly occur unless the very strongest precautions are taken and, since areas of 10^{2}–10^{3} m²/cm³ are involved, the presence of a monolayer of adsorbate will change the chemical composition appreciably. For magnesia of 200 m²/g prepared from hydroxide, water vapour can still be present to the extent of $\sim$3$^{w}/_{o}$ as an adsorbed monolayer. Presumably this could equally be true for other gases present during the thermal decomposition of other salts, such as carbonates, sulphates, oxalates, etc.

Thus it appears that the finest oxide powders obtainable will consist of crystallites of regular shape, probably of expanded lattice parameters, possibly containing residual strains which, however, do not contribute greatly to the energy content of the particles, the excess of which over that of the bulk material results chiefly from the extra surface contribution. Owing to adsorbed vapours the chemical composition of such particles can differ appreciably from that of the bulk material.

These single crystal particles are not present as isolated particles; the next question to be asked therefore is: how are they aggregated?

3. THE CRYSTALLOGRAPHY OF THE AGGREGATE

It is a matter of common observation that oxide powders are found to have macroscopic structures which are relics or pseudo-morphs of the salts from which they have been prepared. Particles of thoria [8, 9] and plutonia prepared from the oxalates have the form of flat plates of square section typical of the shape of the original oxalate crystals. Magnesia prepared by thermal decomposition of nesquehonite ($MgCO_3.3H_2O$) retains the needle-shape of the original carbonate through stages involving volume reduction of $\sim 70\%$.[10] Magnesia prepared from either $Mg(OH)_2$ platelets of hexagonal shape 1,200Å across and 250Å thick, or massive samples of natural brucite retained the shape of the starting material whilst giving MgO products of approximately the same surface area.[11] The most strik-ing example of variation in macroscopic shape of an oxide as a result of variation in shape of starting material comes from the work of CLAYTON et al.[12] on UO_2 where each of nine starting materials gave rise to UO_2 having different pseudomorphs.[12] As a general rule, therefore, the coarsest state of aggregation of a fine powder is likely to be determined by the shape of the particles from which it is derived.

The structure of the material being decomposed may, however, influence the fine structure of the aggregate in a manner which is perhaps not so widely appreciated by investigators working with pure oxides as those working with products derived from naturally occurring minerals.[13]

From studies carried out so far on inorganic oxycompounds, it appears to be the rule rather than the exception for there to be an orientation relationship between the starting material and the pro-duct of decomposition. Thus there may be strong orientation rela-tionships between the crystallites of final product formed within the pseudomorph of the single crystals of the starting material. Many more studies have been made of the behaviour of naturally occurring minerals in this manner than for synthesized inorganic salts because the minerals have been available as large single crystals. This has facilitated the determination of the structure of the starting material, often complex, and of the orientation relationships between starting material and product. The advent of selected-area electron-diffraction techniques will aid the acquisition of information on the latter subject for the synthetic salts.

To confine discussion to those cases where a single oxide results from a decomposition process limits the information available enormously—virtually to a number of oxides derived from hydroxides.

Probably the first topotactic* reaction to be studied by X-rays was the dehydration of brucite, and its nature is now well established.[14]   The hydroxide crystallizes with the CdI_2 structure, the hydroxyl ions being stacked in the hexagonal sequence AB, AB, with the magnesium atoms occupying the octahedral interstices between A and B layers.   After decomposition, the magnesium atoms which were originally in the (001) plane of the hydroxide structure are now in the (111) plane of the oxide structure, the Mg–Mg distance decreasing from 3·14Å to 2·98Å, i.e. a relatively small contraction of 5%.   Normal to the basal plane of the hydroxide there has to be a 50% contraction and the stacking sequence of layers has to be altered from AB AB to ABCABC.   Nevertheless the main feature is that the orientation of the crystallites of MgO within the pseudomorph with respect to one another and the pseudomorph is determined by the orientation of the original hydroxide crystal. Differences in orientation between magnesia crystallites within the pseudomorph of a single hydroxide crystal will be small.

Similar topotactic reactions occur during the dehydration of the hydroxides of aluminium and iron.   In the sequence boehmite $\longrightarrow \gamma\text{-}Al_2O_3 \longrightarrow \delta\text{-}Al_2O_3 \longrightarrow \theta\text{-}Al_2O_3$, orientation relationships are maintained such that the oxygen atoms remain in approximately cubic close packing;[15] for the sequence gibbsite $\longrightarrow Al_2O_3 \longrightarrow \kappa\text{-}Al_2O_3 \longrightarrow \alpha\text{-}Al_2O_3$ and for diaspore $\longrightarrow \alpha\text{-}Al_2O_3$ the oxygen atoms remain in approximately hexagonal close packing.[16]   In the reactions lepidocrocite $(\gamma\text{-}FeO.OH) \longrightarrow \gamma\text{-}Fe_2O_3$ and $FeO \longrightarrow Fe_3O_4$, the oxygen atoms remain in the close-packed cubic positions whilst in the reaction goethite $(\alpha\text{-}FeO.OH) \longrightarrow \alpha\text{-}Fe_2O_3$ the hexagonal close-packed oxygen lattice is retained.[17]

Unlike magnesium hydroxide, the calcia resulting from dehydration of $Ca(OH)_2$ has been reported to be poorly oriented.[18]

Data on other oxysalts is very limited.   Ferrous carbonate decomposes topotactically to FeO and Fe_3O_4 [19] and some form of orientation relationship would seem to exist between nickel carbonate and the nickel oxide derived from it.[20]

There is no evidence on the relationships between oxalate and resulting oxide, although the fact that the original oxalate cubes

* Used in the same sense as in Reference 17.

laminate into thin sheets of oxide suggest that some form of topo-tactic or epitactic reaction may be involved.

It has been suggested that no very close relationship exists be-tween $FeCl_2.4H_3O$ and the β-FeO.OH which results from it on oxida-tion, so there would be expected to be no relationship between the oxide and originating chloride.[21] This situation would also appear to be probably true for alumina derived from aluminium chloride hydrate.[22]

To summarize, it would seem that fine oxide powder particles will be aggregated on the coarsest scale within pseudomorphs of the crystals of the salt from which they were derived: if the transforma-tion to the final product occurs by one or a series of topotactic or epitactic reactions, then those oxide powder particles derived from a single crystal of the starting material may be present as aggregates in which the individual particles may have a strong preferred orienta-tion with respect to the initiating structure, and hence towards one another.

4. STRUCTURE OF THE AGGREGATE

To what extent are the individual crystallites, as defined by X-ray line broadening, associated? Volume contractions accompanying the decomposition are large and the oxides powders are usually present in pseudomorphs, the changes in linear dimensions of which during decomposition are less than can account for the overall volume change, i.e. the pseudomorphs are porous.

General information on the pore structure can be deduced from X-ray data alone. During the decomposition of $Mg(OH)_2$ there has to be a contraction of 50% normal to the basal plane and a con-traction of only 5% parallel to it to produce the MgO structure. Major fissures parallel to the basal plane of the pseudomorph would therefore be expected. Again, since the smallest equiaxed crystallite sizes recorded are 40Å, the aggregates of crystallites must presum-ably be at least of this average thickness when formed.

More detailed information on the pore structure must invoke the use of some other technique to supplement the X-ray evidence, and studies of the physical adsorption behaviour of gases on fine powders have been widely used to this end. From the adsorption isotherm, surface areas can be calculated, and from the hysteresis exhibited on desorption, information on distribution of pore sizes can be obtained.

For regularly shaped perfect crystallites, comparison of the sur-face area derived from X-ray crystallite size-measurements with that obtained from adsorption data should enable the state of aggrega-tion of the crystallites to be assessed, since adsorption does not take account of boundaries between aggregated crystallites. In practice, complications can be envisaged, because irregular surfaces and cracks would not affect the crystallite size determined by X-ray techniques but would contribute to the surface area measured by adsorption: the reverse situation would hold for closed porosity. There is also the further problem of the absolute accuracy of the crystallite-size and surface-area measurements.

Nevertheless it has been shown for MgO prepared by decomposition of the hydroxide in water vapour and in vacuo at $\sim$360°C. that the crystallite sizes obtained from line-broadening agreed with those calculated from surface-area data, assuming uniformly cubic crystallites.[23] For hydroxide decomposed in vacuo the crystallite size was 75 ± 5Å and in 1·9 mm water vapour, 50 ± 5Å. The experimental uncertainty was such as make it possible to distinguish a perfect cube from a figure of sides 1, 1, and 31. In these experiments the decomposition temperature was kept as low as possible compatible with complete decomposition, specifically to avoid sintering.

Not all of the other oxides for which data on crystallite-size and surface-area measurements are available have been decomposed at temperatures so close to their decomposition temperature. Thus for beryllia prepared from beryllium hydroxide the lowest temperature for which the relevant data is available is $\sim$500°C., whereas the hydroxide will decompose completely $\sim$300°C., given time. At 500°C. the surface area (S), derived from the relationship

$$S = 6/\rho d$$

where ρ = density and d = particle diameter or cube edge, is approximately 1·5 [24] to 2 [7] times greater than the surface area measured by adsorption. This could be explained in terms of change of crystallite shape from the equiaxed shape assumed in the above expression. However, it has been shown that for material prepared in this manner the crystallites are sensibly equiaxed.[7] Basic inaccuracy in the data apart, these discrepancies for beryllia can only be explained in terms of crystallite agglomeration.

The same argument cannot be applied in the case of thoria prepared from the oxalate at temperatures very close to its decomposition temperature ($\sim$400°C.). Under these conditions the surface areas derived from crystallites of size 60Å were again about twice those measured by adsorption [9] and the crystallites have been shown to be reasonably equiaxed;[5] if, therefore, these results are to be explained in terms of crystallite agglomeration, a reason has to be advanced for its occurrence for thoria but not for magnesia. Here it is possible only to surmise that experimental conditions might have played a critical part. It has been observed for magnesium hydroxide decomposed in vacuo that the escape of water vapour was impeded if layers of powder >0.5 mm thick were used and, as will be seen later, the presence of water vapour markedly affects sintering behaviour. The experimental details published for the decomposition of thorium oxalate are not sufficient to more than suggest that the bed thickness was probably greater than 0.5 mm and so " self-steaming " would occur. Again, for the latter case, decomposition times of about 14 h were used, compared with a few hours for the magnesia preparation.

Thus the experimental evidence discussed does not make it possible to place high reliance on the use of X-ray crystallite-size data and surface measurements for the deduction of the state of the crystallite agglomeration. For magnesia it remains to be shown that the single-crystal cuboids on agglomeration give rise to differences in the surface areas derived from X-ray crystallite size and by adsorption measurements; for thoria and beryllia it has to be demonstrated that, under carefully controlled conditions of preparation of the finest particles, the two measurements of surface area do coincide.

Determination of pore-size distribution within aggregates of " active " oxide powders have been reported for alumina [25, 26] and magnesia.[23] During the formation of alumina from gibbsite, in the early stages of dehydration the particles rupture along the basal plane of the gibbsite giving rise to plate-like pores of $\sim$30Å width. With further dehydration, the plate-like particles $\sim$200Å wide divide further into rod-like particles separated by pores $\sim$10Å across.[25] Microcrystalline active corundum prepared by decomposition of boehmite under pressure has been shown to consist of aggregates 300-800Å in size of small primary particles separated by pores 100-150Å in diameter.[26] For magnesia prepared from the hydroxide it has already been pointed out that plate-like pores could be formed parallel to both [100] and [001] direction of the parent lattice, and they could be as narrow as 40-60Å and 6-8Å in these two directions respectively. Adsorption hysteresis loop measurements have confirmed the presence of pores over this whole size range.[23]

To sum up, for the very finest powders prepared by low-temperature decomposition, the crystallites may be present within the pseudomorph singly or as aggregates of a few hundred units: the evidence available at present is inconclusive. If the oxide is produced by a topotactic or epitactic reaction, the pores separating these aggregates will have very definite orientations and sizes.

5. BEHAVIOUR OF AGGLOMERATES ON CALCINATION

So far only powders of particle size in the range up to $\sim$100Å have been discussed. Since powder particles of $\sim$2,000Å can still be thought of as "fine", their formation by aggregation of finer crystallites during calcination has to be considered.

If the difference in surface areas derived from crystallite size and adsorption measurements is considered significant, then obviously agglomeration must be occurring at very low temperatures. Above the decomposition temperature, loss of surface area has been shown to occur very rapidly with increase of calcination temperature. Magnesia prepared from magnesium ammonium carbonate by heating for 16 h in air at $\sim 300\,°C$. had a surface area of 400 m^2/g; after the same time at 600°C., the surface area was ~ 75 m^2/g.[10] Beryllia prepared by calcination of the hydroxide at 500°C. had a surface area of 185 m^2/g and at 900°C. of 40 m^2/g.[7] Starting with beryllium oxalate, the surface area of the oxide formed at 400°C. was 314 m^2/g decreasing to 16 m^2/g at 900°C.[7] Thorium oxalate decomposed at 500°C. gives thoria of 32 m^2/g whilst at 800°C. the area is reduced to $\sim 4\cdot 5$ m^2/g.[27]

Great care is needed in the comparison and interpretation of published results, because of the very marked effect that impurities both in the solid and gaseous phases may have on the agglomeration process or processes. Fig. 1 (curves 1, 2, 3) shows surface area/temperature plots for beryllia, using a calcination time of 1 h in air and starting with beryllium hydroxides of varying purity. Whilst the loss of area appears to follow the same pattern for all the powders, the curves are displaced to higher and higher temperatures with increasing purity. An even more striking effect in delaying loss of surface area with increasing calcination temperature is afforded by change of decomposition and calcination atmosphere from air to vacuum for the most impure powder[28] (Fig. 1, curves 1 and 4 respectively).

A similar effect has been demonstrated for magnesia. Calcination of a powder of area 220 m^2/g at 1,050°C. in vacuo for 20 h caused its reduction to 200 m^2/g; using a 4 mm pressure of water vapour at the same temperature, an area of 100 m^2/g was attained in 1 min. The final area loss in 4 mm water-vapour pressure at 600°C. is about 100 times greater than that in vacuo at 1,000°C. The most dramatic effects occur at the higher vapour pressures, but easily measurable effects occur at pressures as low as 10^{-2} mm. In this context, it is important to recall from Section 4 that the crystallite size of magnesia prepared by decomposition in the presence of water vapour was less than that prepared in vacuo, i.e. the presence of water vapour diminishes the crystallite size at the lower decomposition temperatures, but augments it at higher temperatures. Finally the surface area developed under given calcination conditions is a function also of time at temperature and, whilst the loss of

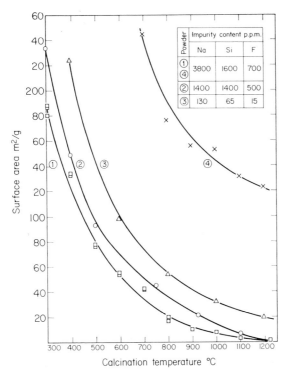

Fig. 1.—Variation of surface area with calcination temperature for several types of beryllia

surface area may eventually saturate, the process may take a hundred hours. It could therefore be illogical to compare the surface areas developed in a fixed time at various temperatures.

When the available data are examined with these strictures in mind, only the most qualitative conclusions can be educed.

Measurements of changes in pseudomorph size by sedimentation [9] and electron micrography [27] for thoria and by air permeability for two types of beryllia,[7] taken in conjunction with surface-area measurements, show that, during calcination, surface-area loss occurs chiefly by aggregation within and not between pseudomorphs. For magnesia, pore volume as measured by adsorption hysteresis alters little during calcination, again suggesting that aggregation occurs mainly within the relic structures.[23]

Information on the state of aggregation within the pseudomorph can, at present, again only be obtained by comparison of surface areas derived from crystallite size and from adsorption data. The

data available for thoria, beryllia and magnesia are plotted in Figs.
2, 3, and 4 as X-ray crystallite size against measured surface areas.
The line representing the theoretical relationship between surface
area and crystallite size for spheres and cubes is included, and also
parallel lines representing factors of deviation of up to three from
this relationship. Variations in crystallite and surface area for
thoria and beryllia were obtained by calcining for a fixed time at
different temperature. For these materials the surface area derived
from X-ray crystallite-size measurement is always greater than that
from adsorption by a factor of ~ 1.5 to 3, which is not apparently
related to crystallite size: the situation is therefore exactly similar
to that already discussed for the finest crystallite size. The variations in crystallite size and surface area for the magnesia were
obtained by calcining powder at $1,050^\circ$C. for various periods of
time in water vapour and vacuo, i.e. at vastly differing rates of
surface area loss. In this case the discrepancy between the two
measurements was zero at the start of calcination and gradually
increased to a factor of 2–3 as calcination proceeded. For this case
it can be taken that the discrepancy is significant and supports the
belief that the discrepancy observed for the other oxide powders is
also significant.

Assuming the measurements from which the discrepancies are
derived to be basically accurate, what information can be obtained
on the state of aggregation? The number of crystallites available
for aggregation within a pseudomorph will decrease with time and
temperature during calcination and potentially may reach unity.
The discrepancy factor e should therefore attain some maximum
value, which in fact never appears to exceed three for the powders

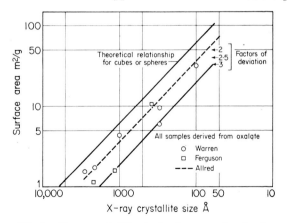

FIG. 2.—X-ray crystallite size/surface area for thoria

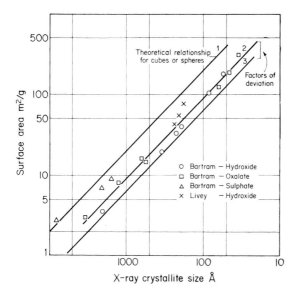

FIG. 3.—X-ray crystallite size/surface area for beryllia

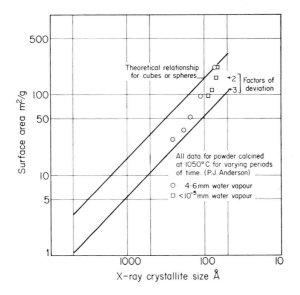

FIG. 4.—X-ray crystallite size/surface area for magnesia

studied. Taking the simplest case of uniform packing of cubic crystallites, the minimum number which have to be aggregated to give a discrepancy of e is e^3, packed to give a cube of side e: any other mode of packing will give a lower value of e. The limit in physical size of the aggregate will be determined by the dimensions of the pseudomorph. The magnesium hydroxide used in the calcination experiments consisted of platelets ~ 250Å thick, which could, therefore, when decomposed to magnesia, contain no more than about four layers of crystallites initially, and between one and two by the time e has reached three. For uniform packing of cubes two layers thick the minimum number of crystallites to give $e = 3$ is 32, arranged $4 \times 4 \times 2$; if packed only one layer thick, then no number of crystallites can give a value of $e > 3$. Thus an upper limit of about 3 to the discrepancy factor for magnesia will arise naturally from limitations in size of the pseudomorph, coupled with the reduction in number of crystallites as calcination proceeds. The same may equally well be true for beryllia and thoria, where the pseudomorphs are known to be of a limited thickness, presumably imposed by the volume changes which have to be accommodated as the result of decomposition. The corollary to this is of course that little information on the state of aggregation can be deduced from values of e without additional information on the dimensions of the pseudomorph and on the limiting size in one dimension that the crystallite aggregates might thereby reach.

In considering the mechanism of material transport whereby the changes in surface area are brought about the following facts have to be borne in mind:

(1) For MgO, BeO and ThO$_2$ decomposed and calcined in air, the process occurs very rapidly at temperatures of around 300°C.

(2) For magnesia the process is extremely sensitive to the presence of water vapour, to the extent that its absence virtually prevents agglomeration.

(3) For magnesia and probably for the other oxides the individual crystallites are closely oriented with respect to one another, which is not likely to aid sintering by bulk diffusion.

(4) As the pseudomorphs do not change in outer shape to any marked extent, the material transport process has only to redistribute material and not to effect densification.

Whilst it is impossible at the present state of knowledge to be definite, it would seem that a surface-transport process such as diffusion or evaporation/condensation rather than a volume transport process will be involved.

6. CONCLUSIONS

The paucity of information on the topics discussed makes it difficult to draw many firm general conclusions but an overall picture of what could occur can be envisaged.

The finest oxide powders obtainable ($\sim$40Å) will consist of crystallites of equiaxed shape, probably of expanded lattice parameter compared with the bulk material. Residual strains will be present within the crystallites but will not contribute greatly to the energy content of the particles, the excess of which over that of the bulk material will result from the extra surface-free-energy contribution. The crystallites will be aggregated on the coarsest scale within pseudomorphs of the crystals of the salts from which they are derived. If the transformations to the final product are oriented, as seems to be the rule rather than the exception, then those oxide particles derived from a single crystal of the starting material will be present within the pseudomorph as aggregates in which there is a strong preferred orientation of crystallites.

Under very closely controlled conditions of preparation at temperatures close to that of decomposition, the crystallites may be so weakly aggregated that virtually their whole surface area is available for gas adsorption. Normally, however, the crystallites will be aggregated in groups the sizes of which cannot be defined from the data presently available. It follows that, if the oxide is produced by an oriented transformation, the pores separating these aggregates will have definite orientations. With increase of calcination temperature above the decomposition temperature, loss of surface area and crystallite growth can occur rapidly, given the correct atmosphere. In this context the presence of water vapour is critical as far as magnesia and beryllia are concerned. During vacuum calcination virtually no loss of area occurs for magnesia up to 1,050°C. Other gaseous impurities may be equally critical for these and other oxides. The agglomeration of crystallites which accompanies these changes in area and crystallite size occurs within the pseudomorphs, which change little in shape and do not themselves agglomerate. The mechanism of material movement during these changes cannot be accurately defined at present but it seems more probable that a process of surface-transport rather than one involving a volume-transport is responsible.

The main conclusion that emerges from this overall picture is that the physical and chemical properties of the compound from which the fine oxide powder is derived can determine the characteristics of the latter to a major extent: they will determine the size and shape of pseudomorphs, the orientation of the oxide crystallites towards themselves and the pseudomorph, the pore structure within the pseudomorph and, possibly, the rate of aggregation of the crystallites during calcination. In this latter respect the importance of impurities both in the solid and gaseous phases must be emphasized.

A final and rather obvious conclusion is that considerably more work in this field of research is very desirable.

ACKNOWLEDGMENTS

The author wishes to express his appreciation to his colleagues, Dr. P. J. Anderson, Mr. T. W. Baker and Dr. D. T. Livey, for valuable discussions and for permission to use unpublished data.

REFERENCES

1. Livey, D. T., *A.E.R.E. Report R 4090,* 1962.
2. Anderson, P. J., and Livey, D. T., *Powder Metallurgy,* (7), 189, 1961.
3. Baker, T. W., and Wilkinson, D. Unpublished results.
4. Thomas, D. K., and Baker, T. W., *Proc. Phys. Soc.,* **74,** 673, 1959.
5. Ferguson, I. F., *A.E.R.E. Report R 3459,* 1960.
6. Livey D. T. et al., *A.E.R.E. Report M/R 1957,* 1956.
7. Bartram, S. F., "Advances in X-ray Analysis," **4,** 40, 1961.
8. Beckett, R., and Winfield, M. E., *Aust. J. Sci. Res.,* **A4,** 644, 1951.
9. Allred, V. D., et al., *J. Phys. Chem.,* **61,** 117, 1957.
10. Dell, R. M., and Weller, S. W., *Trans. Farad. Soc.,* **55,** 2203, 1959.
11. Anderson, P. J., and Horlock, R. F., *Trans. Farad. Soc.,* **58,** 1993, 1962.
12. Clayton, J. C., and Aaronson, S., *J. Chem. Eng. Data,* **6,** 43, 1961.
13. Dent Glasser, L. S., et al., *Quart. Rev. Chem. Soc.,* **16,** 343, 1962.
14. Aminoff, G., *Geol. Fören. Forh. (Stockholm),* **41,** 407, 1919; Garrido, J., *Ion. Rev. Espan., Quin. Applic,* **11,** 206, 220, 453, 1951.
15. Saalfeld, H., "Proceedings of the 4th International Symposium on the Reactivity of Solids" (Amsterdam: 1960), p. 310.
16. Brindley, G. W., and Choe, J. O., *Amer. Min.,* **46,** 771, 1961.
17. Mackay, A. L., "Proceedings of the 4th International Symposium on the Reactivity of Solids" (Amsterdam, 1960). p. 571.
18. West, C. D., *Amer. Min.,* **19,** 281, 1934.
19. Bernal, J. D., et al., *Clay. Min. Bull.,* **4,** 15, 1959.
20. François, J., *C. R. Acad. Sci. Paris,* **230,** 2183, 1950.
21. Mackay, A. L., *Min. Mag.,* **33,** 270, 1962.
22. Stirland, D. J., et al., *Trans. Brit. Ceram. Soc.,* **57,** 69, 1958.
23. Anderson, P. J., and Horlock, R. F., *Trans. Farad. Soc.,* **59,** 721, 1963.
24. Livey, D. T. Private communication.
25. de Boer, J. H., et al., "Proceedings of the 2nd International Congress on Surface Activity," Vol. II, p. 93. (Butterworths, 1957.)
26. Krischner, H., and Torkar, K., "Science of Ceramics," Vol. I, p. 63. (British Ceramic Society, 1962.)
27. Warren, D. Private communication (A.E.I. Research Laboratories, Rugby).
28. Livey, D. T. Private communication.
29. Anderson, P. J. Private communication.

2—Das Reaktionsverhalten verschiedener Aluminiumoxyde mit Lithiumkarbonat

von K. TORKAR, H. P. FRITZER, und H. KRISCHNER

Aus dem Institut für Physikalische Chemie der Techn.
Hochschule Graz., Österreich.

INHALT H5253

Es wurde das Reaktionsverhalten verschiedener reinster Aluminiumoxyde mit Lithiumkarbonat mit einem dynamischen Differenzkalorimeter mit Simultaneichung und auch röntgenographisch untersucht. Die relativen Reaktionszeiten sind: (1) η-Al_2O_3 schneller als (2) aktiver Korund (durch hydrothermale Zersetzung metallischen Aluminiums hergestellt) schneller als (3) stabiler Korund schneller als (4) KI-Al_2O_3. Die Endprodukte bei 850°C. sind: (1) die Tieftemperaturform des $LiAlO_2$; (2), (3), (4) ein Gemisch der Hoch- und Tief-temperaturmodifikation des $LiAlO_2$. Die Al_2O_3-Form KI reagiert langsam. Als Zwischenprodukte der Reaktion treten die Abbauform KII sowie eine neue Form auf, die wir als $LiAlO_2$-K bezeichnen. Das Reaktionsverhalten des Al_2O_3-KI führen wir auf eine gittermässige Behinderung der Reaktion zur Tieftemperaturform des $LiAlO_2$ zurück. Wenn man nämlich bei der Al_2O_3-Form KI eine vorwiegend tetraedrische Sauerstoffkoordination annimmt, so lässt sich nicht nur das Reaktionsverhalten mit Lithiumkarbonat erklären, sondern es wird auch eine zwanglose Einordnung in das bekannte Abbauschema der verschiedenen Aluminiumhydroxyde und -oxyde ermöglicht.

The reaction of different types of alumina with lithium carbonate

The speed of reactivity of different types of pure Al_2O_3 with Li_2CO_3 was investigated by differential calorimeter with automatic recording and by X-ray methods. The relative rates of reactivity are: (1) η-$Al_2O_3 >$ (2) active corundum (prepared by hydrothermal decomposition of metallic Al) $>$ (3) stable cordundum $>$ (4) K1-Al_2O_3. The end-products at 850°C. are: (1) low-temperature $LiAlO_2$; (2), (3), (4) mixture of high- and low-temperature $LiAlO_2$. With K1-Al_2O_3, which reacts slowly, the decomposition product K1l-Al_2O_3 is found, as well as a new substance referred to as $LiAlO_2$-K. The behaviour of Al_2O_3-K1 can be seen as a lattice obstruction to the reaction to form low-temperature $LiAlO_2$. The assumption that Al_2O_3-K1 has a mainly tetragonal oxygen coordination accounts for the reaction with Li_2CO_3 and also makes the decomposition pattern of the hydroxides and oxides of aluminium.

La réaction de différents types d'alumine avec le carbonate de lithium

La vitesse de réactivité de différents types d'Al_2O_3 pur avec Li_2CO_3 est étudiée au moyen du calorimètre différentiel avec enregistrement automatique et au moyen des méthods aux rayons X. Les vitesses relatives de réactivité sont: (1) Al_2O_3-étha $>$ (2) corindon actif (préparé par décomposition hydrothermale de Al métallique) $>$ (3) corindon stable $>$ (4) K1-Al_2O_3. Les produits finals à 850° sont: (1) du $LiAlO_2$ basse température; (2), (3), (4) un mélange de LiAlO₂ haute et basse températures. Aves Kl-Al₂O₃ qui réagit lentement on trouve le produit de décomposition Kll-Al₂O₃ ainsi qu'une substance nouvelle que l'on désigne sous le nom de LiAlO₂-K. Le comportement de Al₂O₃-Kl peut être considéré comme une obstruction de réseau à la réaction pour former du LiAlO₂ basse température. L'hypothèse selon laquelle Al₂O₃-Kl présenterait principalement une coordination quadratique de l'oxygène rend compte de la réaction avec Li₂CO₃ et donne également le modèle de décomposition des hydroxydes et des oxydes d'aluminium.

1. EINLEITUNG

Vor zwei Jahren hatten wir Gelegenheit in Oxford [1] über Versuche zu berichten, die wir über die Darstellung und Untersuchung reinster Aluminiumhydroxyde und -oxyde angestellt haben. Im Verlaufe dieser Untersuchungen wurde durch Zersetzung metallischen Aluminiums mit Wasserdampf unter Druck ein aktives α-Al₂O₃ dargestellt, dessen Bewässerung zu Diaspor unter Wasserdampfdruck erstmals gelang. Außerdem berichteten wir über zwei neue Aluminiumoxyde, das Autoklavengamma und die Al₂O₃-Form Kl.

Die heutigen Ausführungen beschäftigen sich nun mit dem Reaktionsverhalten dieser verschiedenen Aluminiumoxydformen. Als Reaktionskomponente verwendeten wir Lithiumkarbonat, da bei dieser Substanz mit einem frühen Reaktionsbeginn gerechnet werden kann. Das war für uns von Wichtigkeit, da eine Umwandlung der Aluminiumoxyde vor Erreichen der Reaktionstemperatur vermieden werden muß. Außerdem versprach diese Reaktion interessante Aufschlüsse über die Natur der Endprodukte zu geben, worüber in der Literatur uneinheitliche Angaben zu finden sind.

2. DIE REAKTION DES Al₂O₃ MIT Li₂CO₃
(Kurze Literaturübersicht)

Erhitzt man Al₂O₃ mit Li₂CO₃ bei Temperaturen unter 600 °C., so erhält man, wie LEHMANN und HESSELBARTH [2] nachgewiesen haben, unabhängig vom molaren Mischungsverhältnis eine Tieftemperaturform des Lithiumaluminats (T-LiAlO₂). Bei höheren Temperaturen bildet sich das Lithiumaluminat in seiner Hochtemperaturform (H-LiAlO₂), die von HUMMEL [3] röntgenographisch untersucht wurde. Bei höheren Temperaturen ändern sich mit wechselndem Lithiumgehalt die Röntgeninterferenzen der entstehenden Verbindungen.

Verwendet man Li₂O anstelle von Li₂CO₃, so bildet sich auch unterhalb von 650° bei einem Molenverhältnis von 1:5 eine basenreichere Verbindung der Zusammensetzung Li₅AlO₄.[4] Bei Verwendung von LiF entsteht bei einem Mischungsverhältnis von 5:1 der von KORDES [5] beschriebene Spinell LiAl₅O₈.

3. VERWENDETE PRÄPARATE

Im Verlaufe unserer Untersuchungen haben wir reinste Aluminiumoxyde in den verschiedensten Formen dargestellt und untersucht. Aus dieser großen Anzahl von Präparaten wollen wir drei Grundtypen herausgreifen und deren Reaktionsverhalten mit Lithiumkarbonat beschreiben.

3.1 γ-Aluminiumoxyde

Als Repräsentant dieser Gruppe haben wir das η-Al_2O_3 herangezogen, das bei der Entwässerung von Bayerit entsteht. Ein ähnliches Reaktionsverhalten zeigt auch das bei der Entwässerung von Hydrargillit entstehende χ-Al_2O_3 sowie γ-Al_2O_3, das sich beim Erhitzen von Böhmit bildet. Autoklaven-γ sowie die Hochtemperaturformen θ- κ- und δ-Al_2O_3 reagieren merklich langsamer als η-Al_2O_3.

Als Ausgangsmaterial für die Darstellung von η-Al_2O_3 verwendeten wir einen Reinstbayerit, der durch Hydrolyse von Aluminiumaethylat dargestellt worden war.[6] Der gut kristallisierte Bayerit wurde bei 450°C. entwässert und das entstandene η-Al_2O_3 bei dieser Temperatur einige Stunden gealtert.

3.2 α-Aluminiumoxyd

α-Aluminiumoxyd wurde von uns sowohl in seiner stabilen Form als auch als aktiver Korund untersucht.

(1) Stabiles α-Al_2O_3 (Korund). Dieses Präparat wurde durch mehrstündiges Glühen reiner Aluminiumoxyde bei 1200°C. erhalten. Die Teilchengröße dieses Präparates lag bei 5 μm.

(2) Aktives α-Al_2O_3 (Aktiver Korund). Zur Darstellung dieses Präparates zersetzten wir metallisches Aluminium im Autoklaven im Zustandsgebiet des ungesättigten Wasserdampfes.[7] Das aktive α-Al_2O_3 wies eine Teilchengröße von 700–1000 Å auf.

3.3. Al_2O_3-Form KI

Dieses von uns erstmals beschriebene Aluminiumoxyd ensteht bei der hydrothermalen Zersetzung metallischen Aluminiums bei Temperaturen um 400°C. und Wasserdampfdrucken von 150 atm.[8] Aber auch aus verschiedenen Aluminiumhydroxyden und -oxyden kann diese Form KI unter Wasserdampfdruck erhalten werden. Die Teilchengröße des Präparates lag bei 0,5–1 μm.

Die beschriebenen Aluminiumoxyde wurden mit Lithiumkarbonat (p. A. Teilchengröße kleiner als 40 μm) in Molverhältnis 1:1 vermischt und durch mehrstündiges Schütteln homogenisiert. Auf ein Mahlen der Mischungen wurde verzichtet, um die Präparate nicht zu verändern.

4. VERWENDETE APPARATUR

Zur Durchführung der Versuche verwendeten wir eine in unserem Institut entwickelte Dynamische Differenz-Kalorimetrie mit Simultaneichung.[9] Die dynamische Differenz-Kalorimetrie (DDK) unterscheidet sich von der Methodik der Differential-Thermoanalyse (DTA) bekanntlich insoferne, als die Differenztemperatur nicht in der Substanz selbst gemessen wird, sondern an metallischen Hilfskörpern bestimmt wird. Da der Gesamtwärmebedarf der Proben über diese Metallkörper geführt wird, übernehmen diese die Funktion kleiner Kalorimeter, die überdies einem programmierten Aufheizen unterworfen sind. Es handelt sich also um ein kalorimetrisches Verfahren, also um eine DDK.[10]

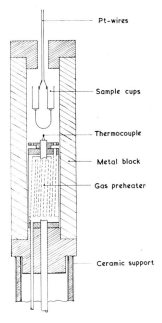

- Pt-wires
- Sample cups
- Thermocouple
- Metal block
- Gas preheater
- Ceramic support

ABB. 1.—DDK-Apparatur

In Abb. 1 ist das Schema der verwendeten DDK/SE Apparatur zu sehen. In einem vertikal stehenden Ofen üblicher Bauart ist ein starkwandiger Metallblock angebracht, der neben guter Wärmeleitfähigkeit eine genügende Wärmekapazität besitzt um temperatur-homogenisierend zu wirken. Die in diesem Bild gezeigte Anordnung ist mit einer Gaseinleitung und Gasvorwärmung versehen, die die Durchführung der Versuche gegebenenfalls unter Schutzgas er-möglicht. Ein Thermoelement, das sich direkt unter den Substanz-bechern befindet, dient zur Temperaturkontrolle. Die Substanz-becher bestehen aus Platin und sind durch einen kurzen Drahtbügel aus Platin-Rhodium verbunden.

Die Tiegelanordung unterscheidet sich also wesentlich von den allgemein in DTA-Anordnungen verwendeten Substanzbechern. (Patent angemeldet.) Durch die Kombination eines Platinbechers mit einem Platinrhodiumdraht wirken die Becher selbst als Thermo-element. In der Substanz auftretende kalorische Effekte werden sofort von der Tiegelwandung aufgenommen und rufen eine Thermo-spannung hervor, die durch dünne Platindrähte, die gleichzeitig zur Aufhängung der Substanzbecher dienen, abgeleitet wird. Da die gesamten auftretenden Reaktionswärmen über die Becherwand zu- oder abfließen müssen, können die Wärmetönungen quantitativ erfaßt und kalorisch ausgewertet werden.

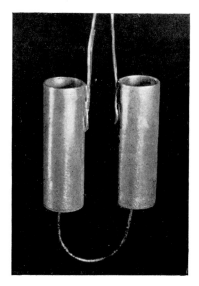

ABB. 2.—Tiegelanordnung

Abweichend von der bisher üblichen Versuchsdurchführung bei der DTA and DDK verzichten wir auf eine inerte Vergleichs-substanz. Anstelle einer Inertsubstanz befindet sich im zweiten

Becher eine Eichsubstanz, die bekannte thermische Effekte aufweist. Mittels dieser Simultaneichung kann man durch Vergleich bekannter Umwandlungs oder Schmelzwärmen aus einem einzigen Versuch—die bisher notwendige Aufstellung von Eichkurven erübrigt sich—eine unbekannte Reaktionswärme mit guter Genauigkeit bestimmen.

Darüberhinaus besteht noch die Möglichkeit mit mehr als zwei Bechern gleichzeitig zu fahren. Bei Verwendung von drei oder vier Bechern ist es möglich, entweder mehrere Eichsubstanzen zu verwenden oder auch Diffenzversuche mit Simultaneichung durchzuführen. Vorallem durch Differenzversuche kann die Empfindlichkeit der DDK wesentlich vergrößert werden.

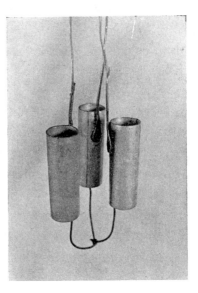

ABB. 3.—Dreitiegelanordnung

Der Ofen der DDK wurde mittels eines Programmgebers elektrisch mit einer Aufheizgeschwindigkeit von $10°$/Min. aufgeheizt. Die durchschnittliche Einwaage betrug 100 mg. Die thermischen Effekte wurden mit Hilfe eines Kompensationsschreibers registriert. Die gleichzeitige Registrierung der Eichreaktionen sowie der Nullinie wurde durch einen Umschaltmechanismus ermöglicht. Die Auswertung der Thermogramme erfolgte planimetrisch, wobei die gute Nullpunktsstabilität der verwendeten Meßanordnung die Auswertung sehr erleichterte.

5. ERGEBNISSE DER DDK/SE VERSUCHE

Die Reaktionswärmen zwischen verschiedenen Aluminiumoxyden und Lithiumkarbonat sind in allen Fällen endotherm. Durch einen Mehrgehalt an Energie des Aluminiumoxydes wird die Reaktionswärme vermindert, die auftretende Peakfläche also kleiner. In Abb. 4 ist das Originaldiagramm eines DDK/SE Versuches wiedergegeben. Es wurde mit Dreitiegelanordnung gearbeitet, wobei die Auswahl der Eichsubstanzen so getroffen wurde, daß

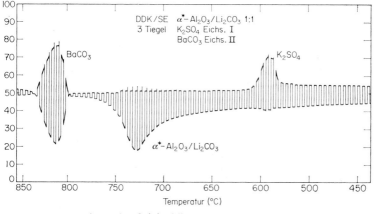

ABB. 4.—Originaldiagramm DDK/SE

deren thermische Effekte vor Beginn bzw. nach Beendigung der Reaktion gelegen waren. Es wurde die $\alpha-\beta$ Umwandlung des K_2SO_4 und des $BaCO_3$ verwendet.

In Abb. 5 sind DDK-Kurven verschiedener Aluminiumoxydformen mit Lithiumkarbonat schematisch zusammengestellt. η-Al_2O_3 zeigt den frühesten Reaktionsbeginn und die kleinste Fläche, da es als γ-Aluminiumoxyd erwartungsgemäß den höchsten Energieinhalt aufweist. Der Reaktionsbeginn verschiebt sich in der Reihenfolge η-$Al_2O_3 \longrightarrow$ aktiver Korund $\longrightarrow$ stabiler Korund $\longrightarrow Al_2O_3$-Form KI gegen höhere Temperaturen.

Bei der Auswertung der Peakflächen erhält man für die Reaktion des η-Al_2O_3 mit Li_2CO_3 eine Wärmetönung von 3,5–4 kcal/Mol. Aktiver Korund zeigt eine Reaktionswärme von 14–15 kcal/Mol, während bei stabilem Korund eine Auswertung durch den unvollständigen Reaktionsablauf erschwert wird. Trotzdem steht der ermittelte Wert von 16 kcal/Mol in guter Übereinstimmung mit dem aus thermochemischen Daten errechneten Wert. Bei der Al_2O_3-

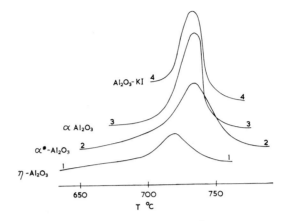

Al₂O₃-KI
α Al₂O₃
α*-Al₂O₃
η-Al₂O₃

650   700   750
T °C

ABB. 5.—Verschiedene DDK-Diagramme

Form KI ist unter diesen Reaktionsbedingungen keine Reaktionswärme festzustellen, sondern es wurde praktisch nur die Schmelz-
wärme des Lithiumkarbonates registriert. Als weiterer Beweis für
das Ausbleiben einer Reaktion kann das Auftreten des fast un-
veränderten Schmelzpeaks von Lithiumkarbonat beim Abkühlen
angesehen werden. Auch röntgenographisch war keine Aluminatbildung nachweisbar.

6. RÖNTGENOGRAPHISCHE VERFOLGUNG DER REAKTION

Zur röntgenographischen Charakterisierung der Reaktions-
produkte verwendeten wir eine Guinierkammer nach JAGODZINSKI.[11]
Durch das hohe Auflösungsvermögen dieser Anordnung konnten
relativ komplizierte Stoffgemische noch analysiert und geringe
Beimengungen einzelner Phasen nachgewiesen werden.

Bei der röntgenographischen Untersuchung der Endprodukte der
DDK-Versuche zeigte es sich, daß η-Al₂O₃ quantitativ zur Tieftemperaturform des LiAlO₂ reagiert. Aktiver Korund reagiert zwar
auch quantitativ mit Lithiumkarbonat, doch entsteht als Endprodukt
ein Gemisch der Tieftemperaturmodifikation mit der Hochtemperaturform des Lithiumaluminates. Dasselbe Endprodukt zeigt
auch stabiler Korund, doch verläuft hier die Reaktion nur zu etwa
75%. Bei der Al₂O₃-Form KI war keine Aluminatbildung nachzu-
weisen.

Zur röntgenographischen Charakterisierung der Reaktions-
produkte haben wir außerdem die verschiedenen Aluminiumoxyd-

formen mit Lithiumkarbonat gemischt und auf eine Temperatur von 675 °C. erhitzt. Nach bestimmten Zeiten wurden Proben entnommen und röntgenographisch untersucht. Die Ergebnisse dieser Untersuchungen sind in Abb. 6 schematisch zusammengestellt. Bei der gewählten Temperatur von 675 °C. beginnt das η-Al_2O_3 fast augenblicklich mit Lithiumkarbonat zur Tieftemperaturform des $LiAlO_2$ zu reagieren. Nach etwa 30 Minuten ist die Reaktion beendet. Bemerkenswert ist, daß sich das gebildete T-$LiAlO_2$ auch nach Reaktionszeiten von 100 Stunden nicht in die Hochtemperaturform unwandelt.

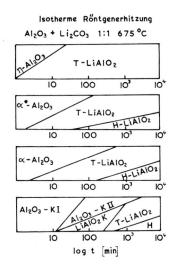

ABB. 6.—Isotherme Röntgenerhitzung

Auch das aktive α-Al_2O_3 reagiert rasch, wobei sich zunächst die Tieftemperaturform des Lithiumaluminats ausbildet. Allerdings entsteht daneben noch vor Beendigung der Reaktion die Hochtemperaturform. Als Endprodukt erhält man ein Gemisch der Hochtemperatur- und Tieftemperaturform des $LiAlO_2$.

Stabiler Korund reagiert ähnlich wie aktiver, doch ist die Reaktionsgeschwindigkeit geringer.

Wesentlich unübersichtlicher sind die Verhältnisse bei der Al_2O_3-Form KI. Die Reaktion beginnt später als bei Korund, wobei hauptsächlich die auch beim Erhitzen an Luft in diesem Temperaturgebiet auftretende Abbauform K II entsteht. Daneben bildet sich aber noch eine neue Form, die wir als $LiAlO_2$-K bezeichnen und deren Röntgeninterferenzen neben denen der Hochtemperatur-

B

form und der Tieftemperaturform des $LiAlO_2$ in Tab. 1 angegeben sind. Erst nach langen Erhitzungszeiten entsteht sowohl die Hochtemperaturform als auch die Tieftemperaturform des $LiAlO_2$.

7. DISKUSSION DER ERGEBNISSE

Unsere Untersuchungen haben gezeigt, daß sich der Reaktionsbeginn in der Reihenfolge η-Al_2O_3 $\longrightarrow$ aktiver Korund $\longrightarrow$ stabiler Korund $\longrightarrow$ Al_2O_3-Form KI gegen höhere Temperaturen verschiebt. In derselben Reihenfolge nimmt auch die Reaktionsgeschwindigkeit ab, wobei sich aber die Peakflächen vergrößern, was mit dem endothermen Reaktionsverlauf in Einklang steht.

Tabelle 1

Tieftemp. Form		Hochtemp. Form		$LiAlO_2$-K	
d Å	rel. Int.	d Å	rel. Int.	d Å	rel. Int.
4,70	10	3,99	10	4,55	2
2.38	4	3,65	5	4.26	2
2,00	10	3,16	7	3.30	5
1,557	2	2.67	10	2,77	4
1,43	4	2.58	10	2,56	4
1,402	5	2,38	2	2,55	1
1,342	1	2,35	1	2,40	1
		2,16	5	2,36	8
		1,93	1	2,32	7
		1.86	6	2,12	10
		1,826	5	1,883	4
		1,794	5	1,68	2
		1,659	2	1,649	1
		1,633	4	1,56	5
		1,622	2	1,45	5
		1,580	5	1,38	10
		1,565	5		
		1,551	1		
		1,508	8		
		1,439	1		
		1,405	3		
		1,373	1		
		1,339	5		
		1,303	6		

Vergleichen wir zunächst das Reaktionsverhalten des η-Al_2O_3, das als Repräsentant der γ-Formen herangezogen wurde, mit dem des stabilen Korundes, so überraschen weder der frühere Reaktionsbeginn noch der raschere Ablauf der Aluminatbildung. Auch der relativ hohe Unterschied in den Reaktionswärmen steht mit anderen Ergebnissen in Übereinstimmung. Während aber als Endprodukt bei der Reaktion von Korund mit Lithiumkarbonat unter den herrschenden Reaktionsbedingungen (Aufheizgeschwindigkeit 10°/

Min; Endtemperatur der DDK 850°C.) ein Gemenge der Hochtemperatur und der Tieftemperaturform des $LiAlO_2$ erhalten wurde,
reagiert η-Al_2O_3 quantitativ zur Tieftemperaturmodifikation.
Vergleicht man das Reaktionsverhalten von aktivem mit stabilem
Korund so erkennt man eine erhöhte Reaktionsfähigkeit des aktiven
Präparates. In der DDK setzt die Reaktion früher ein und verläuft,
im Gegensatz zu stabilem Korund, quantitativ. Der Unterschied in
der Reaktionswärme ist aber gering. Als Endprodukt entsteht in
beiden Fällen ein Gemisch der Hochtemperatur- und der Tieftemperaturform des $LiAlO_2$. Dieses Ergebnis deutet darauf hin, daß
es sich bei aktivem Korund, der sich im Gegensatz zum stabilen
Produkt unter Wasserdampfdruck quantitativ zu Diaspor bewässern
läßt, um keine neue Phase handelt. Aktiver Korund ist als Korund
in besonders feinem Verteilungszustand und damit in erhöhter
Reaktionsbereitschaft anzusprechen.
Schwieriger ist das Reaktionsverhalten der Al_2O_3-Form KI zu
erklären. Obwohl sich die Form KI beim Erhitzen an Luft in
Korund umwandelt, wobei eine Zwischenform K II durchschritten
wird, zeigt die Al_2O_3-Form KI ein trägeres Reaktionsverhalten mit
Li_2CO_3 als stabiler Korund. Darüberhinaus ist aber auch der
Reaktionsablauf ein anderer als bei den anderen Aluminiumoxyden.
Es bildet sich neben der Abbauform KII noch eine neue Form, die
wir als $LiAlO_2$-K bezeichnen. Erst nach langen Reaktionszeiten
bilden sich sowohl die bekannten Hochtemperatur bzw. Tieftemperaturform des $LiAlO_2$ aus.
Um dieses Reaktionsverhalten erklären zu können, möchten wir
einen Vorschlag machen, die Al_2O_3-Form KI sowie die anderen
von uns neu gefundenen Aluminiumoxydformen, in das allgemeine
Abbauschema der Aluminiumhydroxyde und -oxyde einzuordnen.

8. DER ENTWÄSSERUNGSMECHANISMUS DER ALUMINIUMHYDROXYDE

In Abb. 7 ist die Abbaufolge verschiedener Aluminiumhydroxyde
und- oxyde zusammengestellt, wie sie von H. SAALFELD[12] und
unabhängig davon in ähnlicher Weise auch von K. SASVÀRI[13] angegeben wurde. Von beiden Autoren wurde versucht, den Abbau-
mechanismus der Al-Hydroxyde und -oxyde unter Berücksichtigung
der Sauerstoffschichtfolge und der Stellung des Aluminiumions im
Sauerstoffgitter zu erklären. Das Aluminiumion ist im allgemeinen
von sechs Sauerstoff- oder Hydroxylionen umgeben, sitzt also in der
Mitte eines Sauerstoffoktaeders. Manchmal allerdings tritt auch
eine Viererkoordination auf, wobei das Aluminiumion in einem
Sauerstofftetraeder sitzt. Unter Berücksichtigung dieser gittergeo-

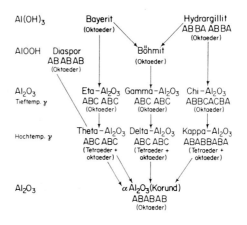

ABB. 7.—Abbaufolge der Aluminiumhydroxyde

metrischen Verhältnisse läßt sich der Entwässerungsmechanismus der Al-Hydroxyde erklären.

In den beiden Trihydroxyden des Aluminiums, in Bayerit und Gibbsit sitzt das Aluminiumion auf Oktaederplätzen. Bei Hydrargillit wurde eine Sauerstoffschichtfolge AB BA AB BA nachgewiesen. Bei der Entwässerung bildet sich entweder Böhmit, in dem das Al^{3+} ebenfalls in Sauerstoffoktaedern sitzt, oder es entsteht direkt eine Tieftemperaturform des γ-Aluminiumoxyds. Die γ-Aluminiumoxyde weisen annährend kubische Symmetrie auf, und haben eine Sauerstoffschichtfolge ABC ABC in mehr oder minder gutem Ordnungszustand. Das Al-Ion sitzt auch hier hauptsächlich in Oktaederlücken. Bei fortschreitender Entwässerung wechseln nun die Al-Ionen von Oktaederplätzen auf Tetraederbesetzung, wobei sich die Hochtemperaturformen des γ-Aluminiumoxydes ausbilden. Diese wandeln sich bei höheren Temperaturen in Korund um, der eine hexagonale Sauerstoffschichtfolge AB AB AB mit Oktaederbesetzung aufweist.

Diaspor kann dank seiner hexagonalen Sauerstoffschichtfolge mit Oktaederbesetzung ohne Ausbildung von γ-Formen direkt zu Korund entwässert werden.

Betrachten wir nun die Al_2O_3-Form KI. Die hexagonale Symmetrie dieser Form weist auf eine hexagonale Sauerstoffschichtfolge ähnlich der des Korund hin. Nimmt man aber für die Form KI im Gegensatz zu Korund vorwiegend eine Besetzung der Tetraederlücken im Sauerstoffgitter durch das Aluminiumion an, so lassen sich alle bekannten Eigenschaften der Al_2O_3-Form KI sowie der beiden anderen neuen Formen KII und Autoklavengamma mit Hilfe dieses Abbauschemas erklären.

Damit die Form KI in Korund übergehen kann, müssen die Aluminiumionen von Tetraederbesetzung auf Oktaederplätze wechseln. Als Zwischenform bildet sich also die κ-Al_2O_3-ähnliche Abbauform K II aus, die sowohl Tetraeder als auch Oktaederbesetzung zeigt. Der Hauptunterschied zwischen κ-Al_2O_3 und der Form K II dürfte also im Ordnungszustand des Sauerstoffgitters gelegen sein. Der

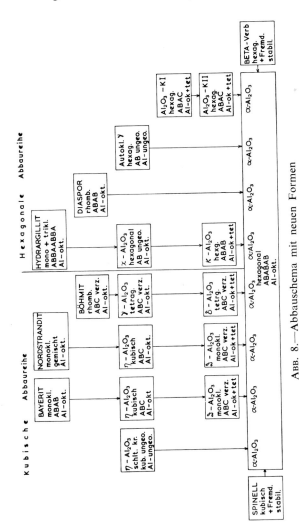

ABB. 8.—Abbauschema mit neuen Formen

Übergang zu Korund tritt hier also durch Platzwechsel der Al-Ionen ein.

Als weiterer Hinweis für die Richtigkeit dieser Vorstellung kann der direkte Übergang des Autoklavengamma zu Korund angesehen werden. Autoklavengamma [8] bildet sich bei der Zersetzung metallischen Aluminiums mit Wasserdampf unter Druck als Vorstufe zu den meisten anderen hydrothermal entstehenden Formen, also auch zu Al_2O_3-KI. Die Intensitätsverteilung der Röntgeninterferenzen von Autoklavengamma weist, trotz einer ziemlich ungeordneten Sauerstoffschichtfolge, auf eine bevorzugte Besetzung der Tetraederlücken im Sauerstoffgitter hin. Bei den Entwässerung müssen die Al-Ionen daher nicht mehr ihre Plätze wechseln und die Ausbildung einer Hochtemperaturform der γ-Aluminiumoxyde unterbleibt daher.

Mit Hilfe dieser gittergeometrischen Überlegungen könnte man auch das Reaktionsverhalten der verschiedenen Aluminiumoxyde, insbesonders der Al_2O_3-Form KI, mit Lithiumkarbonat erklären. Da die Tieftemperaturform des $LiAlO_2$ eine oktaedrische Sauerstoffkoordination aufweist, erfolgt unter den betrachteten Verhältnissen der direkte Übergang des η-Al_2O_3 sowie des Korund in diese Form leicht. Die Form KI ist aber strukturmäßig behindert und bildet zunächst eine Zwischenform aus. Erst über diese Zwischenform des $LiAlO_2$-K sowie über die Abbauform K II mit teilweiser Besetzung der Oktaederplätze, ist der Übergang in die Tieftemperaturform möglich.

Für die Erklärung der teilweisen Bildung der Hochtemperaturmodifikation müßten nähere Einzelheiten über die einzelnen Strukturen bekannt sein.

Dieses Beispiel hat gezeigt, wie sehr das Reaktionsverhalten der Aluminiumoxyde durch deren Struktur beeinflußt wird.

Die verschiedenartige Reaktionsmöglichkeit besonders der hier besprochenen neuen Formen eröffnet auch weite Anwendungsmöglichkeiten in der Keramik.

LITERATUR

1. Krischner, H., und Torkar, K., "Science of Ceramics," Vol. I, S.63-76 (1961).
2. Lehmann, H. A., und Hesselbarth, H., Z. anorg. Chem., (313), 117, 1961, und (315), 14, 1962.
3. Hummel, F. A., J. Amer. Ceram. Soc., **34**, 235, 1951.
4. Lehmann, H. A., und Hesselbarth, H., Z. anorg. Chem. (315), 14, 1962.
5. Kordes, E., Z Krist., **91,** 193, 1935.
6. Torkar, K., und Mitarbeiter, Mh. Chem., **91,** 450, 1960.
7. Torkar, K., und Krischner, H., Mh. Chem., **91,** 757, 1960.
8. Torkar, K., und Krischner, H., Mh. Chem., **91,** 658, 1960.
9. Torkar, K., Lasser, K., und Fritzer, H. P., Sprechsaal (10), Jahrg. 96, 1962.

10. Schwiete, H. E., und Ziegler, G., *Ber. Dtsch. Keram. Ges.*, **35**, 193, 1958.
11. Hofmann, E. G., und Jagodzinski, H., *Z. Metallkunde*, **9**, 601, 1955.
12. Saalfeld, H., *N. Jb. Miner. Abh.*, **96**, 1, 1960.
13. Sasvari, K., und Zalai, A., *Acta Geol.*, IV, 415, 1957.

3—A New Look at X-ray and D.t.a. as applied to Quantitative Analysis of Kaolinitic Clays

By P. S. Keeling

British Ceramic Research Association

ABSTRACT   A553–D642–D551

The concept that the clay mineral in kaolinitic clays belongs to a continuous series implies that X-ray and d.t.a. results are influenced by the nature as well as the proportion of clay mineral. Quantitative comparisons could therefore only be made if the nature of the clay mineral is the same. On the other hand, both the nature and proportion of clay mineral can be estimated from IL and MA values without reference to standard samples.

Un point de vue nouveau concernant l'application de l'analyse par diffraction des rayons X et de l'analyse thermique différentielle à l'analyse quantitative des argiles kaoliniques

Le concept que, dans les argiles kaoliniques, le minéral de l'argile appartient à une série continue, implique que les résultats de diffraction-X et d'A.T.D. sont influencés par la teneur en minéral de l'argile aussi bien que par sa nature. Des comparaisons quantitatives ne pourraient donc être faites que si la nature du minéral de l'argile est la même. Par contre la teneur en minéral de l'argile et sa nature peuvent toutes deux être estimées à partir de valeurs obtenues sans référence à des échantillons normalisés.

Neue Betrachtungen über die Anwendung von Röntgenstrahlen und DTA auf die quantitative Analyse von kaolinitischen Tonen

Die Vorstellung, die die Tonminerale in kaolinitischen Tonen zu einer kontinuierlichen Serie gehören, führt dazu, dass Ergebnisse, die mit Röntgenstrahlen und DTA erhalten werden, sowohl von der Natur als auch vom Anteil des Tonminerals abhängen. Quantitative Vergleiche können deswegen nur angestellt werden, wenn die Natur des Minerals die gleiche ist. Andererseits können sowohl die Natur als auch der Anteil des Tonminerals aus IL- und MA-Werten bestimmt werden, ohne dass man sich auf Standardproben zu beziehen braucht.

1. INTRODUCTION

The clays reviewed in this paper are normal and disordered kaolinites such as are widely used in the ceramic industries. Their quantitative analysis, particularly the nature and proportion of clay mineral, is a matter of considerable interest to the industries concerned, and various methods, of which X-ray and d.t.a. are the most common, have been tried.

Many clay mineralogists have commented on the difficulties involved. BRINDLEY,[1] for example, regards the variable chemical compositions of most clay minerals as the main cause of difficulty, while VAN DER MAREL [2] regards differences in particle size, thickness of amorphous coatings, and degree of structural disorder as the main factors that disturb quantitative investigation.

A common basis for these points of view, as applied to kaolinitic minerals, may be found in the theory put forward by KEELING [3, 4] in which such factors are seen to be outward expressions of a continuously variable composition based on the kaolinite lattice. This has been called the " kaolinite series ".

2. THE KAOLINITE SERIES

Kaolinite is a layer lattice mineral whose ideal structural composition can be expressed in terms of the unit cell as follows:

$$O_6Si_4[O_4(OH)_2]Al_4(OH)_6. \qquad . \qquad . \qquad . \qquad . \qquad . \qquad (1)$$

China clays contain a well-ordered kaolinite of approximately this formula. But china clay is composed of plate-like crystals each of which is made up with a large number of unit lattices. Specific surface area measurements give values around $10 \, m^2/g$ and from the basal spacing, which is known from X-ray to be 7·15Å, it is calculated that the average crystal is about 100 unit lattices thick. The comparatively weak force holding the lattices together across the thickness of the crystal plate (c axis) is generally regarded as a hydrogen bond between the H of the (OH) and the O of the adjacent lattice.

From an examination of the chemical analyses of 26 clays consisting virtually of clay mineral and mica, and covering the range from well-ordered kaolinite through disordered kaolinite to illite, a general formula based on the kaolinite lattice was deduced for the clay mineral [5]:

$$O_6Si_4[O_4(OH)_2] [(Al,Fe)_{4-2n}^{3+} X_n^{2+}](OH)_{6-4n} . \qquad . \qquad (2)$$

in which X represents divalent cations such as Mg^{2+} and Fe^{2+}, and n covers the range 0–1.

This formula gives the average structural composition for the whole sample. In terms of individual lattices, it can be envisaged as crystals composed of unit lattices in which a proportion of the lattices are at $n=1$, i.e.

$$O_6Si_4[O_4(OH)_2] [Al_2 Mg](OH)_2 \qquad . \qquad . \qquad . \qquad (3)$$

This seems to involve an essentially octahedral layer with six anions on one side and two on the other, whereas in the ideal lattice there are six on each side. To give a more even distribution of anions around the cations it would seem better to express the kaolinite series in the form:

$$O_6Si_4[O_4(OH)_{2-2n}][Al, Fe]_{4-2n}^{3+}X_n^{2+}](OH)_{6-2n} \quad . \quad (4)$$

which at $n = 1$ would give

$$O_6Si_4O_4[Al_2Mg](OH)_4 \quad . \quad . \quad . \quad . \quad . \quad (5)$$

with the same number of anions on either side of the octahedral cations.

The modified general structural formula (4) retains the same ionic composition as (2) and also has a reduction of outer (OH) anions which, it has been suggested, is responsible for reduced hydrogen bonding, and therefore reduced crystal thickness, reduced particle size and increased specific surface area of disordered kaolinites. Variations in chemical composition, particle size, and structural disorder are believed to be attributable to the underlying structural composition which is characterized by the value of n in the general formula given above.

3. IL/MA

KEELING [6] has developed a simple method from which it is possible to estimate both the nature and proportion of the clay mineral in kaolinitic clays by determining the ignition loss due to combined water (IL), and the moisture adsorption under standard conditions (MA). The former represents (OH) groups and the latter, specific surface area. The method does not yet appear to be widely known but it has been endorsed by SVEJDA.[7]

The samples whose X-ray and d.t.a. results are illustrated below are shown on IL/MA graphs in order to bring out variations in the nature and proportion of the clay mineral. They have been chosen from the previously mentioned 26 samples consisting virtually of clay mineral and mica.

4. X-RAY RESULTS

The X-ray results shown below consist of diffraction traces taken on samples pressed into rectangular recesses, and using Co Kα radiation at a scanning speed of $\frac{1}{4}°$ (2θ) per minute on a Philips diffractometer. The values of n (OH deficiency divided by 4) and proportions of clay mineral calculated from the chemical analyses have been taken from Tables 3 and 4 of a previous paper.[5]

Figure 1 shows the diffraction traces of a group of clays in which the proportion of clay mineral varies from 82 to 90% (Table 1).

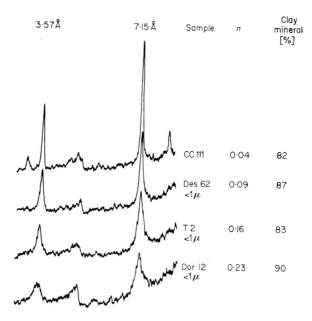

FIG. 1.—X-ray diffractometer traces of kaolinitic clays with 82–90% clay mineral arranged in order of increasing *n* value.

The IL/MA plot for these clays is shown in Fig. 2. CC 111, a Cornish china clay used in the British pottery industry, has a low *n* value of 0·04 and the kaolinite 00*l* peaks at 7·15 Å and 3·57 Å are intense and sharp. The second clay with an *n* value of 0·09 is a S. Devon ball clay with a rather less well-ordered clay mineral, and although the proportion of clay mineral is greater than in CC 111, the 00*l* peaks are less intense and sharp. T2 is a fireclay with an *n* value of

Table 1

Characteristics of Clays examined by X-ray Diffraction

Sample	n	Clay mineral (%)	IL (%)	MA (%)
CC 111	0·04	82	12·0	1·4
Des 62 <1μ	0·09	87	12·1	3·2
T2 <1μ	0·16	83	11·3	4·6
Dor 12 <1μ	0·23	90	11·6	5·7
Des 14 <1μ	0·23	67	9·8	4·2
T12 <1μ	0·37	68	9·3	5·6
EM 265 <1μ	0·44	73	9·3	7·1
LC 81 <1μ	0·90	69	7·3	9·3

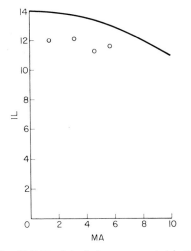

FIG. 2.—IL/MA plot of clay represented in Fig. 1.

0·16, and a further broadening of the 00*l* peaks is apparent. The drop in intensity and broadening of these peaks is even more pronounced in Dor 12, a Dorset ball clay which is calculated to have the highest proportion of clay mineral and an *n* value of 0·23.

The diffraction traces for a second group of clays in which the calculated clay mineral content varies from 67 to 73% is shown on Fig. 3, and the IL/MA plot on Fig. 4 (Table 1). Des 14 is a S. Devon ball clay with a disordered kaolinite clay mineral giving an *n* value of 0·23. The second clay, T12, is a fireclay with a more disordered clay mineral with *n* value of 0·37. EM 265 is an Etruria Marl with an *n* value of 0·44. LC 81 is a London clay used for brickmaking and would be described as illitic; its *n* value is 0·90. This group of clays shows a rather more marked loss of intensity coupled with broadening of the 00*l* peaks as *n* increases.

A relationship between the 7.15 Å peak and value of *n* which, in effect, characterizes the chemical composition of the clay mineral, can be obtained by plotting the width of the peak at half height from the base line, divided by the area of the peak (W/A) against *n*. This is approximately the same as plotting the reciprocal of peak height against *n*, but the ratio W/A takes some account of peak shape. The relationship is shown in Fig. 5 for a number of clays including the ones illustrated in Figs. 1 and 3.

Although it could be argued, as BRINDLEY [8] has done, that the variation in the 7·15 Å peak is due to variation in preferential orientation, it must be remembered that all the samples had the

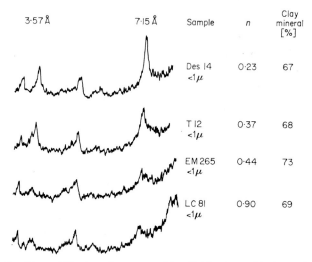

FIG. 3.—X-ray diffractometer traces of kaolinitic clays with 67–73% clay mineral arranged in order of increasing n value.

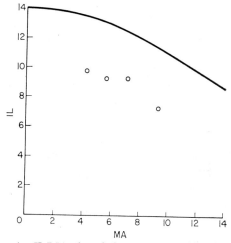

FIG. 4.—IL/MA plot of clays represented in Fig. 3.

same preparatory treatment. The fact that variation in this peak can be closely correlated with the value of n suggests that the shape of the peak is yet another expression of the underlying structural composition. Even when completely random orientation was obtained by the use of a thermoplastic cement, BRINDLEY [8] found that the basal ($00l$) reflection intensities tended to diminish slightly as

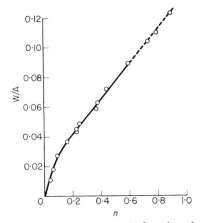

FIG. 5.—Relationship between 7·15 Å peak and n value.

the reflection width increased, and he recommended that in analytical work a standard kaolinite should be used which would give basal reflections of the same angular width as those from the kaolinite to be determined. In terms of IL/MA this would mean a standard sample with the same IL/MA characteristics as the clay to be examined; or in terms of structural composition, a standard sample with the same n value as the clay to be examined. IL/MA, however, is not subject to such a restriction since the position of a sample on the IL/MA plot allows both the nature and proportion of the clay mineral to be estimated.

5. D.T.A. RESULTS

With the d.t.a. results, it has been possible to show more clearly the separate effects of the nature and proportion of the clay mineral. The samples were originally chosen from a graph of combined water, representing (OH) groups, plotted against potash, representing mica. This is shown as Fig. 6, and the points represent samples consisting virtually of clay mineral and mica previously examined by the author.[5] Vertical lines crossing the sample area may be taken as representative of a fixed proportion of clay mineral but with disorder, (OH) deficiency and n value increasing from top to bottom. Lines from the direction of the muscovite apex of the sample area to the combined water axis, may be regarded as representing increasing proportions of essentially the same type of clay mineral.

Groups of clays on two fairly vertical lines, AB and CD, representing roughly the same proportions of different types of clay mineral, and a group on line EF, representing different proportions of the same type of clay mineral, have been investigated. The n values, proportions of clay mineral calculated from the chemical analyses, and IL and MA values are given in Table 2, and the IL/MA plots are shown in Figs. 7, 9, and 11.

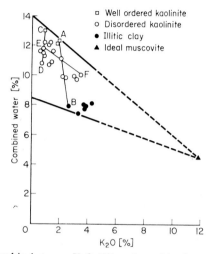

FIG. 6.—Relationship between K_2O (%) and combined water (%)* for clays examined by d.t.a.

Table 2
Characteristics of Clays examined by D.t.a.

Sample	n	Clay mineral (%)	IL (%)	MA (%)
A – B				
CC 111	0·04	82	12·0	1·4
T6 < 1μ	0·25	78	10·7	5·3
EM 265 < 1μ	0·44	73	9·3	7·1
LC 24 < 1μ	0·91	75	7·3	10·9
C – D				
Des 18	0·02	90	12·8	2·1
Dor 12 < 1μ	0·23	90	11·6	5·7
EM 278 < 1μ	0·28	88	11·1	6·5
EM 256 < 1μ	0·41	87	10·3	7·9
E – F				
Dor 12 < 1μ	0·23	90	11·6	5·7
T2 < 1μ	0·17	83	11·3	4·6
T6 < 1μ	0·21	78	10·7	5·3
Des 14 < 1μ	0·23	67	9·8	4·2

* The combined-water values in Fig. 6 have been calculated on a 100% clay mineral/mica basis and, because of small proportions of impurities in the samples, are slightly higher than the IL values in Table 2.

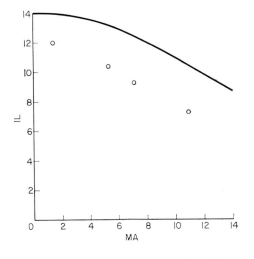

FIG. 7.—IL/MA plot of clays on line AB.

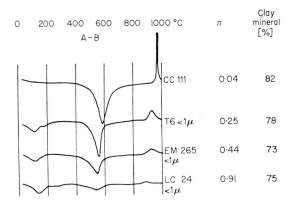

FIG. 8.—D.t.a. results in order of increasing *n* value for clays on line AB.

Figure 8, showing the d.t.a. curves for the samples on line AB, starts with the china clay CC 111, consisting mainly of well-ordered kaolinite with an *n* value of 0·04. The second clay is a fireclay with a disordered kaolinite—*n* value, 0·25. The third clay is an Etruria Marl with a more disordered kaolinite, and an *n* value 0·44, and the fourth clay is a London clay with an *n* value of 0·91. The main features as *n* value and disorder increase are:

(1) Increase in size and peak temperature of the low-temperature endotherm, representing loss of adsorbed moisture, corresponding with MA value;

(2) Decrease in size and peak temperature of 500°–600°C. endotherm, representing loss of combined water,

(3) Decrease in intensity and peak temperature of 900°–1,000°C. exotherm, representing recrystallization of alumino-silicate.

The same effects can be seen in Fig. 10 (line CD), representing a higher proportion and somewhat narrower range of clay mineral,

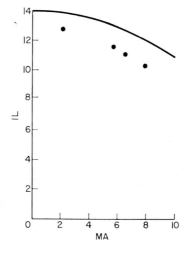

FIG. 9.—IL/MA plot of clays on line CD.

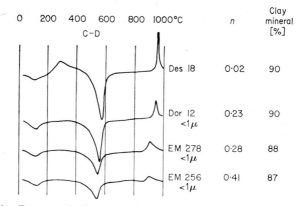

FIG. 10.—D.t.a. results in order of increasing n value for clays on line CD.

from Des 18, a well-ordered S. Devon ball clay, to EM 256, a very disordered Etruria Marl. On the other hand, Fig. 12 (line EF), with clays of essentially the same type arranged in order of decreasing clay mineral content, shows rather similar types of endotherm and exotherm with a general diminution of peak area as the proportion of clay mineral decreases, but with little or no tendency for peak temperatures to change.

It seems clear that optimum peak temperature is controlled by the nature of the clay mineral and that peak area depends as much on the nature of the clay mineral as on the proportion present.

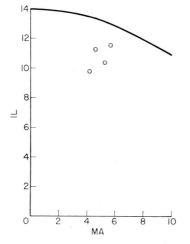

FIG. 11.—IL/MA plot of clays on line EF.

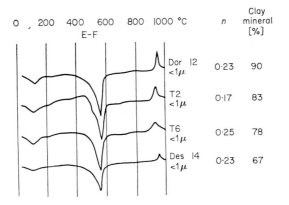

FIG. 12.—D.t.a. results for clays on line EF.

Quantitative analysis could only be safely undertaken by comparing a clay with a standard containing essentially the same type of clay mineral.

6. CONCLUSIONS

The difficulties associated with the use of X-ray and d.t.a. for the quantitative analysis of kaolinitic clays arise because the structural compositions of the clay minerals show a continuous variation. X-ray and d.t.a. results reflect both the nature and the proportion of clay mineral, and there is no obvious way of separating the two. Errors will inevitably arise unless the sample to be analysed is compared with a standard sample containing the same type of clay mineral. In the IL/MA method, with which the X-ray and d.t.a. results have been compared, the determinations are of combined water representing (OH) groups, and of MA representing specific surface area. The specific surface area is inversely proportional to the average thickness of the crystal plates, and depends on the strength of the inter-lattice hydrogen bond provided by the hydrogen of the outer (OH) groups. The IL and MA values of the clay mineral having been worked out,[5] and the relationship plotted on a graph, it is possible to estimate both the nature and proportion of clay mineral for any kaolinitic clay without reference to standard samples.

ACKNOWLEDGMENTS

The author is indebted to Mr. F. G. Wilde for the X-ray results and to Dr. N. F. Astbury, Director of the British Ceramic Research Association, for permission to publish.

REFERENCES

1. Brindley, G. W., "X-ray Identification and Crystal Structures of Clay Minerals" (Ed. G. Brown. Min. Soc., London, 1961), Chapter XIV.
2. Van der Marel, H. W., "Quantitative Analysis of Kaolinite," *Silicates Industriels*, **25**, pp. 23 and 76, 1960.
3. Keeling, P. S, "The Common Clay Minerals as a Continuous Series," "Science of Ceramics," Vol. 1, 153–165, 1962.
4. Keeling, P. S., "The Kaolinite Series," "Trans. VIII Int. Ceram. Congr., Copenhagen," pp. 53–57, 1962.
5. Keeling, P. S., "A New Concept of Clay Minerals," *Trans. Brit. Ceram. Soc.*, **60**, 449, 1961.
6. Keeling, P. S., "The Examination of Clays by IL/MA," *Trans. Brit. Ceram. Soc.*, **60**, 217, 1961.
7. Svejda, H., "Ein Beitrag zur Untersuchung des Mineralbestandes von Tonen," *Ziegelindustrie*, **15**, 336, 1962.
8. Brindley, G. W., and Kurtossy, S. S., "Quantitative Determination of Kaolinite by X-ray Diffraction," *Amer. Min.* **46**, 1205, 1961.

4—Adsorption of Basic and Acidic Dyes by Clays and their Relations to Specific Surface

By G. Boardman and W. E. Worrall

Ceramics Division, Houldsworth School of Applied Science,
University of Leeds

ABSTRACT A451

Experiments on several clays of predetermined surface area indicated that basic dye-adsorption is likely to predict the total specific surface area to within $+10\%$, but the values may be in error by as much as 50%. Within these limits, the technique is the simplest and quickest for the purpose. Some acid dyes are strongly adsorbed and appear to form a monolayer, similar to basic dyes. Results for different clays suggest that the weight of dye thus adsorbed is not directly related to specific surface. Other acid dyes are less strongly adsorbed, in a manner showing some similarities to Gibbsian adsorption. Fundamentally the weight adsorbed is proportional to the adsorbing area and the supernatant concentration, but the constant of proportionality varies from clay to clay, making predictions of surface area impossible. There are also some deviations from this mechanism: certain clays appear to have a small anion-exchange capacity; with some, the dye and acid, when added to aid adsorption, compete for the surface and, above a critical supernatant concentration, there is a sharp increase in weight adsorbed.

Adsorption par les argiles des colorants acides et basiques et sa rélation avec la surface spécifique

Des expériences faites avec plusieurs argiles, dont on connaissait la surface spécifique, ont indiqué que l'adsorption d'un colorant basique a quelque chance de permettre de prédire la surface spécifique totale à $+10\%$ près mais que la valeur de l'erreur peut atteindre 50%. Entre ces limites c'est là la technique la plus simple et las plus rapide pour obtenir le résultat cherché. Certains colorants acides sont fortement adsorbés et semblent former une couche monomoléculaire, comme le font les colorants basiques. Les résultats obtenus avec des argiles différentes donnent à penser que le poids du colorant ainsi adsorbé n'est pas en rapport direct avec la surface spécifique. D'autres colorants acides sont moins fortement adsorbés, de façon similaire à l'adsorption gibbsienne. En principe le poids adsorbé est proportionnel à l'aire adsorbante et à la concentration du liquide surnageant, mais la constante de proportionnalité varie d'une argile à une autre, ce qui rend impossible toute prédiction de surface spécifique. Ce mécanisme n'est pas toujours respecté: certaines argiles semblent posséder une petite capacité d'échange d'anions; dans le cas de certaines autres le colorant et l'acide, lorsque l'on en ajoute pour faciliter l'adsorption, entrent en compétition pour la surface, au-dessus d'une concentration critique du liquide surnageant et l'on observe une nette augmentation du poids adsorbé.

Die Adsorption von basischen und sauren Farbstoffen an Ton und Beziehungen zur spez. Oberfläche

Versuche an verschiedenen Tonen, deren Oberflächenverhalten bestimmt worden war, zeigten, dass die Adsorption von basischen Farbstoffen die gesamte spez. Oberfläche innerhalb $\pm 10\%$ genau voraussagt, aber die Werte können bis zu 50% falsch sein. Innerhalb dieser Grenzen ist diese Technik die einfachste und schnellste. Einige saure Farbstoffe werden stark adsorbiert und scheinen Monoschichten zu bilden, ebenso wie die basischen Farbstoffe. Ergebnisse für verschiedene Tone zeigen, dass das Gewicht der so adsorbierten Farbstoffe nicht in direkter Beziehung zur spez. Oberfläche steht. Andere saure Farbstoffe werden weniger stark adsorbiert und zeigen Ähnlichkeit mit einer Gibbschen Adsorption. Grundsätzlich ist die adsorbierte Menge der adsorbierenden Fläche proportional und der überbleibenden Konzentration. Die Proportionalitätskonstante ist aber von Ton zu Ton verschieden und macht Voraussagen über die Oberfläche unmöglich. Es gibt auch Abweichungen von diesem Mechanismus. Einige Tone scheinen ein geringes Anionenaustauschvermögen zu haben. Bei einigen treten Farbstoff und Säure in Konkurrenz um die Oberfläche und oberhalb einer kritischen Konzentration gibt es eine scharfe Zunahme in der adsorbierten Menge.

1. INTRODUCTION

Several properties involved in the production of clay-based ceramic articles depend on the specific surface area of the raw material. Such properties include plasticity of a clay–water paste and shrinkage characteristics. In order to be able to control these properties better industrially, it is desirable to be able to measure easily both the ultimate surface area, when all the individual clay particles are dispersed, and the area actually available for a given process owing to aggregation of the particles. The present work is concerned with the former of these topics, with special reference to the building-brick industry.

Most of the convenient methods of measuring specific surfaces, e.g. by turbidimetry or permeability, measure only a superficial surface area. Methods which are accepted as yielding an accurate value of the total surface area, e.g. gas adsorption, are laborious and need complex apparatus. Studying the adsorption of solutes from solutions has often been suggested as a more convenient method (e.g. EWING and RHODA,[1] MARON, BOBALEK and FOK[2]) and the use of dye-solutions presents a particularly simple technique. The objects of the present work were to examine the existing basic dye-adsorption technique for determining specific surfaces of clay and to investigate the possible use of acidic dye adsorption.

2. EXPERIMENTAL

2.1 Dye Adsorption

The technique was kept as simple as possible in view of possible industrial use, and was therefore restricted to aqueous dye-solutions.

In general, carefully measured quantities of the clay and the dye-solution to be used were placed in a test-tube which was then closed with a rubber stopper, shaken vigorously for 1 min and left to stand overnight. It was not found necessary to use any more prolonged agitation than this, or to purify any of the dyes used. Some of the brick- and fire-clays were washed in HCl to remove impurities which gave rise to effervescence in the acidic solutions used in Section 3.33.

The supernatant solutions were determined colorimetrically by means of a Spekker colorimeter (Hilger and Watts Ltd). In some cases they were centrifuged first; in others, turbidity was either absent or could be allowed for by making measurements with Spekker filters of two different colours. pH measurements were made with a Cambridge pH meter.

Tests were made on the dyes to ensure that, under the conditions in which they were to be used, they were not subject to appreciable fading or colour change with pH.

2.2 Calibration of the Clays

Accurate values of the specific surface areas of the clays to be used were obtained by means of the gas-adsorption technique of BRUNAUER, EMMETT and TELLER,[3] using nitrogen as adsorbate.

3. RESULTS AND DISCUSSION

3.1 B.E.T. Results

Table 1

B.E.T. Specific Surfaces of the Clays Used

Clay	Specific surface (m²)
China	13·2
Ball	27·8
Fireclay	12·3
Brick-clay 1	26·9
Brick-clay 2	18·2
Brick-clay 3a	8·86
Brick-clay 3b	8·71

3.2 Basic-dye Adsorption

3.21 Theory to be Tested

The theory of this type of adsorption, as given by WORRALL,[4] may be summarized as follows. Basic dyes in solution ionize to give a large organic cation and a simple anion. A clay, by virtue of its cation-exchange capacity (c.e.c.), has a strong affinity for the dye cations which, because of their organic nature, tend in aqueous solution to displace completely the initial cations on the clay. Unless a clay has a low c.e.c., however, the large cations will cover the surface completely before they have satisfied the c.e.c. It is assumed that only this monolayer is adsorbed, it screening off the unsatisfied part of the c.e.c., and that the orientation and packing-density of the adsorbed ions is the same in all circumstances.

This last assumption is open to objection; e.g. it is known that some basic dyes can take up several different orientations on different adsorbents (see KIPLING and WILSON [5]) and so the theory needs to be tested thoroughly. The results below were intended as a contribution to this.

3.22 Experiments

Experiments were carried out with two dyes, methylene blue and malachite green. Figure 1 shows the variation of the proportion of methylene blue adsorbed by various clays from a $0.01M$ initial solution with total area of clay.

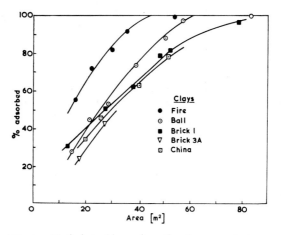

FIG. 1.—Methylene blue adsorption by several clays

3.23 Discussion

According to the theory of Section 3.21, all the points in Fig. 1, for adsorption of less than 100%, should lie on a single straight line. In fact, the points for six of the clays fall within a band which enables areas to be predicted to within about $\pm 10\%$ in the region of 60–80% adsorption. The results for the fireclay diverge widely from this band however, showing about 50% greater adsorption than the other clays. This same type of divergence was found also with malachite green adsorption, and with a 0·1M initial solution of methylene blue.

It appears therefore that basic-dye adsorption is likely to yield specific surface values for any clay within 10% of the B.E.T. value but this cannot be entirely relied on and there may be a divergence of as much as 50%. Provided that no greater accuracy than this is required, basic-dye adsorption is probably the simplest way of measuring the specific surface areas of clays.

The curvature of the curves in Fig. 1 is probably owing to a small amount of physical adsorption in addition to the monolayer, varying with supernatant concentration. It is therefore desirable to use a separate calibration curve for each initial concentration of dye used.

3.3 Acidic-dye Adsorption

3.31 Theory: Monolayer Adsorption

Acidic dyes ionize in solution into a complex anion and a simple cation. Clays have very little affinity for anions. There may, however, be sufficient affinity, e.g. through –OH bonding or van der Waals forces, between the clay and the dye for a monolayer of undissociated molecules to be formed.

3.32 Theory: Gibbsian Adsorption

The types of adsorption so far discussed have involved strong attractive forces between the dye-molecules and the clay surface, and are therefore open to the objection mentioned in Section 3.21. It was decided therefore to investigate possible types of adsorption in which no attraction by the surface for the adsorbate occurs. GIBBS[6] treated theoretically a form of adsorption which arises from the thermodynamic requirement of the solution to reduce its surface tension to a minimum and not from the nature of the adsorbing surface, and therefore falls into the required category.

Gibbs derived the following equation for this type of adsorption:

$$w = - \frac{Ac}{RT} \frac{d\gamma}{dc} \qquad \cdot \quad \cdot \quad \cdot \quad \cdot \quad (1)$$

where w is the weight absorbed; A, γ, are the area and tension respectively of the interface; c is the bulk concentration of the solution, $T°$K the temperature and R the gas constant.

At very low concentrations this becomes

$$w = kAc \quad . \quad . \quad . \quad . \quad . \quad (2)$$

where k is a constant (see ADAM [7]).

If it is assumed that γ is the same at all surfaces having no attraction for the dye, k will be independent of the nature of the surface.

Now $\qquad\qquad w = V(c_0 - c)$

where V, c_0 are the volume and initial concentration of the dye solution, and

$$A = SM$$

where M is the mass of clay used and S the specific surface of the clay. Hence

$$\frac{V(c_0 - c)}{c} \equiv kA = kSM \quad . \quad . \quad . \quad . \quad (3).$$

Thus a graph of $\dfrac{V(c_0 - c)}{c}$ versus A for a clay of predetermined specific surface should give a line of slope k; and graphs of $V(c_0 - c)/ck$ versus M for unknown clays should then yield lines of slope S.

3.33 Experiments

Preliminary experiments showed that Napthol Green (C.I. 10025)[8] appeared to attain a monolayer beyond which little adsorption occurred. It was therefore used to check the theory of Section 3.31. In some cases HCl had to be added, as little adsorption took place at high pH, showing that only undissociated molecules were adsorbed. The pH could not be reduced below about 4, however, as a colour change took place.

The dyes Orange G (C.I. 16230) and Orange II (C.I. 15510) were found in preliminary experiments to show no sign of forming monolayers, and their adsorption seemed consistent with Equation (3). Their structures are as follows:

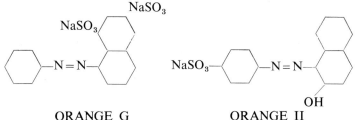

ORANGE G   ORANGE II

The simple structures make it likely that van der Waals adsorption will be negligible, and –OH bonding is ruled out by the fact that the only –OH group is in a shielded position.[9] It was therefore decided to investigate thoroughly the adsorption mechanism of these dyes, to see if they could be used in determinations of specific surface either by the theory of Section 3.32 or otherwise.

Presumably because of the extra ionizable Na atom, Orange G adsorbed less than Orange II in similar circumstances, so the latter was preferred. Orange G was used in a few of the experiments, however. The general mechanisms of adsorption of the two dyes appeared to be very similar. It was found that over the acid pH range the dyes underwent no colour change.

The weight of dye adsorbed by a given clay in any experiment may be expected to depend on (1) the pH, (2) the initial dye-concentration, and (3) the area of clay. Accordingly the variation in the weight adsorbed obtained by varying each one of these properties and keeping the other two constant was found for several clays.

3.34 Results: Naphthol Green Adsorption

Table 2

**Apparent Specific Surface Areas, Monolayer Formation by
Naphthol Green being Assumed
(China clay is taken as standard)**

Clay	Apparent specific surface ($m^2\ g^{-1}$)
China	13·2
Ball	17·0
Fireclay	5·7
Brick-clay 1	11·9

Comparison with Table 1 shows that this type of acidic-dye adsorption is not promising as a method of measuring the specific surface areas of clays.

3.35 Results: Orange G and Orange II Adsorption

Figure 2 shows the results of adsorptions by constant areas of various clays from Orange G of constant c_o and varying pH. The increase in fraction adsorbed with decrease of pH from 6 to 2 fits the theory of section 3.32 provided that it is assumed that only undissociated molecules are substantially adsorbed, so that k is a function of H (the H^+ concentration), k increasing continually with

H. The existence of several widely separated curves, however, also means that the vital assumption that k is the same for all clays is invalidated. The fall in fraction adsorbed below pH = 2 indicates that a more complex mechanism must occur here. (There is a lack of points between pH 2 and pH 4·5 in Fig. 2, but other experiments have shown that the curves are of the form drawn here.)

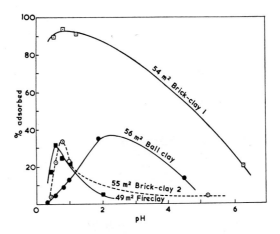

FIG. 2.—Effect of pH on Orange G adsorption

The variations of weight of dye adsorbed by constant areas of several clays from solutions of varying c_o and constant pH were next considered. Two different mechanisms of adsorption were found as shown in Fig. 3 (full lines; for the china and ball clays) and Fig. 4 (for brick-clay 1).

From Equation (3)

$$c/c_o = V/(kA + V)$$
$$\therefore (c_o - c)/c_o = kA/(KA + V) \quad . \quad . \quad . \quad (4)$$

so that if the theory of Section 3.32 held, the fraction of dye adsorbed would be constant for each pH and A value. When c_o becomes too large for Equation (2) to hold, the fraction adsorbed may be expected to decrease, so the increase actually found, as in Fig. 3, must have a different explanation.

If it is assumed that HCl (presumably the undissociated molecule) is also adsorbed and that there is competition for places between the two types of molecule, it is possible to explain Fig. 3 and account for the fall in fraction adsorbed at low pH in Fig. 2.

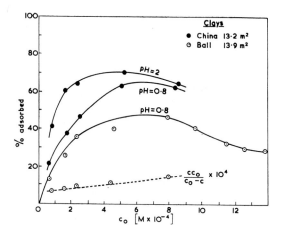

FIG. 3.—Relation between fraction of Orange II adsorbed and initial concentration for a china- and a ball-clay

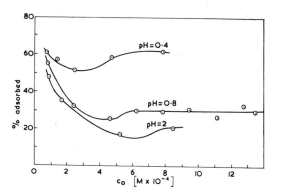

FIG. 4.—Relation between fraction of Orange II adsorbed and initial concentration for a brick-clay

Suppose that the surface area is divided into a part A_{dye}, covered by the dye in accordance with the mechanism of Equation (2), and a part A_{HCl}, covered by HCl molecules and not available for dye adsorption. Suppose also that these areas are determined by the initial concentrations of the dye and acid, in accordance with the equation

$$A_{HCl}/A_{dye} = c_0/KH \quad . \quad . \quad . \quad (5)$$

where K is a constant. Then

$$A_{dye}/A = c_o/(c_o + KH). \qquad . \qquad . \qquad . \qquad (6)$$

and Equation (2) becomes

$$w = \frac{k(H)Ac_oc}{c_o + KH} \qquad . \qquad . \qquad . \qquad . \qquad (7).$$

The presence of H in the denominator now accounts for the maxima obtained in Fig. 2. At constant pH, Equation (7) gives

$$V(c_o - c) = kAc_oc/(c_o + k') \qquad . \qquad . \qquad . \qquad (8)$$

where $\qquad\qquad\qquad k' = KH$

i.e. $\qquad\qquad \dfrac{c_oc}{V(c_o - c)} = \dfrac{c_o}{kA} + \dfrac{k'}{kA} \qquad . \qquad . \qquad . \qquad (9).$

Thus the proposed mechanism implies a linear relationship between $c_oc/V(c_o - c)$ and c_o. The broken line in Fig. 3 shows this relationship to hold in the case of the ball clay. The china clay does not have this exact relationship, but the form of the curves in Fig. 3 makes it likely that the theory applies qualitatively. At the higher c_o values shown in Fig. 3, the fraction adsorbed tends to decrease. No explanation is as yet offered for this effect.

In Fig. 4, for brick-clay 1, the curves tend to a large value of the ordinate $c_o = 0$ instead of to the origin as in Fig. 3. Similar curves were obtained with the fireclay. Suppose that, in addition to the weight of dye adsorbed according to Equation (8), a weight w' is adsorbed independently of the concentration, so that

$$w' = k''A \qquad . \qquad . \qquad . \qquad . \qquad (10).$$

Then the fraction of dye adsorbed by this mechanism

$$\frac{w}{Vc_o} = \frac{k''A}{V} \cdot \frac{1}{c_o} \qquad . \qquad . \qquad . \qquad . \qquad (11).$$

This component of the fraction adsorbed will thus decrease rapidly with increasing c_o. The curves of Fig. 4 fit in well with the possibility that a component of this type is superimposed on curves similar to those obtained in Fig. 3. The independence of concentration of this component indicates that it is owing to strong chemical attraction. It is suggested that the lattice imperfections inherent in brick- and fire-clays give rise in some cases to a small anion-exchange capacity.

The final set of experiments was performed with various areas of clay and solutions of constant c_o and pH. In these circumstances, the weight adsorbed is likely to be given by Equation (2) for a clay without an anion-exchange capacity (a.e.c.) and, for a clay possessing one, by

$$w = V(c_0 - c) = kAc + k''A . \quad . \quad . \quad (12).$$

Thus a plot of $V(c_0 - c)/Av. c$ should yield a straight line of slope k and, where appropriate, intercept k''. Figure 5 shows that adsorption from very dilute solution does in fact give rise to curves of this form, and confirms the previous results that the ball clay has no a.e.c. and that the fireclay and brick-clay [1] have a.e.c. of 0·11 m.e/100 g and 0·04 m.e/100 g respectively (compared with c.e.c. of the order of 20 m.e/100 g). At the high end of the concentration range, i.e. for small areas of clay, the ball clay and fireclays 3a and b are seen to deviate widely from the straight line obtained at low c. It appears that, with some clays, the density of adsorbed molecules increases beyond the value predicted by Equation (12) above a critical concentration of the supernatant dye.

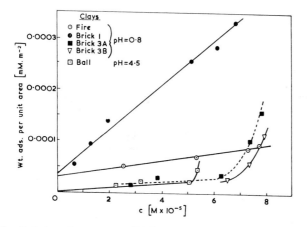

FIG. 5.—Relations between equilibrium concentrations of adsorbed and supernatant Orange II for several clay adsorbants

Clays 3a and b were taken from the same seam and apparently were virtually identical in many properties, including B.E.T. specific surface; they differed in that 3a had a works classification of " good " and 3b one of " very bad " for suitability for brickmaking. It is interesting that these clay samples gave very distinguishable curves in Fig. 5.

As none of the mechanisms discussed in this chapter allow k and A to be determined independently, they do not appear to have any usefulness for determining specific surface areas of clays. It is suggested, however, that further consideration of the various mechanisms may throw some light on the structure of the various clays.

ACKNOWLEDGMENT

The Brick Development Association are thanked for their financial support of the work, and for providing a maintenance grant for one of us (G.B.).

REFERENCES

1. Ewing, W. W., and Rhoda, R. N., *Anal. Chem.,* **22**, 1453, 1950.
2. Maron, S. H., Bobalek, E. G., and Fok, S., *J. Colloid Sci.,* **11**, 21, 1956.
3. Brunauer, S., Emmett, P. H., and Teller, E., *J. Amer. Chem. Soc.,* **60**, 309, 1938.
4. Worrall, W. E., *Trans. Brit. Ceram. Soc.,* **57**, 210, 1958.
5. Kipling, J. J., and Wilson, R. B., *J. Appl. Chem.,* **10**, 109, 1960.
6. Rideal, E. K., " Surface Chemistry " (Cambridge University Press, 1930).
7. Adam, N. K., " The Physics and Chemistry of Surfaces " (Oxford University Press, 1941).
8. Colour Index (Society of Dyers and Colourists: Bradford), 2nd Edition.
9. Allingham, M. M., Cullen, J. M., Giles, C. H., Jain, S. K., and Woods, J. S., *J. Appl. Chem.,* **8**, 108, 1958.

5—Bound Water on Clay

By P. H. DAL and W. J. H. BERDEN

Laboratory N.V. Kon. Sphinx-Céramique,
Maastricht, Netherlands

ABSTRACT
A72

A survey of the literature. The "Webb effect" is discussed in relation to facts and theories from general colloid chemistry. Some measurements have been made on bound water to clarify the discrepancies in the literature; it was found that the specific gravity of water in contact with all types of clay minerals is increased. The accuracy of these determinations is stressed. Measurements of the influence of electrolytes on casting-slips and clay suspensions indicate that the "Webb effect" does not exist.

L'eau liée à l'argile

Etude critique de la littérature. "L'effet WEBB" est étudié en relation avec les faits et les théories de la chimie colloïdale générale. Des mesures ont été faites au sujet de l'eau liée en vue de clarifier les divergences existant dans la littérature; on a constaté que le poids spécifique de l'eau en contact avec tous les types de minéraux de l'argile est augmenté. L'exactitude de ces déterminations est soulignée. Des mesures relatives à l'influence d'électrolytes sur des barbotines de coulage et sur des suspensions d'argile indiquent que "l'effet WEBB" n'existe pas.

Im Ton gebundenes Wasser

Eine Übersicht der Literatur wird gegeben, Das "Phänomen von Webb" wird diskutiert in Zusammenhang mit den Theorien der Kolloidchemie. Mehrere Untersuchungen sind gemacht zur Erklärung der Widersprüche in der Literatur über gebundenes Wasser Im Ton; dabei ist festgestellt worden, dass das spezifische Gewicht von Wasser in Kontakt mit den Tonmineralen zunimmt. Die Genauigkeit dieser Bestimmungen wird betont. Messungen über den Einfluss von Elektrolyten auf Gießschlicker und Tonsuspensionen zeigen dass das "Phänomen von Webb" nicht besteht.

1. PROBLEM AND LITERATURE

Being engaged in a factory making sanitary ware by slip-casting, we are interested in the problems arising in the preparation and handling of clay slips. In 1934 WEBB [1] published an article which contains an important observation. He measured the specific gravity of a bone-china slip to which waterglass had been added and, simultaneously, the viscosity by a flow viscometer, and his results are shown in Table 1.

Table 1

Original Data of the "Webb Effect"

Flow Time (sec.)	Pint weight (oz.)	Specific gravity (g/ml.)
25·0	33·3	1·665
18·2	33·1	1·655
17·0	32·8	1·640
15·0	32·6	1·630
12·5	32·5	1·625
16·2	32·8	1·640
21·9	33·0	1·650

From this table it follows that optimal peptization, which is shown by a minimum flow-time, correlates with minimal pint weight. WILLIAMSON [2] mentions that the decrease in specific gravity with increasing deflocculation is even more marked in an earthenware slip.

In the slip, the quantities of solid matter and water were kept constant. *A priori* one would expect that eventually the specific gravity of this mixture would be constant, except for a small correction for the addition of waterglass, but unfortunately Dr. Webb did not describe how his experiment was performed. According to him, this supposed constancy does not exist, because the experiment shows a change in pint weight, which may be considered relatively large.

It is difficult to assume that the true specific gravity of the mixture of solid materials which makes up the raw bone china body changes by deflocculation because, according to the concept of modern colloid chemistry, peptization only means a change in the surface of the matter by ion exchange, adsorption, charge or potential. This change takes place practically only in the finest grains with the greatest specific surface—the clay minerals.

If the solid matter does not change in specific gravity, one has to assume that the specific gravity of the water phase changes. Because the slip contains much filterable water, which may be called free, this change can only take place in that part of the water that is more or less closely associated with the solid matter in which a colloid chemical change can occur.

To explain the experiment of Webb in this way, one has to accept two assumptions:

(1) Coagulated clay possesses a hull, layer or mantle of bound water with a higher specific gravity than normal.

(2) By deflocculation this layer is released and changed to free water of normal specific gravity.

In this way the volume of the water phase increases by deflocculation and the pint weight of the mixture decreases. Conversely, by flocculation of the suspension the total volume decreases, because part of the water is immobilized with the raising of its specific gravity. Of course, the reverse can also be assumed. Coagulated clay has no water around its particles, whereas peptized clay has a layer of bound water with a lower specific gravity than normal. Whichever assumption is chosen depends on the measurement of the specific gravity of this film of bound water.

In ceramic literature this phenomenon has been given the name of the "Webb effect". Whether the explanation is right or wrong, this "Webb effect" should be very important, provided that Dr. Webb's measurements are correct:

(1) In ceramics for the understanding of the mechanism of the preparation of casting-slips.

(2) In general colloid chemistry for the understanding of stability and the double-layer.

Now it is remarkable that, despite the considerable literature on casting-slips, apparently nobody has taken the trouble to reproduce this Webb effect and study it systematically, although it is mentioned uncritically in several handbooks [3, 4, 5] and in some publications.[2, 6, 7] Of these, KEPPELER and SCHMIDT found that a minimum water content occurred in filter-cakes from optimally deflocculated slips. Although these experiments can be explained even better by a different interpretation, these authors explained their results by the Webb effect. Eventually a small remark was found in the dissertation of GAUGLITZ,[8] who wrote that he found no difference in specific gravity between natural and deflocculated kaolinite. It is even more remarkable that this "Webb effect" is unknown in colloid chemistry, although in this science one can work with model substances which are far more hydrophilic (e.g. gelatin) than ordinary clays can be.

The first assumption that underlies the Webb effect postulates that only coagulated clay contains a layer of bound water, necessarily of higher specific gravity. In making measurements of this kind, generally such a small volume of water is added that practically no double layer is developed and so the adjective "coagulated" has no meaning. Apart from the influence of peptization and coagulation, the concept of bound water is well known in colloid chemistry, soil science and soil mechanics, and as a working definition bound water can be regarded as water with other properties than are usually ascribed to it.

The important abnormal ways in which bound water can manifest itself are that:

(1) It cannot freeze
(2) It has lost its solvent properties
(3) It has a different specific gravity
(4) No heat of hydration or contraction occurs once a certain quantity of water has been adsorbed.

The first property is exhibited by water formed by capillary condensation in a rigid skeleton; it fills the small angles between adjacent grains and has a negative curvature and therefore a lower vapour pressure, resulting in a more or less lower freezing-point or higher boiling-point.[9] This kind of water is not very interesting because, by adding more water, the curvature of the air–water boundary as well as the rigidity of the clay sample is generally destroyed.

The second property is responsible for the origin of the colloid chemical concept of bound water (e.g. references 10 and 11). It is worth mentioning that we tried this method by measuring the concentration of a known quantity of urea added to a clay–water mixture by chemical analysis after centrifuging. A negative result was obtained because traces of soluble humus interfered with the analysis.[12] A polarimeter for making the analysis by physical means was not available.

The third manifestation of bound water (different specific gravity) is the most direct one for our purpose. Much work has been done on this method of estimation, and a comprehensive review has been published recently.[13] Although all investigators agree that bound water on clay really exists, there are two opinions about the value of its specific gravity. One group of authors states that this specific gravity is lower than normal,[14, 15] the first portion of water having an ice-structure.[16] The other group thinks that the specific gravity is higher.[17, 18] The first group mostly used bentonite and an indirect method of estimation. In a trial to resolve this discrepancy, we estimated the specific gravity of the bound water on three clay minerals by a direct method (Section 2), irrespective of the fact that the resulting figures were needed for the estimation of the Webb effect (Section 3). We could not find literature on the fourth property of bound water, which is understandable because the method of estimation is asymptotic, i.e. not very accurate. As a result of our work on the determination of specific gravity, this method was also tried, but its accuracy was quite low.

2. THE DENSITY OF WATER ADSORBED ON CLAY IN RELATION TO MOISTURE CONTENT

2.1 Method

The best method of measuring the density of dry clay and of clay–water mixtures would be that proposed by HEERTJES,[19] by the displacement of helium, but this method is too difficult for an ordinary ceramic laboratory. Therefore density was measured in the next best way—by the well-known pycnometer method using non-polar liquid. The highest accuracy was obtained by avoiding the errors of commonly used pycnometer flasks[21] and by repeating the measurements so that they could be analysed statistically.

The average specific gravity of bound water is calculated from the specific gravity of dry clay and a non-polar liquid and from the quantity of water present in the mixture. It will no doubt be clear that if there are small quantities of water in the clay, very accurate figures are needed for the specific gravity of both clay and non-polar liquid if the specific gravity of this water is to be determined with sufficient accuracy. To satisfy these requirements we used pycnometer flasks of 50 cm^3, according to RUBY and LOVELAND.[20] We are of the opinion that with this kind of apparatus systematic errors are practically eliminated.

Weighings were made to 0·2 mg against an empty pycnometer used as tare. In this way the moisture film on the outer surfaces of the pycnometers, which can amount to 1 mg, is compensated for. Although buoyancy proved to have no effect, all weighings were corrected for it. In a booklet, HARMS[21] mentions that, for a substance with a thermal expansion coefficient of 0·002 and a coefficient of compressibility of 100. 10^{-6} (rather high figures for organic liquids), the following levels of accuracy for the specific gravity determination can be attained:

Some units in the 3rd decimal place when temperature varies $\pm 1\,°C$.

Some units in the 4th decimal place when temperature varies $0·1\,°C$.

Some units in the 5th decimal place when temperature varies $0·01\,°C$.,

whereby normal changes in atmospheric pressure can be neglected.

For substances with lower thermal expansion, such as water and solids, 0·1 of the desired constancy in temperature would suffice. Our pycnometers were thermostatted in a water bath at $25 \pm 0·01\,°C$. In contradiction to the above statement, we only attained an uncertainty factor of 3.10^{-5} in the specific gravity of the non-polar liquid by taking the average of 10 estimations and guessing the probable error at the 5% level.

In connection with the necessary de-airing, it was found that not more than 12–15 g of clay could be used, depending on the type of clay. With this quantity, by measuring twice, it was only possible to calculate the specific gravity to the third decimal place, which is too inaccurate. By repeating this measurement 10 times, the limits of accuracy of the specific gravity of the dry clay could be reduced to $\pm$ 4.10^{-4}. Owing to uncertainty in the specific gravity of the liquid, the accuracy in the specific gravity of the dry clay is only $\pm$ 9.10^{-4}. The limits of accuracy for the specific gravity of the water in wetted clay depends on its quantity: at a moisture content of about 0.25%, $\pm$ 0.2; at about 0.5% moisture, $\pm$ 0.1; at about 1% moisture, $\pm$ 0.05; and at about 10% moisture, $\pm$ 0.005. We consider that these calculations are important, because one is inclined to overestimate the accuracy of the specific gravity values of bound water.

2.2 Materials

The investigation has been carried out mainly with a Dutch clay of the illite type from Brunssum, from which all particles $> 50\ \mu$ had been removed. For comparison, some experiments were made with the American Monarch kaolin and with Wyoming bentonite. Their properties are given in the Appendix.

2.3 Specific Gravity of Dry Clays

The necessary quantity of clay was first dried in the pycnometer for 24 h in a dryer at $105°$ and after that for 8 h at $100°C.$ under vacuum with P_2O_5. No further loss of weight could be demonstrated after drying for a longer period.

The following values for specific gravity were found by using cyclohexane:

Brunssum clay	2·6592
Monarch kaolin	2·6133
Wyoming bentonite	2·6215

In water the figures for Brunssum clay and Monarch kaolin are 2·7124 and 2·6245 respectively. A few other organic liquids which we tested (benzene, decalin) gave slightly higher values than the results obtained with cyclohexane.

This liquid therefore proved to be the best, being easily obtained free of aromatics, while the solubility of water in it can be neglected.

In agreement with the lowest figure for the specific gravity, it follows that there is no, or only minimal, volume compression. The use of cyclohexane yields the true specific gravity of clays or at least a value which approximates to the actual value as well as possible.

Of course, other pure aliphatic hydrocarbons such as hexane or octane could be used equally well. Purified aliphatic kerosene has been used, but it has the disadvantage that, in de-airing, the most volatile fraction can evaporate, with a possible alteration to the specific gravity of the resulting liquid.

2.5 Measurement of the Specific Gravity of the Water adsorbed on Clay

The fully dried clay in the pycnometer flasks was wetted with various quantities of water. A water content up to 4% was obtained by adsorption from the air during periods varying from a few hours to a few weeks, with regular mixing to get as homogeneous wetting as possible. The higher water contents were obtained by adding definite quantities of water. Apart from chance error, systematic errors could be made. From the figures in Table 2 it can be concluded that no air was left on or between the clay particles, to cause unreproducible diminution of the specific gravity. We feel sure that no water was evaporated during the de-airing, because we did not use exactly equal periods of time for evacuation. If an unequal percentage of the water present had evaporated, the results should have fluctuated far more than they actually did.

Moreover, another reason for choosing cyclohexane instead of kerosene for the specific gravity determinations was its boiling point of 81 °C. at normal pressure. It could therefore be expected that, at the working temperature of 25°, the maximum vapour pressure of cyclohexane would be higher than that of water, consequently only cyclohexane would boil off during the de-airing by evacuation.

The results of Table 2 are illustrated in Figure 1, together with the measurements of TSCHAPEK.[17]

In the three types of clay studied, the specific gravity of the adsorbed water increases as the water content diminishes and the increase in specific gravity is least with the kaolin. This is probably due to its low specific surface and the low exchange-capacity. Except for the general trend, we were not interested in this material. It is, however, of particular interest that Wyoming bentonite with its expanding lattice shows the same trend as the other clays, because in the literature conflicting results have been published.[14, 15] As X-ray investigations show that the hygroscopic moisture is adsorbed first of all between the layers, expanding in the c direction,

Table 2

Relation between the Water Content and its Properties on Different Clays

BRUNSSUM CLAY

Water content (g/g clay)	0·0029	0·0053	0·0107	0·0202	0·0417	0·0884	1·122	1.354	2·45.
Average specific gravity of water	1·7	1·5	1·38	1·25	1·15	1·069	1·0040	1·0027	1·00(
Volume compression (ml/g clay)	0·0012	0·0018	0·0029	0·0040	0·0054	0·0060	0·0077	0·0076	0·00
Hypothetical thickness of water layer (Å)	0·18	0·37	0·81	1·68	3·80	8·6	117	141	256

MONARCH KAOLIN

Water content (g/g clay)	0·0030	0·0077	0·0096	0·213	0·412	0·870	2·950
Average specific gravity of water	1·2	1·1	1·02	1·02	1·01	1·000	0·9976
Volume compression (ml/g clay)	0·0005	0·0007	0·0002	0·0004	0·0004	0·0003	0·0015
Hypothetical thickness of water layer (Å)	1·67	4·2	6·3	14	27	58	1970

WYOMING BENTONITE

Water content (g/g clay)	0·0026	0·0050	0·0119	0·0240
Average specific gravity of water	1·9	1·7	1·29	1·15
Volume compression (ml/g clay)	0·0012	0·0021	0·0027	0·0031
Hypothetical thickness of water layer (Å)	0·07	0·14	0·43	0·99

NOTE: Specific gravity of water at 25°C: 0·9971

it must be concluded that this water too has a higher specific gravity, which is in disagreement with HENDRICKS [22] but in agreement with OAKES.[18]

In principle, similar results have been obtained by TSCHAPEK [17] using some Russian soils (with much organic matter), although he obtained a value of 1·7 for specific gravity at a moisture content as low as 2%. Both the results of Tschapek and those in Table 2 can be extrapolated to a value of 1·9 at zero moisture content. So the question arises as to the physical meaning of such a high value of specific gravity, which cannot be solved experimentally, because there is no sense in making measurements at a moisture content even lower than 0·25%; the chance error is then becoming prohibitive.

One can calculate that the specific gravity of water in closest packing in one flat layer will be 1·57, if the radius of the O^{2-} ion is taken as 1·4 Å. If there are two layers, the specific gravity rises

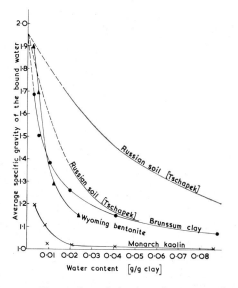

FIG. 1.—Average specific gravity of the bound water as function of the
water content of different clay types

to 1·73, and if there are very many superimposed layers the specific
gravity rises to the ideal maximum of 1·93. The course of the
decreasing specific gravity does not follow the pycnometer measurements because only the average specific gravity of the whole water
content is estimated.

If one makes the unrealistic assumption that the bound water
hull is a continuum, and further that this average specific gravity
for a distance x or up to a total water content x is called z and the
real specific gravity at distance x is y, then $z = \dfrac{1}{x} \displaystyle\int_{o}^{x} y \, dx$, from
which it can be deduced by simple differentiation that $y = z + x \dfrac{dz}{dx}$.

By graphical differentiation it is possible to construct a new graph
of the real specific gravity at each distance from the clay surface or
for each increment of the water content, and Fig. 2 does so for the
Brunssum clay. On the abscissa are plotted the water content and
the hypothetical thickness of the water film surrounding the clay
surface. The diameter of the O^{2-} ion $= 2·8$ Å, and the H_2O molecule
will have this same value. A thickness of the water film less than
2·8 Å means that the clay surface is only partly wetted, in which
case one cannot understand why the specific gravity of this water
is higher than normal, as there should be room for this content of

water to distribute itself in the state of least energy—i.e. evenly. Knowing the specific surface values of the clays used, it is easy to calculate the water content at which the clay surface is just covered with a layer one molecule thick in the closest possible packing (specific gravity 1·57). This must take place, for

Brunssum clay	at 4·2%
Wyoming bentonite	at 9·3%
Monarch kaolin	at 0·7%

For Brunssum clay Table 2 shows that at a moisture content of 4·17% the specific gravity of this water is only 1·15 instead of the expected 1·57. The calculated thickness of the water film is accordingly 3·80 Å instead of 2·80 Å. Figure 2 also shows that the specific gravity of 1·57 is attained at 0·4% moisture with a calculated film thickness of only 0·25 Å.

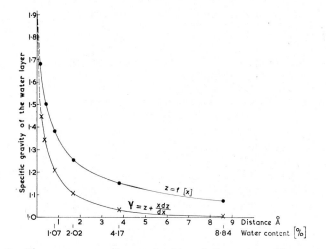

FIG. 2.—The average specific gravity (z) and the real specific gravity (y) in relation to the hypothetical thickness of the water layer and the water content (x)

At a thickness of 2·80 Å the specific gravity of the water is increased only to 1·18 at a moisture content of 3·35%. It is therefore impossible to associate the calculated specific gravity of 1·57 with the necessary film thickness 2·80 Å and a moisture content of 4·2%, calculated from a specific surface value, even by supposing an error of ± 100% in determining the specific surface.

The conclusion must be that there is no direct correlation between adsorbed water and the total specific surface of the clay. Next it can be assumed that only a certain part of the total surface acts as the agent in raising the specific gravity of the water present, but in doing so this active part of the surface must satisfy some possible assumptions which will be discussed now.

It can be understood qualitatively that water will be adsorbed on a flat clay plate (e.g. reference 9) if the plate has a homogeneous electrical charge. From the double-layer theory it follows that the potential and strength of the field diminish exponentially with distance from the plate. In this electric field the water molecules, acting as dipoles, will be directed. As the strength of field changes considerably in the immediate neighbourhood of the plate surface, the one pole of the water molecule will be attracted more than the other pole will be repelled, resulting in an adsorption of one or more layers of water.

The attraction as well as the directional force decrease rapidly as the distance from the plate surface increases, and so does bound water of high packing-density and specific gravity. If a plate has a charge, there must be an equal quantity of counter ions forming a condensor in the dry state and a double layer in water. In the double-layer theory these counter ions are considered as point charges, but in practice they are normal ions with a very small but definite radius. These counter ions must therefore be hydrated even more strongly, because the strength of field at the small curved surface will be greater but it will decrease more rapidly. This phenomenon is known in physical chemistry as the hydration number and electrostriction of salts in solution. One can even imagine special chains of water dipoles between charge points on the plate surface and the counter ions having a certain extension, and thus a higher specific gravity.

An uncharged surface of a hydrophilic substance like clay or glass generally consists of an ionic lattice with more or less hetero-polar binding forces. This means that on the surface unsatisfied valencies will be present which can both direct and adsorb water molecules.

So at least four causes for the adsorption of water can be summed up in order of decreasing importance.

(1) The cations in the double layer
(2) The negative charge centres at the surface
(3) The chain formation of water dipoles between them
(4) The unsatisfied valencies at the hydrophilic surface.

If in the first instance it is assumed that the lower moisture contents are used in hydrating the available cations only, some calculations can be made. The exchange capacity of Brunssum clay is about 0·2 m.e/g and consists of 0·123 mg-ion of different species (see Appendix).

To hydrate every exchangeable cation with one molecule of water needs 0·123 mmol = 0·0022 g H_2O/g clay. The lowest quantity of moisture used in the measurements was 0·25% and so is ample to hydrate every cation present with 1 molecule of water. If one imagines that this water, which is presumably insufficient to build up a shell round the cations, will insert itself between the cation and the negatively charged points, then about 70% of the valencies present are thus hydrated (0·2 m.e. = 0·0036 g H_2O). If the charge were evenly distributed, every negative charge point would have about 80 Å² available.

Although it is known, or at least believed, that the charge is more or less concentrated at the edges, distances will still be so great and the charge density so small that one cannot speak of densest packings. Yet there is the experimental fact, which cannot be doubted, that the specific gravity of these small particles of water is very much higher than that of free water in bulk. This fact is rather strange, because this small particle of water will be divided into single molecules in its reaction with exchangeable ions and clay surface, but it can be understood as follows. The concept of "specific gravity" is that of a property of matter in polymolecular dimensions, i.e. in bulk, and loses its significance in the region of molecular dimensions, i.e. if separate molecules are considered. So the calculated figures for the specific gravity at low moisture contents are limiting values, tending to the volume of one molecule as if it were in densest packing $\left(\dfrac{\pi\sqrt{2}}{6}\right)$.

Table 2 also summarizes the calculated values of the volume-compression of the water present in the mixture. For the Brunssum clay, this volume-compression reaches an asymptotic value of about 0·0075 ml/g clay, if the water content is high enough to form a clay–water suspension (Fig. 3). The volume-compression is then

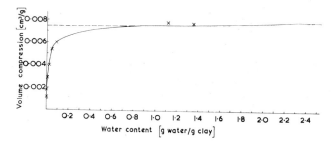

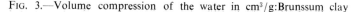

FIG. 3.—Volume compression of the water in cm³/g:Brunssum clay

completely reached and the addition of more water has no further influence and can be regarded without any restriction as free.

From experiments of DEEG and HUBER [23] on the behaviour of the dielectric properties of clay–water mixtures, it can be concluded that the water layer round the clay particles is influenced for a distance of 10 H_2O molecules into the layer. In our case this means that all water up to a content of 30 to 40% is more or less bound. From Fig. 3 it follows that the results of Deeg and Huber can agree with our measurements, but in our case it is difficult to say where the volume-compression is completely ended, as this value cannot be interpolated exactly from the asymptotically rising curve. Figure 2 shows that the true specific gravity of an incremental increase in moisture content diminishes so slowly that at a moisture content above 10% the normal specific gravity has been reached.

In physical chemistry, hydration numbers for ions can be found which differ widely according to the method of estimation. If we take as an example figures from KORTÜM [26]

$$H^+ = 4; \; Na^+ = 3; \; K^+ = 2; \; Mg^{2+} = 10; \; Ca^{2+} = 7 \cdot 5,$$

the total quantity of water bound by the cation content of Brunssum clay can be calculated as 1·50%. As this water will envelop the cations as closely as possible, its calculated specific gravity will be somewhat lower than the calculated ideal value of 1·93 because of the curved surfaces of the different cations. The hydration numbers mentioned will probably form one shell around the ion, and so more water can be bound with decreasing specific gravity.

Anyhow, this figure of 1·50% is rather low compared with the 40% of water, which is definitely influenced by the presence of clay, which means that more factors have to play a part—for example, the other three already mentioned (negative surface charge, chain formation and unsatisfied valencies).

If the first 1·50% of water were only used in hydrating the cations, then from 0 till 1·50% a constant specific gravity of about 1·9 had to be found. This picture contradicts the experimental fact of the smooth curve relating specific gravity to water content. This means that all the probable mechanisms of adsorption will work at the same time, perhaps even with different probabilities, depending on the force of attraction. So up to the present it is impossible to offer a satisfactory explanation of the adsorption of water on clay and it is not even known if more mechanisms are at work, which is not so surprising considering that even hydration numbers of a simple salt in a dilute solution are not known precisely.

Considering the existence of a Webb effect, the experimental results show that:

(1) Bound water on clay exists and is recognizable by an increase in the specific gravity.

(2) The limiting value of this specific gravity corresponds to the calculated figure for the closest packing.

(3) The influence of the adsorbed water can be measured even with dilute clay suspensions.

3. INFLUENCE OF ELECTROLYTES ON THE SPECIFIC GRAVITY OF CLAY SUSPENSIONS

3.1 Further Additions of Peptizer to Casting-slips

Two experiments were made by adding more peptizer to industrial casting-slips. In imitation of WEBB,[1] a bone-china slip was made by deflocculation with water and 5 ml waterglass of specific gravity 1·3680 per kg of dry materials. The specific gravity of this slip after de-airing was measured by the pycnometer method and found to be 1·7686 at 25°C.

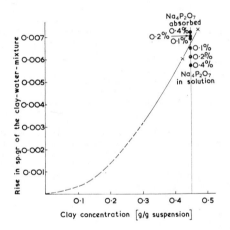

FIG. 4.—Influence of the addition of electrolyte ($Na_4P_2O_7$)

Then 2·30 g waterglass was added per 100 g bone china slip and the pycnometer was filled immediately after careful stirring because of the onset of thixotropy. The measured specific gravity was 1·7556. If no volume contraction or expansion had occurred, the specific gravity should be:

$$\frac{100 + 2·30}{\dfrac{100}{1·7686} + \dfrac{2·30}{1·3680}} = 1·7570$$

Although there was a great difference in rheological behaviour, the difference in specific gravity was less than 2 units in the third decimal place, in contradiction to Webb's results.

A similar experiment was made with an industrial porcelain slip (specific gravity 1·7926) which contained 50·8 g of H_2O and 128·5 g of dry material (specific gravity = 2·61) per 100 cm³; 0·15 and 0·30 g respectively of dehydrated $Na_4P_2O_7$ (specific gravity = 2·534) was added per 100 ml of slip. Needless to say, the rather well deflocculated porcelain slip became very thixotropic on the addition of excess peptizer. The measured specific gravity of these slips were 1·7932 and 1·7936 respectively. For the calculation of the resulting specific gravity two assumptions can be made:

(1) The added salt is fully dissolved in the water phase of the casting-slip and stays there unaltered. Consequently the salt behaves as a neutral electrolyte, contracting the double layer. If an exchange reaction takes place between this salt and the double layer, this exchange will be stoicheiometric and the small error in the specific gravity of the resulting electrolyte will be negligible. For the addition of 0·30 g $Na_4P_2O_7$ the salt concentration is $0·30/50·8 = 0·59\%$ and the measured specific gravity of this solution was 1·0056. The calculated specific gravity is then:

$$\frac{179·26 + 0·30}{\dfrac{128·4898}{2·61} + \dfrac{50·7702 + 0·300}{1·0056}} = 1·7953$$

The true specific gravity of the solid material in this porcelain slip was not estimated, but an error of $\pm 0·01$ has no influence on this result.

(2) The added salt is fully adsorbed on the clay content of the slip. Then the calculated specific gravity for the 0·30 g addition becomes:

$$\frac{179·26 + 0·30}{100 + \dfrac{0·30}{2·534}} = 1·7935$$

Both assumptions cannot be right and the truth will be somewhere in between. The results are summarized in Table 3:

From this result it can be concluded that no Webb effect exists, or at least the results are not statistically significant. Even if Dr. Webb had used the measured figures without correction for the added electrolyte, the rise in specific gravity is more than one order smaller than given in his table. So his results are inexplicable.

Table 3

Influence of the Electrolyte on the Specific Gravity of Porcelain Slip

	Measured specific gravity	Calculated specific gravity	
		No adsorption	Fully adsorbed
Porcelain slip	1·7926	—	—
0·15 g Na$_4$P$_2$O$_7$/100 cm^3	1·7932	1·7939	1·7930
0·30 ,, ,,	1·7936	1·7953	1·7935

3.2 Clay Suspensions with Different Contents of Electrolytes

If it is still possible to demonstrate the existence of a Webb effect, even if this effect be ten times smaller than Dr. Webb believed, we have to work with pure clay suspensions because:

(1) The stability and rheological behaviour of casting-slips depends on the kind and quantity of clay present;

(2) Some bound water exists on the clay particle;

(3) It is plausible that the non-clay materials in a common slip simply behave as diluants because the specific surface is too small to influence the quantity of bound water and its eventual density.

Although we are quite sure that no air was included in the casting-slips when the specific gravity was being measured in the above two experiments, as can be demonstrated by the figures themselves, it was difficult to fill the pycnometer flask with the highly thixotropic or coagulated slip. In continuing the investigation with pure clay slips an easier way of working was followed, but with the disadvantage that no exact duplicate measurement could be made.

Some clay was dried thoroughly in a pycnometer flask and then weighed. Next a known weight of water, with or without electrolyte, was added and weighed after de-airing. The quantities of clay, water and salt were therefore known and the specific gravity was measured by filling the flask with cyclohexane. The specific gravity of dry clay and water being known exactly, the specific gravity of the mixtures of both in any concentration can be calculated. On the other hand, the specific gravity of some mixtures at lower concentration can be determined by the pycnometer method. From the calculated and the measured results the increase in specific gravity due to the volume-contraction in relation to the clay concentration can be determined.

This increase in specific gravity is caused by the existence of bound water on the clay particles. The Webb effect is only the secondary increase or decrease of the expected change in specific gravity brought about by adding some electrolyte to the clay–water mixture.

In the same way can be measured and calculated the specific gravity of mixtures of clay and water to which some electrolyte has been added, provided that the specific gravity of the electrolyte as solid and dissolved in water of definite concentration is known. So by interpolation the rise in specific gravity at the given concentration at which the electrolytes are used is accurately known. This value is compared with the specific gravities measured and calculated according to the two assumptions mentioned previously (added salt: either in solution or fully adsorbed).

In Table 4 Brunssum clay $<50\,\mu$ with specific gravity of 2·6592 is used with solutions of $Na_4P_2O_7$ in three concentrations.

Table 4 shows that the change from the coagulated clay suspension in water to the fully deflocculated suspension with 0·4% pep-

Table 4
Estimation and Analysis of the "Webb Effect"

Kind of liquid	Specific gravity of liquid	Clay concentration	Measured specific gravity	Calculated specific gravity	Rise in specific gravity
Water	0·9971	0·2996	1·2206	1·2175	0·0031
Water	0·9971	0·4248	1·3634	1·3574	0·0060
Water	0·9971	0·4712	1·4204	1·4131	0·0073

Expected rise in specific gravity for clay concentration 45%: 0·0067

| $Na_4P_2O_7$ solution | | | | Calculated specific gravity for salt | |
				In solution	Fully adsorbed
0·1%	0·9981	0·4494	1·3939	1·3874	1·3870
0·2%	0·9991	0·4491	1·3943	1·3882	1·3873
0·4%	1·0009	0·4491	1·3957	1·3900	1·3885

| | Rise in specific gravity of salt | | Expected rise in specific gravity | Quantity adsorbed |
	In solution	Adsorbed		
0·1%	0·0065	0·0059	0·0067	50%
0·2%	0·0061	0·0070	0·0067	67%
0·4%	0·0057	0·0072	0·0067	67%

tizer is not accompanied by a change in specific gravity of the right order. By assuming that the added salt will either stay in the inter-micellar liquid or will be fully adsorbed on the clay particles, the difference from the expected value is still small (0·001 maximum), but of the opposite sign. It must therefore be definitely concluded that there is no such phenomenon as the " Webb effect ".

If no corrections for the salt content were made, the measured specific gravities would even increase gradually from the inter-polated value of 1·3933 to 1·3957, in contradiction to the Webb results.

Finally an estimate can be made by interpolation of the quantity of salt adsorbed. Although this estimate cannot be even fairly accurate, the order of magnitude agrees remarkably well with figures found by one of us [24] with another method, more suitable for this purpose.

In Table 5 some additional work with hydroxides and some floccu-lating agents along the same lines is summarized. A new portion of Brunssum clay $<50\,\mu$ and oxidized with 30% H_2O_2, having a specific gravity of 2·6588, had to be used.

Table 5

Influence of some Deflocculants and Coagulants

Addition (mol/litre)		Rise in specific gravity		Expected rise in specific gravity according to the clay–water concentration
		If electrolyte was dissolved	If electrolyte was adsorbed	
0·04	LiOH	0·0046	0·0053	0·0055
0·08	LiOH	0·0040	0·0053	0·0055
0·02	LiOH	0·0066	0·0069	0·0069
0·04	LiOH	0·0057	0·0064	0·0066
0·04	NaOH	0·0054	0·0063	0·0066
0·04	KOH	0·0053	0·0058	0·0066
0·04	NaCl	0·0070	0·0072	0·0069
0·04	BaCl₂	0·0065	0·0079	0·0069
0·04	AlCl₃	0·0069	0·0079	0·0069

This Table shows that the specific gravity calculated on the assumption of adsorption of the added hydroxide nearly equals the expected specific gravity, which means that the quantity adsorbed must be nearly 100%. There is, however, a systematic error of 0·0003 at most, except with the addition of KOH. The two reasons for this error can be summed up as follows:

(1) It is possible that the error is caused by absorption of CO_2 from the air, and in particular the KOH solution was not free from carbonate.

(2) The assumption of total adsorption of the hydroxide is less probable than an exchange reaction.

A clay contains H^+ ions in the double-layer and dissociable OH groups on its surface, together with the usual and normal cation content. The reaction with a small amount of a dilute hydroxide solution can be written as:

$$\text{Ca-H-clay} + \text{KOH} \longrightarrow \text{Ca-K-clay} + H_2O$$

As according to this reaction, some water results, the expected rise in specific gravity is over-estimated.

After the addition of a hydroxide, just enough to replace H^+ by K^+ or less, the pH of a clay suspension increases. If this substance were fully adsorbed, the pH would not alter. So hydrolysis takes place, according to the schematic equation:

$$\text{Ca-K-clay} + H_2O \longrightarrow \text{Ca-K-H-clay} + \text{KOH}$$

This means that the greater the addition, the more will be left in the intermicellar liquid and so the less can be adsorbed. The last part of the Table demonstrates that inorganic coagulants compress the double layer without being physically adsorbed.

Of course an exchange reaction will take place:

$$\text{Ca-clay} + \text{NaCl} \rightleftharpoons \text{Na-clay} + \text{CaCl}_2$$

$$\text{Ca-clay} + \text{BaCl}_2 \rightleftharpoons \text{Ba-clay} + \text{CaCl}_2$$

An analogous schematic equation for $AlCl_3$ cannot be given, because the exchange depends on the pH of the suspension. It is believed that the added NaCl will stay practically complete in the intermicellar liquid, in accordance with the calculated result. On the other hand, much of the added $BaCl_2$ will be exchanged, changing the specific gravity of the dry clay and of the intermicellar liquid, and resulting in an apparent adsorption of 30%.

All that can be said about the added $AlCl_3$ is that it will be fully exchanged in a valence state between 1 and 3. In contrast with the $BaCl_2$ solution, the difference in specific gravity between the original $AlCl_3$ solution and the resulting $CaCl_2$ solution is not very great, and the final result is therefore similar to one in which no adsorption had taken place.

APPENDIX

BRUNSSUM CLAY $< 50\ \mu$

Chemical Analysis (%)		Grain Size (μ)	(%)
SiO_2	65·7	< 50	100
Al_2O_3	20·4	< 20	96
Fe_2O_3	1·95	< 10	89
TiO_2	1·01	< 5	80
CaO	0·34	< 2	69
MgO	0·96	< 1	60
K_2O	1·94	Exchangeable cations	(m.e./100g.)
Na_2O	0·30	Ca^{2+}	16·30
Loss on ignition	7·1	Mg^{2+}	2·89
Organic matter	0·8	Na^+	1·21
Quartz	37·8	K^+	0·80
		H^+	0·70

Specific surface (glycerol method[25]): 96 m^2/g.

MONARCH KAOLIN

Chemical Analysis	(%)	Rational Analysis	(%)
SiO_2	46·09	Kaolinite	96·7
Al_2O_3	38·3	Mica	0·5
Fe_2O_3	0·38	Nontronite	1·0
Na_2O	0·10	TiO_2	1·3
K_2O	0·07	Organic matter	0·26
Loss on ignition	13·76	Quartz	0·4

Specific surface: 15 m^2/g.

WYOMING BENTONITE

Specific surface: 212 m^2/g.

REFERENCES

1. Webb, H. W., *Trans. Brit. Ceram. Soc.*, **33**, 129, 1934.
2. Williamson, W. O., *Trans. Brit. Ceram. Soc.*, **46**, 77, 1947.
3. Salmang, H., " Die Keramik, physikalische und chemische Grundlagen " (3. Auflage 1954), pp. 68–72.
4. Eitel, W., " The Physical Chemistry of the Silicates " (Chicago 1954), pp. 540–542.
5. Searle, A. B., and Grimshaw, R. W., " The Chemistry and Physics of Clays " (3rd Ed., London, 1959).
6. Keppeler, G., and Schmidt, H., *Sprechsaal*, **70**, 269, 1937.
7. Dale, A. J., *Ceramics*, **12**, (146), 24; (147), 32, 1961.
8. Gauglitz, R., and Schwiete, H. E., Mitteilung aus dem Institut für Gesteinshüttenkunde der Rheinisch-Westfälischen Technischen Hochschule Aachen 1958. " Ueber die Verflüssung von wässrigen Mineralschlämmen, insbesondere von Tonmineralschlämmen ".
9. Alexander, A. E., and Johnson, P., " Colloid Science ", Vol. II, Oxford 1949, p. 605.
10. Gortner, R. A., *Trans. Faraday Soc.*, **26**, 678, 1930.
11. Briggs, D. R., *J. Phys. Chem.*, **36**, 367, 1932.
12. van der Meulen, J. H., *Chem. Wbl.*, p. 550, 1930.

13. Martin, R. T., *Clays and Clay Minerals,* **9,** 28, 1962.
14. von Nitzsch, W., *Koll. Z.,* **93,** 110, 1940.
15. Anderson, D. M., and Low, P. F., *Nature,* **180,** 1194, 1957.
16. Macey, H. H., *Trans. Brit. Ceram. Soc.,* **41,** 73, 1942.
17. Tschapek, M. W., *Ztschr. Pfl. ern.,* **34,** 265, 1934.
18. Oakes, D. T., *Clays and Clay Minerals,* **5,** p. 46, 1958.
19. Heertjes, P. M. Dissertation, Delft 1938.
20. Ruby, W. R., and Loveland P. P., *J. Phys. Chem.,* **50,** 345, 1946.
21. Harms, H., " Die Dichte flüssiger und fester Stoffe " (Braunschweig 1941).
22. Hendricks, S. B., and Jefferson, M. E., *Amer. Min.,* **23,** 851, 1938.
23. Deeg, E., and Huber, O., *Ber. Dtsch. Keram. Ges.,* **32,** 261, 1955.
24. Dal, P. H., *Klei,* **7,** 263, 1957.
25. Diamond, S., and Kinter, E.B., *Clays and Clay Minerals,* **3,** 334, 1956.
26. Kortüm, G., " Elektrolytlösungen " (Leipzig 1941).

6—Über die Untersuchung keramischer Feldspäte und ihr Verhalten bei hohen Temperaturen

Von O. E. Radczewski

Institut für Gesteinschüttenkunde *
Technische Hochschule, Aachen

INHALT   A53d

Die Verfahren der mineralischen und technologischen Untersuchung keramischer Feldspäte werden kurz geschildert. Sodann wird über Versuche berichtet, die an mehr oder weniger reinen Feldspäten, z.T. mit unterschiedlichem Glimmerzusatz durchgeführt wurden, um ihr Verhalten beim Brennen und in der Masse zu prüfen. Neben diesen Schalen- und Kegelproben wurden die keramischen Feldspäte und deren Mischungen mit Kaolin im Griffin-Telin-Heiztisch nach Welch lichtmikroskopisch untersucht. Mikrophotographien geben Auskunft über ihr Schmelzverhalten bis zu Temperaturen von etwa 1600°C. Die hierbei erhaltenen Ergebnisse werden mit den Erhitzungsmikroskopkurven nach Zwetsch verglichen.

Investigations on feldspars and their behaviour at high temperatures

The methods by which feldspars were investigated are briefly considered. The results are given of tests on more or less pure feldspars, in some cases with the addition of mica, in order to check their behaviour during firing and in bodies. Besides the " dish-and-cone " tests, the feldspars and mixtures of them with kaolinites were examined by a high-temperature microscope with the Griffin-Telin heating-table developed by Welch. Photomicrographs give information about their melting behaviour up to temperatures of about 1,600°C. The results obtained are compared with the curves obtained by Zwetsch with the high-temperature microscope.

Recherches sur les feldspaths et leur comportement à haute températures

On examine brièvement les méthodes employées pour l'étude des feldspaths. On donne les résultats d'essais effectués sur des feldspaths plus ou moins purs, comportant dans quelques cas une addition de mica afin de contrôler leur comportement durant la cuisson et dans les pâtes. En dehors des essais sur cônes pyrométriques les feldspaths et leurs mélanges avec des kaolinites ont été examinés au moyen d'un microscope haute-température à l'aide de la table chauffante de Griffin-Telin mise au point par Welch. Des microphotographies renseignent sur leur comportement à la fusion jusqu'à des températures de l'ordre de 1600°C. On compare les résultats obtenus avec les courbes obtenues par Zwetsch à l'aide du microscope haute température.

1. EINLEITUNG

Der Feldspat ist ein wichtiger keramischer Rohstoff, der in der Feinkeramik, in den Massen von Porzellan, Feldspatsteingut und in

* Direktor, Prof. Dr. phil. nat. H. E. Schwiete.

der Glasur Verwendung findet.   Die keramischen Feldspäte sollen
eine weiße, transparente Schmelze liefern.

Mineralogisch unterscheiden wir drei Arten von Feldspäten:

Kalifeldspat oder Orthoklas ($KAlSi_3O_8$),
Natronfeldspat oder Albit ($NaAlSi_3O_8$) und
Kalkfeldspat oder Anorthit ($CaAl_2Si_2O_8$) (Bild 1).

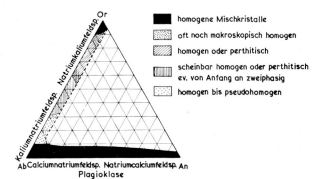

BILD 1.—Konzentrationsdreieck Orthoklas (Or), Albit (Ab), Anorthit (An).
Mischkristalle bei gewöhnlicher Temperatur

Zwischen Orthoklas und Anorthit kommen keine Mischkristalle
vor, während Anorthit und Albit eine auch bei normalen Temperaturen beständige lückenlose Mischkristallreihe bilden, die
Kalknatronfeldspäte oder Plagioklase.   Hiervon sind für die
Keramik wichtig die Oligoklas-Albite mit einem Anorthit-Gehalt
unter 15–20%.   Die Alkalifeldspäte Orthoklas und Albit sind nur
bei hohen Temperaturen mischbar, beim Abkühlen entmischen sie
sich meist in feine Lamellen.   Diese entmischten Feldspäte werden
je nach der Ausbildung als Mikroklin, als Perthit oder Antiperthit
bezeichnet.

Die Feldspäte kommen also in der Natur nicht rein vor, sondern
bilden in Abhängigkeit von den physikalisch-chemischen Bedingungen bei ihrer Entstehung Mischkristalle und im allgemeinen auch
mehr oder weniger starke Verwachsungen mit Quarz, Muskovit oder
Serizit.   Die keramischen Feldspäte mit einem Anorthitgehalt unter
15–20% finden sich in der Natur vorwiegend in sauren magmatischen
Gesteinen, in granitischen Pegmatiten und in daraus entstandenen
Sandsteinen (Arkosen) oder Sanden.

Sie werden heute vorwiegend fein gemahlen und verschnitten ge-
liefert, das heißt, sie werden aus einer Anzahl verschiedener natürlicher Feldspäte, die weitgehend von den Begleitmineralen gereinigt

sind, nach Maßgabe ihrer chemischen Zusammensetzung gemischt, so daß eine gleichmäßige Lieferung über längere Zeiträume auch unabhängig vom Wechsel des natürlichen Vorkommens gewährleistet ist.[6]

Wir haben es daher bei den keramischen Feldspäten nicht mit einheitlichen Mineralen zu tun, sondern mit mehr oder weniger homogen zusammengesetzten Gesteinen, die nebeneinander verschiedene Feldspatarten (Kalifeldspat, Plagioklas) und Quarz sowie Glimmer und Kaolinit enthalten. Für das Verständnis der Eigenschaften dieser zerkleinerten Mineralgemenge ist die Kenntnis ihrer Zusammensetzung notwendig.

2. DIE UNTERSUCHUNG

Die Untersuchung der keramischen Feldspäte hat die Aufgabe, sie in dreifacher Hinsicht zu charakterisieren:

Die Kornverteilung, von der die spezifische Oberfläche und damit die Reaktionsfähigkeit im festen Zustand und in der Schmelze abhängt, wird bestimmt mittels Sieb- und Sedimentationsanalysen. Hierauf soll in diesem Zusammenhang nicht eingegangen werden.

Die mineralische Untersuchung erstreckt sich auf die Ermittlung seines Mineralbestandes und die Bestimmung der Art des Feldspates, während schließlich seine Eigenschaften und insbesondere das Verhalten beim Brennen und Schmelzen durch die technologischen Untersuchungen ermittelt werden.

2.1 Chemische Analyse und Berechnung der Zusammensetzung

Aus der chemischen Analyse, die die Menge der den Feldspat zusammensetzenden Oxyde angibt, wird in der Praxis auf einfache Weise der rationelle Feldspatanteil berechnet, indem das vorhandene K_2O in Orthoklas und das vorhandene Na_2O in Albit umgerechnet wird. Hierbei wird aber weder der stets vorhandene Glimmer noch der Anorthitgehalt und ebenso wenig bei kaolinisierten Feldspäten der Kaolinit berücksichtigt.

Bild 2 zeigt die Schwankungen in der chemischen Zusammensetzung einiger natürlicher Feldspäte; aus der Lage der Punkte geht deutlich hervor, daß bei der Berechnung der Zusammensetzung der Anorthitgehalt zu berücksichtigen ist, der auch bei Alkalifeldspäten bis zu 10% betragen kann.

Daher ist für die Auswertung der chemischen Analyse die Berechnung des modalen Mineralbestandes, wie es in der Petrographie üblich ist, dringend zu empfehlen.[2] Dabei erhält man Ergebnisse, die den tatsächlichen Verhältnissen besser entsprechen.

Hierbei wird zweckmäßig so verfahren, daß zunächst MgO, unter Umständen unter Hinzunahme von FeO, mit K_2O, Al_2O_3, SiO_2 und H_2O als Biotit, $K_2O.6(Mg,Fe)O.Al_2O_3.6SiO_2.2H_2O$, dann ein Teil des K_2O mit Al_2O_3, SiO_2 und H_2O als Muskovit $K_2O.3Al_2O_3.6SiO_2.2H_2O$, verrechnet wird.

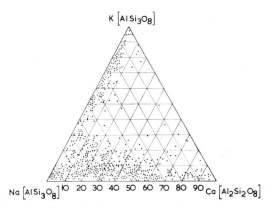

BILD 2.—Konzentrationsdreieck Orthoklas – Albit – Anorthit. Schwankungen in der chemischen Zusammensetzung natürlicher Feldspäte nach BETECHTIN [1]

Na_2O ergibt mit Al_2O_3 und SiO_2 Albit, $Na_2O.Al_2O_3.6SiO_2$, CaO mit Al_2O_3 und SiO_2 Anorthit, $CaO.Al_2O_3.2SiO_2$, und das restliche K_2O mit Al_2O_3 und SiO_2 Orthoklas, $K_2O.Al_2O_3.6SiO_2$.

Das jetzt noch verbleibende Al_2O_3 wird mit SiO_2 und H_2O zu Kaolinit, $Al_2O_3.2SiO_2.2H_2O$, verrechnet, während das überschüssige SiO_2 die Menge des Quarzes angibt. Für eine solche Berechnung ist im allgemeinen die Kenntnis des qualitativen Mineralbestandes Voraussetzung, die am einfachsten durch lichtmikroskopische Untersuchung gewonnen wird.

2.2 Das Lichtmikroskop

Da die keramischen Feldspäte im allgemeinen zu etwa 80% in den Korngrößen über 6μ vorliegen, ist das geeignete Instrument zur Bestimmung ihrer Minerale das Polarisationsmikroskop.[3]

Im Lichtmikroskop ist eine Unterscheidung der Hauptminerale der keramischen Feldspäte bereits aufgrund ihrer Lichtbrechung mit Hilfe der sog. Beckeschen Linie möglich, denn die Brechungsindices von Quarz and Glimmer liegen über 1,54, die des Oligoklas-Albit zwischen 1,54 und 1,528, die Brechungsindices der Kalifeldspäte aber darunter. Da sich bei diesem Verfahren die meist farblosen Minerale vom hellen Untergrund aber nur wenig abheben, ist eine quantitative Bestimmung sehr anstrengend und zeitraubend; es empfiehlt sich daher, die einzelnen Minerale durch die optische Anfärbung im Phasenkontrast oder im Grenzdunkelfeld zu unterscheiden, wobei sich die Körner vom dunklen Untergrund durch ihre leuchtenden Farben deutlich abheben.

Zweckmäßig verwendet man dazu den HEINE-KONDENSOR,* der durch einen beweglichen Spiegelkörper ausgezeichnet ist und mit dem ohne Schwierigkeiten die verschiedenen Beleuchtungsarten Hellfeld, Phasenkontrast und Dunkelfeld, sowie die entsprechenden Übergangsstellungen kontinuierlich eingestellt werden können.

Voraussetzung für die optische Anfärbung ist die Einbettung des Objektes in solche Flüssigkeiten mit hoher Dispersion, daß sich die Dispersionskurve der Einbettungsflüssigkeit mit den entsprechenden Dispersionskurven der Minerale in einem möglichst engen Bereich schneiden.

Im Phasenkontrast zeigen die entsprechenden Mineralkörner abhängig von ihrem Brechungsindex verschiedene Farben, die aber nur in Korngrößenbereichen unter $6,3\mu$ bis etwa $0,63\mu$ charakteristisch sind.

Für gröbere Körner verwendet man zweckmäßig das Grenzdunkelfeld, das bei allseitig gerader Dunkelfeldbeleuchtung entweder durch einen Dunkelfeldkondensor mit entsprechendem Objektiv oder, bei Verwendung eines Phasenkontrastkondensors, durch ein Objektiv mit vollständig absorbierendem Phasenring oder am einfachsten mit dem Heine-Kondensor und den normalen Mikroskopobjektiven erzielt werden kann.[7, 8]   Den Strahlengang für weißes Licht bei Grenzdunkelfeldbeleuchtung zeigt Bild 3.   Daneben findet sich eine Darstellung der Dispersionskurven von Immersionsflüssigkeit und einem isotropen Mineral, welche sich im grünen Bereich des Spektrums schneiden.   In diesem Fall geht das Licht dieser Wellenlänge praktisch unbeeinflußt durch das Korn hindurch, während der restliche Teil des Spektrums an den Korngrenzen gebeugt wird und somit zur Abbildung beitragen kann.   Das Korn erscheint daher in der Komplementärfarbe mit einem rotblauen (violetten) Rand. Allgemein kann man sagen, daß diejenigen Minerale, deren Brechungsindizes wenig über demjenigen der Immersionsflüssigkeit liegen, violett, Minerale mit einem höheren Brechungsindex gelb, bei sehr großem Unterschied aber weiß erscheinen, Minerale mit einem tieferen Brechungsindex als das Einbettungsmittel erscheinen blaugrün.

Zur Bestimmung der keramischen Feldspäte verwendet man zweckmäßig Mischungen von Zimtaldehyd ($n_D = 1,619$) und Oxalsäurediäthylester ($n_D = 1,408$).

* Fa. E. Leitz, Wetzlar

In Tabelle 1 ist das Ergebnis einer quantitativen Analyse des Feldspatsandes Arcos von Weiherhammer (Oberpfalz) aufgrund der mikroskopischen Bestimung im Grenzdunkelfeld verglichen mit dem aus der chemischen Analyse berechneten modalen Mineralbestand; beide zeigen gute Übereinstimmung. Hierbei erfolgte die Auszählung in zwei verschiedenen Flüssigkeiten mit dem Brechungsindixes $n_D = 1,511$ zur Unterscheidung des Orthoklas (violett) von den anderen Komponenten (gelb) und $n_D = 1,535$ zur Unterscheidung der Feldspäte (blau), des Quarzes (violett) und der Glimmer (gelb). In der feinsten Fraktion, 20–6,3μ, wurde zusätzlich auch in eine Mischung mit dem Brechungsindex $n_D = 1,551$ eingebettet, in der eine quantitative Bestimmung des Kaolinits möglich ist: der Kaolinit erscheint neben dem gelben Glimmer und den blauen Körnern von Quarz und Feldspat violett.

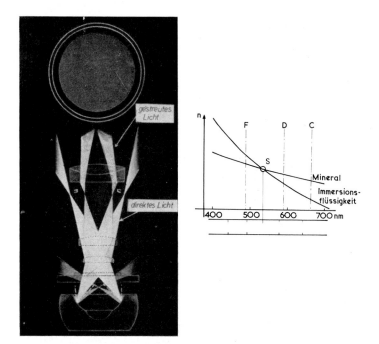

BILD 3.—Strahlengang im Grenzdunkelfeld für weisses Licht.   Direktes (ungestreutes) Licht grün, gestreutes Licht rotblau.

2.3 Technologische Untersuchung

Zur Bestimmung der Eigenschaften der keramischen Feldspäte sind technologische Versuche notwendig, bei denen der Feldspat

Tabelle 1

Mineralbestand des Weiherhammer Feldspat "Arcos"

Fraktion (μ)	Mineralbestand in % jeder Fraktion					Korngrößenanteil (%)	Mineralbetand in % der Gesamtprobe				
	Gl	K	Qu	Ab	Or		Gl	K	Qu	Ab	Or
> 200	0		82	1	17	21	0		17,2	0,2	3,6
200–125	1		69	0	30	18	0,2		12,4	0	5,4
125– 90	3		60	0	37	10	0,3		6,0	0	3,7
90– 63	5		52	2	41	8	0,4		4,2	0,1	3,3
63– 20	10		48	2	40	19	1,9		9,1	0,4	7,6
20– 6,3	3	27	32	4	34	10	0,3	2,7	3,2	0,4	3,4
						86	3,1	2,7	52,1	1,1	27,0
								5,8			
Aus chem. Analyse berechnet						98,8	2,1	10,1	58,4	3,9	24,3
						86	1,9	8,8	50,8	3,4	31,1
								10,7			

Gl = Glimmer   K = Kaolinit   Qu = Quarz
Ab = Oligoklas-Albit   Or = Orthoklas

unter Bedingungen, welche den Verhältnissen in der Praxis möglichst nahe kommen, untersucht wird.[8] Zur Charakterisierung des Brenn- und Schmelzverhaltens erfolgt zunächst die Ermittlung des Kegelfallpunktes nach SEGER, aber zweckmäßig nicht im Kohlegrießofen, wie es für die feuerfesten Baustoffe vorgeschrieben ist, sondern in einem elektrisch beheizten Silitstab-Kammerofen. Sodann werden die bekannten Rinnenproben, die vor allem für die Beurteilung von Glasuren unerläßlich sind, und die Schalen- und Kegelproben durchgeführt. Bei letzteren wird das Aussehen der Probe nach dem Brand beurteilt, wobei die Spitze der Kegel, der Schmelzgrad der Probe, die Beschaffenheit ihrer Oberfläche, sowie das Auftreten von Blasen und die Transparenz der Schmelze charakterisiert werden.

Da in dieser Arbeit in erster Linie über die Charakterisierung des Feldspates als Mineral berichtet werden soll, wird auf diese Verfahren nicht näher eingegangen. Im Rohstoffausschuss der Deutschen Keramischen Gesellschaft werden seit einigen Jahren Gemeinschaftsuntersuchungen an einer Reihe von keramischen Feldspäten durchgeführt, deren Ergebnisse zu gegebener Zeit veröffentlicht werden sollen.

2.4 Verhalten der Feldspäte bei hohen Temperaturen

Im folgenden soll näher auf das Verhalten keramischer Feldspäte bei hohen Temperaturen eingegangen und über Untersuchungen berichtet werden, die hinsichtlich der physikalischen Eigenschaften der Schmelze und der im Feldspat und in der Masse enthaltenen Minerale durchgeführt wurden. Ziel dieser Untersuchungen ist es, das Verhalten der Feldspatschmelze vorauszusagen, die Abhängigkeit ihrer Eigenschaften von der verschiedenen Zusammensetzung zu erklären und Verfahren zu finden, die eine schnelle Charakterisierung ermöglichen.

2.5 Erhitzungsmikroskop

Im Jahre 1956 hat A. ZWETSCH [11] vorgeschlagen, das Verhalten der Feldspäte bei hohen Temperaturen im Erhitzungsmikroskop zu prüfen, in dem zylindrische Probekörper von 3 mm Durchmesser und 3 mm Höhe bis etwa 1450°C. mit einer Geschwindigkeit von 8° pro Minute erhitzt werden. Die Schattenbilder der Prüfkörper werden bei diesem Verfahren in Abständen von 10 zu 10°C. photographiert und die Flächeninhalte der Silhouetten ausplanimetriert. Bild 4 zeigt den Schmelzverlauf von 2 Feldspäten im Erhitzungsmikroskop nach STEGER.[9]

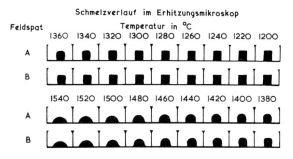

BILD 4.—Schmelzverlauf von zwei Feldspäten im Erhitzungsmikroskop nach STEGER [9]

Trägt man die Flächen der Schattenbilder, das heißt die Änderungen in Form und Größe der Prüfkörper in der Weise als Kurve auf, daß die Abszisse die Temperatur und die Ordinate die Fläche der untersuchten Probe angibt, wobei die Fläche der Ausgangskörper bei 20°C. den Nullpunkt bzw. den 100%-Wert bedeutet, dann ergeben sich charakteristische Kurven, wie sie z.B. Bild 5 für einen Perthit von Uddevalla (Westschweden) zeigt.

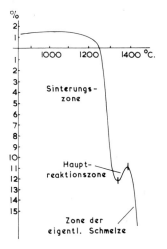

BILD 5.—Erhitzungsmikroskop-Kurve des Feldspats B/S 1, eines Perthit von Schweden

Aus der chemischen Analyse berechnet: Ab : Or = 1 : 4,7.   Quarz 0,19%, nach ZWETSCH [12]

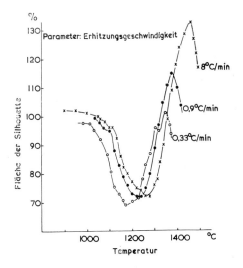

BILD 6.—Einfluß der Erhitzungsgeschwindigkeit auf das Verhalten im Erhitzungsmikroskop (Birkenfelder Feldspat)

Das Verfahren ist allerdings recht empfindlich gegenüber Änderungen in den Versuchbedingungen und in der Beschaffenheit der Probe:

Den Einfluß der Erhitzungsgeschwindigkeit zeigt nacht HARKORT und PETSCH[5] Bild 6 für den Birkenfelder Feldspat: Die Temperaturen der charakteristischen Umkehrpunkte zwischen den einzelnen Zonen werden etwas verändert, der Charakter des Kurvenverlaufs bleibt allerdings erhalten. Bild 7 zeigt nach ZWETSCH den

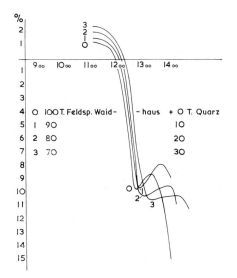

BILD 7.—Verlauf der Erhitzungsmikroskop-Kurven des Feldspats vor Waidhaus in Abhängigkeit vom Quarzgehalt

Einfluß eines unterschiedlichen Quarzzusatzes zum Feldspat vor Waidhaus und Bild 8 nach eigenen Versuchen die Abhängigkeit des Kurvenverlaufs von der Teilchengröße der Probe für einen skandinavischen Kalifeldspat (Feldspat 412 der Fa. Franz Mandt, Krohenhammer) folgender Zusammensetzung:

	%
Orthoklas	73
Plagioklas	23
Quarz	3
Glimmer	1

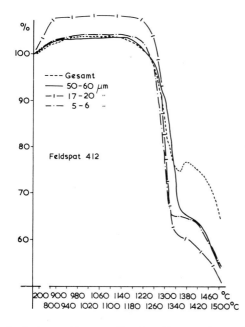

BILD 8.—Verlauf der Erhitzungsmikroskop-Kurven des Feldspat 412 in Abhängigkeit von der Teilchengröße

2.6 Untersuchung im Dünnschliff

Um die Gründe des unterschiedlichen Verhaltens der Feldspäte im Erhitzungsmikroskop zu erklären, haben wir zunächst Proben des gleichen Ausgangsmaterials (Feldspat 412) im Platintiegel unter gleichen Bedingungen wie im Erhitzungsmikroskop bis zu charakteristischen Temperaturen erhitzt, schnell abgekühlt und von den so erhaltenen Schmelzen Dünnschliffe angefertigt. Dabei zeigte sich zu Beginn der Sinterungszone, also bei etwa 1240°C., neben Quarz noch viel Feldspat, der wohl schon stark angegriffen, aber noch nicht geschmolzen war. Mitten in der Sinterungszone, etwa bei 1290°–1300°C. ist nur noch sehr wenig Feldspat vorhanden. Bei der Temperatur des ersten Umkehrpunktes (1360°C.), also zwischen der Sinterungs- und Hauptreaktionszone ist der Feldspat dann ganz verschwunden. Quarzkörner sind aber noch bei der Temperatur des zweiten Umkehrpunktes, also an der Grenze zwischen Hauptreaktionszone und der eigentlichen Schmelzzone, vorhanden und lassen Reaktionssäume im Dünnschliff nicht erkennen.

SOC—D

2.7 Griffin-Telin-Heiztisch

Eine Möglichkeit, das Verhalten des Feldspates heim Schmelzen direkt zu beobachten, bietet das Heiztischmikroskop, und zwar der Griffin-Telin-Heiztisch, der von WELCH[10] entwickelt und von W. GUTT[4] verbessert wurde.

Das Prinzip dieses Heiztisches zeigt Bild 9.   Ein Thermoelement aus Platinrhodiumlegierungen mit 5%, bzw. 20% Rhodium dient

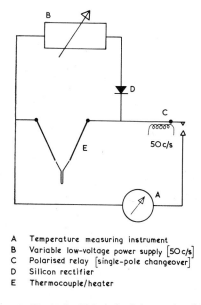

A   Temperature measuring instrument
B   Variable low-voltage power supply [50 c/s]
C   Polarised relay [single-pole changeover]
D   Silicon rectifier
E   Thermocouple/heater

BILD 9.—Griffin-Telin-Heiztisch, Schema der Schaltung

gleichzeitig zur Temperaturmessung, als Präparatträger und als Ofen.   Es wird mit einem 50 Perioden-Wechselstrom beheizt, der Heizstrom fließt jedoch nur während jeder zweiten Helbperiode der Netzspannung.   In den Zwischenperioden wird er vollständig durch Siliziumdioden augeschaltet, so daß während dieser Perioden die Thermospannung und damit die Temperatur gemessen werden kann.   Da der Wechsel zwischen Heizung und Temperaturmessung fünfzigmal in der Sekunde erfolgt, wird die Probe stetig aufgeheizt und ihre Temperatur dauernd gemessen.

Der Pt/Rh-Draht hat einen Durchmesser von 0,2 mm, der Abstand der Schenkel des Thermoelements beträgt 1,5 mm.   Vor jedem Versuch wird das Thermoelement, das nachher z.b. mit Flußsäure wieder gereinigt werden kann, in das mit einem organischen Klebstoff versetzte Pulver eingetaucht und dann langsam erhitzt. Mit dieser Apparatur können ohne Schwierigkeit Temperaturen bis 1600°C. erreicht werden. Zweckmäßig wird aber dann die Heizkammer mit Argon gefüllt, um ein Verdampfen des Metalls und ein Beschlagen der Fenster der Heizkammer bei den hohen Temperaturen zu verhindern.

Bild 10 gibt eine Ansicht der Heizkammer mit herausgezogenen Thermoelement-Heizdrähten fertig zur Aufnahme der Probe, Bild 11 zeigt die gesamte Apparatur während eines Versuchs (bei 1200°C.), die Heizkammer ist auf ein Leitz-Polarsationsmikroskop montiert.

Seit etwa einem halben Jahr haben wir Versuche mit diesem Heiztischmikroskop an keramischen Feldspäten durchgeführt und zunächst einen reinen Feldspatsand, den Feldspat FS 90 der Am-

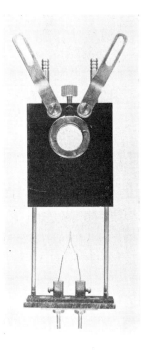

BILD 10.—Griffin-Telin-Heiztisch, Heizkammer mit heraugezogenen Thermoelement-Heizdrähten

berger Kaolinwerke untersucht. Dieser Feldspat hat folgende Zusammensetzung:

	%
Orthoklas	76
Plagioklas	9
Quarz	7
Glimmer	7

Im Erhitzungsmikroskop liegt seine Sinterungszone nach ZWETSCH zwischen 1150° und 1350°C., seine Hauptreaktionszone zwischen 1350° und 1400°C. und die eigentliche Schmelzzone über 1400°C.

BILD 11.—Heiztisch-Mikroskop in Betrieb bei ca. 1200°C. Leitz-Polarisations-
mikroskop mit Griffin-Telin-Heiztisch und Aufnahmekamera

Im Heiztischmikroskop finden wir den Beginn der Schmelze bei 1250°C., also innerhalb der Sinterungszone. In diesem Bereich, bei 1250°–1300°C., treten auch die Blasen auf, und die letzten Mineralkörner verschwinden, um eine vollständige Schmelze zu bilden (Bild 12). Bei weiterem Erhitzen tritt dann eine Läuterung der Schmelze ein, bis schließlich, meist bei 1600°C., eine klare Schmelze vorhanden ist (Bild 13).

2.8 Mischungen von Feldspat mit Kaolin

In einer weiteren Versuchsreihe untersuchten wir Mischungen von Feldspat mit Kaolinit, die bis zum Erreichen einer klaren Schmelze erhitzt wurden. Unter geeigneten Versuchsbedingungen kann beim langsamen Abkühlen der klaren Schmelze das Auskristallisieren von Mullitnadeln beobachtet werden. Wir verwandten

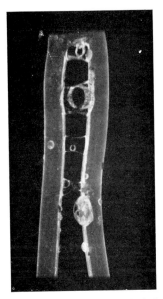

BILD 12.—Feldspat FS 90, bei 1400°C. im Heiztischmikroskop (Vers. 23).
Klare Schmelze mit Blasen (Vergr. 30:1)

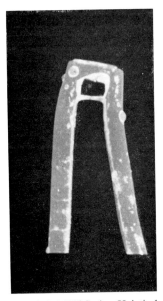

BILD 13.—Feldspat FS 90, bei 1600°C. im Heiztischmikroskop (Vers. 29).
Klare Schmelze an der Spitze der Thermoelement-Heizdrähte
(Vergr. 30:1)

zunächst einen bereits von ZWETSCH[11] untersuchten nordischen Feldspat, einen Perthit aus der Gegend von Kragerø in Südnorwegen mit der Zusammensetzung:

	%
Orthoklas	69
Plagioklas	19
Quarz	5
Glimmer	5

Der Kornanteil zwischen 20 und 63 μ dieses Feldspates wurde mit Schnaittenbacher Kaolin der Feinheit unter 6,3 μ im Verhältnis von etwa 1 : 1 gemischt und in der angegebenen Weise erhitzt. Bei den ersten Versuchen erfolgte die Mischung der beiden Komponenten volumenmäßig, wobei der Kaolin einen geringen Überschuß bildete. Die folgenden Bilder geben verschiedene Stadien dieser Versuche wieder:

Bild 14 zeigt die beginnende Schmelze bei einer Temperatur von 1200°C. nach etwa 15 Minuten. Im weiteren Verlauf des Versuches bildet sich ein Schmelztropfen, der noch Kaolinflocken und schon Blasen enthält (Bild 15 bei 1400°C.). Bei 1500°C. hat sich die gesamte Schmelze in der Spitze des Thermoelementes zusammengezogen, sie enthält noch Flocken von Kaolin und auch Blasen. Nachdem die Temperatur etwa 40 Minuten lang auf 1600°C.

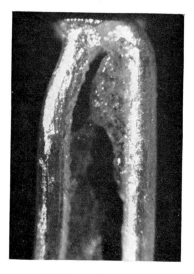

BILD 14.—Mischung von Feldspat (Perthit) und Kaolin, Beginnendes Schmelzen bei 1200°C. im Heiztischmikroskop (Vers. 48) (Vergr. 45:1)

gehalten war, bildete sich eine klare Schmelze, in der weder Blasen noch Kaolinflocken zu erkennen sind (Bild 16).

Von dieser Temperatur an wurde die Probe langsam abgekühlt, und bei 1440°C. konnten die ersten kleinen Mullitnadeln beobachtet werden. Nun wurde die Temperatur über 16 Minuten konstant gehalten, wobei die Mullitnadeln vom Rande aus strahlenförmig in die Schmelze hineinwuchsen. Bild 17 zeigt den Zustand der Probe nach etwa 3 Minuten bei 1440°C., Bild 18 nach 16 Minuten. Beim weiteren Abkühlen bildet sich ein dichtes Gewebe von Mullit, das die ganze Schmelze durchsetzt, so daß die Probe undurchsichtig wird.

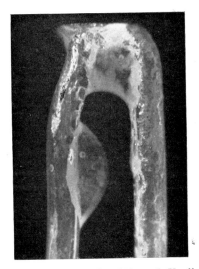

BILD 15.—Mischung von Feldspat (Perthit) und Kaolin bei 1400°C. im Heiztischmikroskop (Vers. 48) (Vergr. 45:1) Schmelztropfen mit Kaolinflocken und Blasen

Die Schmelze dieser Versuche hat folgende Zusammensetzung

		%
SiO_2	etwa	61
Al_2O_3	etwa	28
K_2O		8,6
Na_2O		1,6

sie liegt also im Mullitfeld, wenn wir das Dreistoffsystem Alkalioxyd–Al_2O_3–SiO_2 von SCHAIRER und BOWEN zu Grunde legen.

Diese ersten orientierenden Versuche wurden zunächst mit keramischen Feldspäten ausgeführt, wie sie in der Praxis verwandt

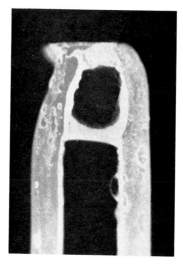

BILD 16.—Mischung von Feldspat und Kaolin bei 1600°C. im Heiztischmikroskop (Vers. 48). Die an der Spitze der Thermoelement-Heizdrähte konzentrierte Schmelze hat sich nach 40 Minuten vollständig geklärt (Vergr. 45:1)

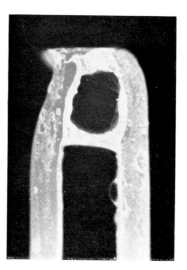

BILD 17.—Mischung von Feldspat und Kaolin im Heiztischmikroskop (Vers. 48). Ausscheiden von Mullitnadeln nach dem Abkühlen der klaren Schmelze von Bild 16 auf 1440°. (Vergr. 45:1)

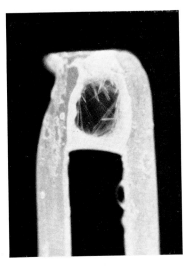

BILD 18.—Mischung von Feldspat und Kaolin im Heiztischmikroskop (Vers. 48). Wie Bild 17, 16 Minuten später bei 1440°C. (Vergr. 45:1)

werden. Weiteren Versuchen liegt ein wechselndes Verhältnis von Feldspat und Kaolinit zugrunde. Außerdem werden Feldspäte mit größeren Quarzgehalten und größeren Glimmergehalten untersucht, bei denen auch der Glimmerzusatz künstlich verändert werden soll. Für diese Versuche ist der Glimmer vom Typ Seidenglanz der Firma Franz Mandt, Krohenhammer vorgesehen, der bei der Reinigung keramischer Feldspäte anfällt.

3. ZUSAMMENFASSUNG

Die Zusammensetzung der keramischen Feldspäte wird zweckmäßig aus der chemischen Analyse berechnet, das Verfahren der Berechnung des modalen Mineralbestandes, wobei auch die Menge des vorhandenen Glimmers und des Kaolinits zu berücksichtigen ist, wird kurz geschildert. Für die Bestimmung des Mineralbestandes im Lichtmikroskop wird das Grenzdunkelfeld (das allseitig gerade Dunkelfeld) empfohlen, welches in geeigneten Einbettungsflüssigkeiten die wesentlichen Komponenten mit charakteristischen Farben erscheinen läßt. Mit dieser Methode ist eine einfache Unterscheidung der Minerale und auch eine schnelle quantitative Bestimmung des Mineralbestandes möglich, die mit den aus der chemischen Analyse errechneten Werten gut übereinstimmt.

Zum Studium des Verhalten der Feldspäte bei hohen Temperaturen ist zunächst das Erhitzungsmikroskop zu empfehlen. Aus den Schattenbildern der Prüfkörper lassen sich in Abhängigkeit von der Temperatur Dehnungs-Schwindungs-Kurven erhalten, aus denen charakteristische Reaktionszonen abgelesen werden können. Auf den Einfluß von Versuchsbedingungen und Probenbeschaffenheit auf den Verlauf dieser Kurven wird hingewiesen.

Eine direkte Beobachtung der Probe während des Schmelzens bis zu Temperaturen von 1600°C. ermöglicht das Heiztischmikroskop unter Verwendung des Griffin-Telin-Heiztisches, in dem Beginn der Schmelze, Auftreten der Blasen und das Läutern der Schmelze zu einem klaren Glas beobachtet werden kann. Beim Abkühlen scheiden sich aus der klaren Schmelze von Feldspat-Kaolin-Mischungen bei etwa 1440°C. Mullitnadeln aus, die im Laufe der Zeit und bei weiterem Abkühlen ein immer dichteres Netz im Schmelztropfen bilden.

LITERATUR

1. Betechtin, A. G., "Lehrbuch der speziellen Mineralogie". 2.verb.u.erw. deutsche Aufl., S.563 (Berlin 1957).
2. Correns, C. W., "Einführung in die Mineralogie" S.185 (Springer, Berlin 1949).
3. Correns, C. W., und Piller, H., "Mikroskopie feinkörniger Silikatminerale". In Freund, H. "Handbuch der Mikroskopie in der Technik", Bd. IV, Teil 1, S.697-780.
4. Gutt, W., *Silicates Industr.*, **27**, 285, 1962.
5. Harkort, D., und Paetsch, D., *Ber dtsch. keram Ges.*, **37**, 402, 1960.
6. Mandt, Franz, (Firmenmitteilung), *Keram. Z.*, **13**, 320, 1961.
7. Radczewski, O. E., *Ber. dtsch. keram. Ges.*, **38**, 389, 1961.
8. Radczewski, O. E., *Silicates Industr.* **27**, 579, 1962.
9. Steger, W., Proceedings of the International Symposium on the Reactivity of Solids, Göteborg 1952, S.689-701.
10. Welch, J. H., Transactions VIIth International Ceramic Congress, London 1960, pp. 197-206.
11. Zwetsch, A., *Ber. dtsch. keram. Ges.*, **33**, 349, 1956.
12. Zwetsch, A., *Bull. Soc. Franç. Céram.*, (36), 3, 1957.

Part Two

PROCESSING OF MATERIALS

7—Neuere Untersuchungen über die Grundlagen des Zerkleinerns

By H. Rumpf

Direktor des Instituts für
Mechanische Verfahrenstechnik
der Techn. Hochschule Karlsruhe

INHALT   C21. C22t

Das Zerkleinern beruht auf der Erzeugung von Brüchen. Die freie Grenz-flächenenergie der neu gebildeten Bruchflächen stellt die Nutzenergie des Zerkleinerns dar. Der Wirkungsgrad ist das Verhältnis dieser Nutzenergie zur aufgewendeten Energie. Er hängt somit von zwei Vorgängen ab: 1. Der Energieaufnahme bis und gegebenenfalls auch noch während der Bruchbildung und 2. der Oberflächenbildung. Es empfiehlt sich, zwischen der Einzelkornzerkleinerung, bei der alle Energie den zu zerkleinernden Teilchen verlustfrei zugeführt wird, und der maschinellen Zerkleinerung zu unter-scheiden. Am Beispiel des Zugversuchs werden die verschiedenen möglichen Mechanismen der Sprödbruchbildung erläutert. Die Festigkeit hängt haupt-sächlich von der Fehlstellenstruktur ab. Bei ähnlichen Teilchen des gleichen Stoffes und ähnlicher Beanspruchungsart sind sowohl die Energieaufnahme als auch die entstehenden Oberflächen von der Beanspruchungsgeschwin-digkeit und der Teilchengrösse abhängig. Man muss also den Wirkungsgrad der Einzelkornzerkleinerung als Funktion erstens der Beanspruchungs-geschwindigkeit und der dadurch erreichbaren Energiekonzentration und zweitens der Korngrösse untersuchen. Die experimentellen Werte werden diskutiert und mit hypothetischen Funktionen verglichen. Es bestehen bei der maschinellen Zerkleinerung die Probleme der optimalen Anpassung der Wirkungsgradfunktion der einzelnen Maschine an die der Einzelkornzer-kleinerung und der Grenzen der Beanspruchbarkeit bei feinsten Korngrössen.

New investigations concerning the principles of size reduction

Size reduction is based on the production of fractures, and the surface energy of the newly formed surfaces represents the useful energy of the size reduction. The efficiency is the ratio of this useful energy to the energy supplied and depends on: (1) the energy absorbed before and sometimes during crack formation; (2) the creation of new surface. However a dis-tinction should be made between the comminution of a single particle, to which the energy is supplied without loss, and size reduction in bulk by machinery. A tensile test enables the possible mechanisms of brittle crack formation to be explained. Strength depends mainly on flaw structure. For similar particles of a same material and for a similar kind of stressing, the energy absorption and the originating surfaces depend on the stressing velocity and the particle size. Therefore the efficiency of comminution of a single particle should be investigated as a function (1) of the stressing velocity and the attainable resulting energy concentration, and (2) particle size. The numerical results of experiments are discussed and compared with hypothetical functional relationships. In reduction of size by machinery, the problem of optimal adaptation of the efficiency relationships of each machine to those of the comminution of single particles and of the limits of stressability for the finest particle sizes remains.

Recherches nouvelles concernant les principes du broyage

Le broyage est basé sur la production de fractures et l'énergie de surface des surfaces nouvellement formées représente l'énergie utile du broyage. Le rendement est le rapport de cette énergie utile et de l'énergie absorbée et il dépend: (1°) de l'énergie absorbée avant, et parfois pendant, la formation des fissures; (2°) de la création de surfaces nouvelles. Il conviendrait toutefois de faire une distinction entre la comminution d'une particule unique, à laquelle l'énergie est transmise sans perte, et le broyage en masse effectué à la machine. Un essai de traction permet d'expliquer les mécanismes possibles de la formation de fissures par rupture fragile. La résistance mécanique dépend principalement de la structure des défauts. Dans le cas de particules semblables, d'une même substance, soumises à des contraintes de même nature, l'absorption d'énergie et las surface qui se forment dépendent de la vitesse d'application des contraintes et de la dimension des particules. En conséquence le rendement de la comminution d'une particule unique devrait être étudié en tant que fonction: (1) de la vitesse d'application de la contrainte et de la concentration d'énergie résultante pouvant être atteinte, et (2) de la dimension de la particule. Les résultats numériques d'experiences sont étudiés et comparés à une fonction de corrélation hypothétique. Dans le cas du broyage à la machine, la solution du problème de l'adaptation optimale des corrélations, relatives au rendement, afférentes à chaque machine, à celles afférentes à la comminution d'une particule unique, reste à trouver de même que reste à résoudre le problème des limites concernant les contraintes auxquelles peuvent être soumises les particules ayant les dimensions les plus fines.

1. EINLEITUNG

Von der wissenschaftlichen Behandlung der vielen Probleme des Chemical Engineering erhoffen wir uns eine bessere Erkenntnis der Phänomene und die Entwicklung von Methoden zur Vorausberechnung von Verfahren und technischen Anlagen. Bei Stoffumwandlungen sind folgende Teilprobleme gestellt: (1) Definition des Ausgangs- und des Endzustandes; (2) Gleichgewichtsbedingung für die Umwandlung; (3) zeitlicher und örtlicher Ablauf der Umwandlung unter definierten physikalischen Bedingungen; (4) Verwirklichung der Umwandlung in einem Apparat oder einer Maschine.

Betrachten wir die Zerkleinerung eines dispersen Feststoffes, so sind der Ausgangs- und Endzustand zunächst durch ihre Kornverteilungen und deren kennzeichnende Mittelwerte, vor allem ihre spezifischen Oberflächen definiert. Das gemahlene Gut ist feiner als das Ausgangsgut, es hat die größere spezifische Oberfläche. Physikalisch geschieht die Oberflächenvergrößerung dadurch, daß in Einzelkörnern des dispersen Gutes Brüche ausgelöst werden. Zur genaueren Definition des Vorganges müssen somit zwei Fragen unterschieden werden:

(1) Welchen Gesetzen folgt die Bruchbildung im Einzelkorn? und
(2) Welche Einzelkörner des Kollektivs werden zerkleinert?

Die erste Frage betrifft das grundlegende physikalische Geschehen. Seine Gesetzmäßigkeiten, z.b. die Abhängigkeit des Oberflächenzuwachses von der Energiezufuhr lassen sich durch Bruchfunktionen darstellen. Sie müssen experimentell bestimmt werden. Die zweite Frage hängt von der apparativen Steuerung des Verfahrens ab. Die Verteilung der beanspruchenden Kräfte und Energien auf die einzelnen Körner kann durch die Abmessungen und Bewegungen der Mahlorgane, die Strömung des gasförmigen oder flüssigen Trägermediums und die von diesen beiden Einflüssen abhängige Bewegung der Teilchen selbst beeinflußt werden. Man kann Auswahlfunktionen definieren, die für die kollektive Beanspruchung zum Beispiel für ein maschinelles Verfahren angeben, welche Mengenanteile welcher Kornfraktionen der vorhandenen Kornverteilungen in Abhängigkeit von Zeit oder Ort zerkleinert werden. Erst wenn wir beide Funktionen: die Bruchfunktionen der Einzelkörner und die Auswahlfunktionen der kollektiven Beanspruchung kennen, können wir die kollektive Zustandsänderung gesetzmäßig darstellen.

Je nach dem erstrebten Ergebnis wird man die Bruchfunktionen und Auswahlfunktionen unterschiedlich definieren. Meine heutigen Ausführungen werden sich auf das Problem der Energieausbeute beschränken. Dieses ist technisch bedeutsam, weil der Energieaufwand vielfach ein wichtiger Kostenanteil ist, und weil die mit dem Energieverlust unmittelbar verknüpfte Erwärmung des Gutes für die Anwendbarkeit des Zerkleinerungsverfahrens und für die anwendungstechnischen Eigenschaften des Gutes oft entscheidend sind. Wir wollen die Frage nach der Energieumsetzung in drei Stufen erörtern:

Zunächst betrachten wir das physikalische Problem der Bruchbildung und des Bruchfortschrittes. Dabei beschränken wir uns auf ein einfaches Modell, nämlich den Ablauf eines Sprödbruches im Zugversuch.

In der zweiten Stufe befassen wir uns mit der Einzelkornzerkleinerung regelmäßig und unregelmäßig geformter Teilchen unter definierten Beanspruchungsbedingungen.

In der dritten Stufe, der maschinellen Zerkleinerung kommen weitere Unsicherheiten hinzu, die das exakte Verständnis erschweren.

Eine gewisse Einsicht gewinnt man aus dem Vergleich der

Energiebilanzen von maschineller und Einzelkornzerkleinerung, obwohl die Beanspruchungszustände in den Maschinen nicht genügend bekannt sind. In meinem Referat werde ich diese Frage nur an einem Beispiel berühren und zum Schluß einige Bemerkungen über die Grenzen der Beanspruchbarkeit feiner Teilchen anfügen.

2. DIE BEDINGUNGEN DER SPRÖDBRUCHBILDUNG UND BRUCHFORTPFLANZUNG BEIM ZUGVERSUCH

Damit sich ein Bruch bilden oder fortpflanzen kann, müssen zwei Bedingungen erfüllt sein, eine Kraftbedingung und eine energetische Bedingung.

2.1 Kraftbedingung

Die Kraftbedingung besagt, daß an der Bruchfront die molekularen Zusammenhaltkräfte überwunden werden müssen. Im Falle des Sprödbruches bedeutet dies, daß die örtlichen Zugspannungen die molekulare Zerreißfestigkeit erreichen müssen. Da die im Zerreißversuch festgestellte Zugfestigkeit bei den meisten Stoffen um zwei bis drei Zehnerpotenzen kleiner ist als die molekulare Zerreißfestigkeit, müssen die örtlichen Zugspannungen an der Bruchfront gegenüber den mittleren Zugspannungen in der Probe um zwei bis drei Zehnerpotenzen erhöht sein. Sofern bereits ein Riß gebildet ist, erklärt man dies Phänomen mit der Kerbwirkung. Der Kerbfaktor ist dann dem Verhältnis der molekularen Zerreißfestigkeit zur Zugfestigkeit gleichzusetzen. Sein Quadrat entspricht dem Verhältnis der Rißlänge zum Krümmungsradius der Rißspitze. Da der Krümmungsradius mindestens einige Atomabstände, d.h. einige Angström groß sein muß, erhält man als Mindestrißlänge den 10^{-4} fachen Wert, das sind einige μm, sofern die Zerreißfestigkeit das 10^{-2}-fache der molekularen Zerreißfestigkeit beträgt.

Die Kraftbedingung postuliert also eine minimale Anrißlänge, die umso größer sein muß, je kleiner die Zerreißfestigkeit eines Stoffes im Verhältnis zu seiner molekularen Zerreißfestigkeit ist.

2.2 Energiebedingung

Die Energiebedingung führt zu dem gleichen Befund und darüber hinaus zu umfassenden Aussagen über die physikalischen Bruchbedingungen. Sie verlangt, daß bei einem differentiellen Rißfortschritt die angelieferten und aufgenommenen Energiebeträge einander gleich sind.

Man erhält damit folgende Bilanzgleichung

$$-\frac{\delta V_a}{\delta l} - \frac{\delta V_F}{\delta l} - \frac{\delta V_{th}}{\delta l} - \frac{\delta F_{ch}}{\delta l} = \frac{dB}{dl} + \frac{dT}{dl} \quad . \quad . \quad (1)$$

$$G_a + G_F + G_{th} + G_{ch} = 2\gamma + \frac{dT}{dl} \quad . \quad . \quad (2)$$

Dabei bedeuten

V_a die Formänderungsenergie des durch die äußeren Kräfte aufgebauten elastischen Spannungszustandes

V_F die Energie der strukturellen Eigenspannungssysteme

V_{th} die Energie evtl. vorhandener thermischer Eigenspannungen

F_{ch} die Reaktionsarbeit einer rißbildenden chemischen Reaktion,
sofern eine solche stattfindet

B die sogenannte Bruchflächenenergie. Sie umfaßt sämtliche
beim Bruchfortschritt an der Bruchfront absorbierten
Energien

T die kinetische Energie der mit dem Bruchfortschritt aus-
gelösten Stoffbewegung.

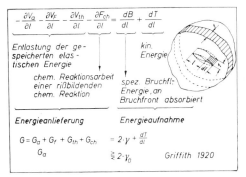

ABB. 1.—Energiebedingung

Alle Energien seien auf die Längeneinheit der Bruchfront bezogen.
(siehe Abbildung 1). Die Energiegradienten haben dann die Dimension Energie pro Fläche oder Kraft pro Länge. Für den Energiegradienten $= -\dfrac{dV_c}{dl}$ hat Irwin die Bezeichnung " crack extension force "
eingeführt. Wir wenden diese Bezeichnung auch auf die übrigen
zum Rißantrieb in Frage kommenden Energien an und bezeichnen
die Größen, G_a, G_F, G_{th} und G_{ch} als spezifische Rißausbreitungs-
energien oder Rißausbreitungskräfte des durch die äußeren Kräfte
aufgebauten Spannungszustandes, der strukturellen Eigenspan-

nungen, der thermischen Eigenspannungen und einer rißbildenden chemischen Reaktion. In welcher Weise diese Energien bei der Rißbildung beteiligt sein können, werden wir noch erörtern.

Entsprechend wird die auf die Flächeneinheit der neugebildeten Bruchfläche $dl \times 1$ bezogene, an der Bruchfront absorbierte Energie als spez. Bruchflächenenergie γ bezeichnet. Da zwei neue Bruchflächen gebildet werden, ist $\dfrac{dB}{dl} = 2\gamma$. Die Energieumsetzung an der Bruchfront setzt sich aus mehreren Teilprozessen zusammen. In Abb. 2 sind diese schematisch dargestellt.

Die frischen Grenzflächen sind in einem hochaktiven Zustand. Es bilden sich amorphisierte oder feinkristalline Strukturen höherer

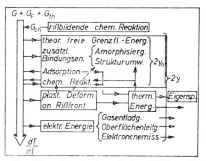

ABB. 2.—Energieaufnahme beim Rißfortschritt

Bindungsenergie. Nach einer überschlägigen Abschätzung kann diese Energieerhöhung größenordnungsmäßig etwa den Betrag der spez. freien Grenzflächenenergie des ungestörten Gitters erreichen. Soweit geeignete Partner an die Grenzflächen gelangen können, finden adsorptive und chemische Folgeprozesse statt. Bei der Adsorption wird die freie Grenzflächenenergie γ_0 herabgesetzt, bei chemischen Reaktionen ist eine Minderung oder Erhöhung von γ_0 möglich.

In der unmittelbaren Umgebung der Rißfront entstehen hohe Schubspannungen, die plastische Verformungen bewirken können. Das Ausmaß der plastischen Verformung hängt von der Größe der angelieferten spez. Energie G_a unde dem Stoffverhalten ab. Bei Metallen und Kunststoffen liegt, wie noch gezeigt wird, die Energieabsorption durch plastische Deformation um mehrere Größenordnungen über der freien Grenzflächenenergie γ_0. Diese Energie wandelt sich hauptsächlich in thermische Energie um und verteilt sich durch Wärmeleitung schnell auf den ganzen Körper. In unmittelbarer Nähe der Rißfront können sehr hohe Konzentrationen thermischer Energie auftreten. Dadurch können chemische Reaktionen mit verhältnismäßig hoher Aktivierungsenergie angeregt werden.

Schließlich absorbieren elektrische Aufladungen einen gewissen Energiebetrag. GILMAN[1] berichtet, daß bei der Spaltung von Lithiumfluorid Aufladungsenergien in der Größenordnung $10\gamma_0$ festgestellt wurden. Die elektrischen Ladungen werden als Gasentladung und Oberflächenentladung abgeleitet. Auch die an frischen Bruchflächen emittierten Exoelektronen sind die Folge angehobener Energiezustände.

Die gesamte an der Rißfront absorbierte Energie 2γ verteilt sich auf die potentielle Energie $2\gamma_0$ der neuen Grenzflächen, unter Umständen auf einen potentiellen Energiebetrag erzeugter Eigenspannungen und auf die thermische und elektrische Energie, die sich auf den ganzen Körper verteilen und zum Teil auch nach außen abgeleitet werden.

Die unmittelbare Erfahrung lehrt, daß die Brüche eine Folge der äußeren Beanspruchungen sind. Sie haben den Spannungszustand V_a aufgebaut, aus dem die spez. Energie G_a zur Ausbreitung des Risses angeliefert wird. Es ist deshalb zu erwarten, daß man aus der Größe G_a eine maßgebliche Information über die Rißfortpflanzungsbedingungen gewinnt. Dies ist auch der Fall. Die Berechnung von G_a ist eine Aufgabe der Elastizitätstheorie und zwar speziell der Kerbtheorie. Irwin bezeichnet diesen Aufgabenbereich als "fracture mechanics". Wir betrachten nun den *Zugversuch* und zwar die gleichmäßige Zugbeanspruchung einer Platte der Dicke 1 mit der Zerreißspannung σ. Für verschiedene Rißanordnungen erhält man die Beziehung:

$$G_a \approx \frac{\sigma^2}{E} \cdot l = \left(\frac{\sigma}{E}\right)^2 \cdot E \cdot l \qquad l/L < 0{,}2 \quad . \quad . \quad (3)$$

Die Formel gilt nur, solange das Verhältnis der Rißflänge l zur Plattenlänge L kleiner als 0,2 ist.

Bei logarithmischer Auftragung erhält man für G_a in Abhängigkeit von l eine Gerade mit 45°-Steigung (Abb. 3). Der die Zugfestigeit σ und den Elastizitätsmodul E enthaltende Faktor $(\sigma/E^2) \times E$ wird als Parameter genommen.

Weitere Werte der Energiegrößen von Gleichung (3) sind zunächst nicht bekannt. Man kennt für einige Stoffe angenähert die Werte der theoretischen freien Grenzflächenergie γ_0. Damit ist eine untere Grenze für die spez. Bruchflächenenergie γ gegeben. Diese untere Grenze ist in dem Diagramm durch eine horizontale Gerade bei dem Ordinatenwert $2\gamma_0$ markiert. Der Schnittpunkt mit der 45°-Geraden für G_a entspricht dem Gleichgewicht der Griffith-Bedingung.

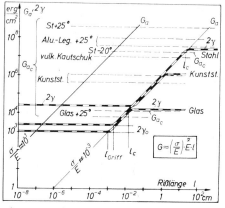

ABB. 3.—Rißausbreitung beim Zugversuch

Griffith, der 1920 als erster die Energiebedingung der Rißausbreitung formulierte, berücksichtigte nur G_a und γ_0. Die zugehörige Rißlänge ist die Griffithlänge.

Eine weitere wichtige Größe ist die kritische Rißlänge l_c. Bei ihr setzt die dynamische Rißphase ein. Sie läßt sich experimentell bestimmen. Eine von IRWIN [2] benutzte Methode besteht darin, den Probenrand mit Farbstofflösung zu benetzen. Sie dringt in den Riß ein, solange er sich langsam ausbreitet, folgt aber nicht dem schnellen Riß. Der farbige Anteil des Bruchbildes zeigt dann die kritische Rißlänge an.

Zu l_c gehört die kritische Rißausbreitungskraft G_{ac}. In Abb. 3 sind einige der von Irwin u.a. veröffentlichten Meßwerte von G_{ac} mit gestrichelten Horizontalen angegeben. Bei einer bestimmten Beanspruchungsanordnung ist die Größe von G_{ac} ein Charakteristikum des Stoffes. G_V und G_{ch} sind gegenüber den großen Beträgen von G_{ac} meist vernachlässigbar, ebenso G_{th}, wenn die Probe thermisch entspannt ist. Somit ist G_{ac} der bei Beginn der dynamischen Rißphase absorbierten spez. Bruchflächenenergie 2γ angenähert gleichzusetzen. Die Werte von G_{ac} der verschiedenen Stoffe liegen um eine bis fünf Größenordnungen über der freien Grenzflächenenergie $2\gamma_0$. Die großen Werte lassen sich nur durch an der Bruchfront ausgelöste mikroplastische Verformungen erklären. In welchem Ausmaß elektrische Energie beteiligt sein kann, ist noch nicht genügend untersucht.

Bei größeren Rißlängen $l > l_c$ wächst die Rißfortpflanzungsgeschwindigkeit schnell bis zu einem konstanten Endwert, wie SCHARDIN [3] 1938 gefunden hat. Bei konstanter Rißfortpflanzungsgeschwindigkeit muß auch die absorbierte Energie einen konstanten maximalen Wert $2\gamma_{max}$ erreichen. Die mit wachsender Rißlänge l zunehmende Differenz zwischen G_a und $2\gamma_{max}$ ist die kinetische Energie der bewegten Massen. Die Kurve für 2γ mündet also in die beiden Horizontalen für $2\gamma_{min}$ und $2\gamma_{max}$ ein und folgt dazwischen angenähert der 45°-Geraden für G_a, weil die angelieferte Energie für $l > l_{griff}$ überwiegend von G_a herrührt. Der untere Grenzwert $2\gamma_{min}$ ist größer als $2\gamma_0$, wenn bereits bei der Rißbildung mehr Energie absorbiert wird, als die freie Grenzflächenenergie. Dies ist nach den Messungen von BERRY [4, 5] bei Kunststoffen der Fall.

Das Diagramm vermittelt eine Anschauung von der Problematik der Rißentstehung. Die Zugfestigkeit ist fast immer wesentlich kleiner als die molekulare Zerreißfestigkeit. Beispielsweise sei $\sigma/E \approx 10^{-3}$ und $\gamma_{min} = \gamma_0$ zugrunde gelegt. Von $l = l_{griff}$ ab wird die Rißausbreitung von der aus dem äußeren Spannungszustand angelieferten Energie G_a übernommen. Falls ein thermischer Eigenspannungszustand vorhanden ist, kann seine Energie G_{th} zusammen mit G_a oder auch, wie beim thermischen Sprengen von Glas, allein den Riß antreiben. Die Werte von G_a und analog auch diejenigen von G_{th} sinken aber schnell unter den erforderlichen Betrag $2\gamma_0$, wenn die Rißlänge kleiner als l_{griff} wird. Für $l = 0,1\ l_{griff}$ ist G_a nur noch ein Zehntel von $2\gamma_0$. Bei noch kleineren Rißlängen ist G_a vernachlässigbar klein.

Für die Rißbildung unterscheiden wir vier Möglichkeiten:

(1) Es sind Anrisse mit hinreichend großer Länge, hinreichend kleinem Krümmungsradius und geeigneter Orientierung zur Zugspannung vorhanden, damit die Energie des äußeren Spannungszustandes die Rißausbreitung übernehmen kann. Die Anrißlängen müssen mindestens der Griffith-Länge gleichen, also größer als etwa 1 bis 10 μm sein. Diese Bedingung dürfte bei vielen Aufgabegütern der Hartzerkleinerung erfüllt sein, vor allem bei Gesteinen. Wenn ausschließlich G_a im Zusammenwirken mit vorhandenen Anrissen den Bruch erzeugt, sind folgende Befunde zu erwarten:

(a) erhebliche Streuung der Bruchfestigkeit, bedingt durch eine statistische Verteilung der Anrißlängen und ihrer Wirksamkeit,
(b) Unabhängigkeit der Bruchfestigkeit von der Temperatur,
(c) Zunahme der Festigkeit mit kleiner werdender Körpergröße.

(2) Es sind keine hinreichend wirksamen Anrisse vorhanden. Dagegen werden Mechanismen betätigt, die die Energie der strukturellen Eigenspannungen zur Wirksamkeit bringen. Hierzu bedarf es geringer Gleitungen. Solche Mechanismen sind für kristalline Stoffe VON COTTRELL, STROH und anderen [6-8] nachgewiesen. Sie

beruhen auf der Anhäufung von Versetzungen an Korngrenzen oder sich schneidenden Gleitebenen. Die Rißausbreitungskraft G_F ist proportional zur Anzahl und Stärke der blockierten Versetzungen und der die Gleitung bewirkenden Schubspannung. Sie ist in erster Näherung unabhängig von der Rißlänge. Dies bedeutet, daß G_F auch bei Anrissen von der Dimension der Atomabstände wirksam werden kann.

Mit der Versetzungstheorie läßt sich die Sprödbruchentstehung in Metallen einschließlich ihrer Abhängigkeit von der Temperatur und der Art des Spannungszustandes quantitativ deuten. Im niedrigen Temperaturbereich kommt die Zwillingsbildung als möglicher rißauslösender Gleitmechanismus hinzu. Diese beiden Gleitmechanismen dürften bei allen kristallinen Stoffen ohne hinreichend wirksame Anrisse maßgeblich sein.

(3) Die dritte Möglichkeit besteht darin, daß die Reaktionsarbeit einer chemischen Reaktion unmittelbar die Grenzflächenenergie aufbaut. Einen Mechanismus der spannungskorrosiven Rißbildung, also einer rißbildenden Reaktion, hat CHARLES [9] für Silikatgläser angegeben. Er besteht in einer mehrstufigen hydrolytischen Reaktion, wobei die Selbstdiffusion der Alkaliionen geschwindigkeitsbestimmend ist. Damit läßt sich erklären, daß die Festigkeit von Gläsern bei Ausschluß von Feuchtigkeit z.b. im Vakuum, erheblich zunimmt.

(4) Wenn keine zusätzliche Energie außer derjenigen des äußeren Spannungszustandes zur Rißbildung angeliefert wird und auch kein Anriß von der Griffithlänge vorhanden ist, muß die angelegte Spannung σ erhöht werden, bis bei dem jeweils noch wirksamen kleineren Anriß Gleichgewicht zwischen G_a und $2\gamma_0$ herrscht. Dies entspricht einer Parallelverschiebung der 45°-Geraden für G_a nach links zu größeren Parametern σ/E. Wenn das Material völlig frei von Anrissen ist, steigt die Festigkeit auf die molekulare Zerreißfestigkeit $\sigma/E \approx 10^{-1}$ an.

Die molekulare Zerreißfestigkeit wurde bei Quarzglasfäden [10] von rd. 3 μm und bei nadelförmigen Eisen-Einkristallen [11] von ca. 1 bis 3 μm Dmr. erreicht. In unserem Institut führten wir Druckversuche [12] mit Glaskugeln aus. Dabei stieg die max. Zugspannung bis zur molekularen Zerreißfestigkeit, wenn der Kugeldurchmesser unterhalb von. rd. 30 μm lag. Auch bei größeren Glasstücken ist es mit sehr sorgfältiger Oberflächenbehandlung [13] gelungen, die Festigkeit bis zur molekularen Zerreißfestigkeit zu steigern.

Wir fassen zusammen: Bei den üblichen technischen Festigkeiten läßt sich die Bruchentstehung entweder dadurch erklären, daß

Anrisse von der Größe der Griffithlänge, d.h. ca. 1–3 μm Länge und ca. 5–10 Å Krümmungsradius vorhanden sind, oder es müssen durch die äußere Beanspruchung zusätzliche Reaktionen ausgelöst werden: entweder plastische Materialverschiebungen, die zu einer Konzentration von Eigenspannungen führen, oder spannungskorrosive chemische Reaktionen.

Die investierte elastische Energie setzt sich während des Bruchablaufes zum größten Teil in freie Grenzflächenenergie um. Der zusätzlich an der Bruchfront absorbierte, durch die Differenz $\gamma-\gamma_0$ bestimmte Energieanteil wird dort in Wärme oder elektrische Energie umgewandelt und stellt einen unmittelbaren Energieverlust dar. Der restliche Energiebetrag bleibt zunächst als kinetische Energie der den Körper durchflutenden elastischen Wellen erhalten. Die elastischen Wellen werden an den Körpergrenzen, an Inhomogenitäten und an den entstehenden Bruchflächen reflektiert, wobei je nach der räumlichen Anordnung bei der Begegnung der Wellen Spannungsspitzen und sekundäre Brüche entstehen können. Diese Vorgänge spielen sich innerhalb sehr kurzer Zeiten ab, die größenordnungsmäßig durch den Quotient aus Körpergröße und Bruchfortpflanzungsgeschwindigkeit bestimmt sind. Nach beendetem Bruchgeschehen bleibt ein großer Teil der kinetischen Energie in Eigenschwingungen, translatorischer und rotierender Bewegung der fortfliegenden Bruchstücke erhalten. In Zerkleinerungsmaschinen besteht meistens eine verhältnismäßig geringe Chance dafür, daß die kinetische Energie bei weiteren Beanspruchungsfällen wieder ausgenutzt wird, so daß sie durch Reibung in Wärme umgewandelt wird.

3. EINZELKORNZERKLEINERUNG

Wir betrachten nun die Zerkleinerung beliebig geformter Einzelteilchen. Das Bruchverhalten sei spröde, d.h. der Bruch erfolge nach elastischer Verformung.

Die Zerkleinerung verläuft stufenweise, ausgehend von einer Ausgangskorngröße x_1 zu einer Kornverteilung, die durch einen Mittelwert oder eine charakteristische Korngröße x_2 bezeichnet werde, z.B. die Korngröße x_{802}, unterhalb der 80% der Masse der entstandenen Körnung liegen möge, zu der also der Durchgang $D = 80\%$ gehört.

Wir bezeichnen ferner mit

A_m die massenbezogene spez. Arbeitsaufnahme
A_v die volumenbezogene spez. Arbeitsaufnahme
$\Delta O_m = O_{m_2} - O_{m_1}$ den Zuwachs der massenbezogenen spez. Oberfläche

$\Delta O_v = O_{v_2} - O_{v_1}$ den Zuwachs der volumenbezogenen spez.
Oberfläche

γ_0 spez. freie Grenzflächenenergie

Der Wirkungsgrad der stufenweisen Zerkleinerung ist dann

$$\eta' = \gamma_0 \frac{\Delta O_m}{A_m} = \gamma_0 \frac{\Delta O_v}{A_v} \quad . \quad . \quad . \quad . \quad (4)$$

3.1 Modellgesetze

Wir fragen, ob sich irgendwelche Modellgesetze aufstellen lassen. Hierzu sind zwei Ähnlichkeitsvoraussetzungen unerläßlich:

(a) *Geometrische Ähnlichkeit der Teilchen*

Ihre Größe ist dann eindeutig durch die charakteristische Länge x_1 bestimmt.

(b) *Ähnliche äußere Beanspruchung*

Folgende Einflüsse können willkürlich gewählt werden

(1) die Stoffart
(2) die Beanspruchungsgeschwindigkeit v
(3) die Teilchengröße x_1

Abhängige Größen sind

(4) der spez. Arbeitsaufwand A_m bzw. A_v
(5) die entstehende Bruchfläche ΔO_m bzw. ΔO_v

Die Stoffart läßt sich nicht durch definierte physikalische Größen repräsentieren. Wohl ließe sich das elastische Verhalten eindeutig durch Stoffgrößen, beim Hookeschen Verhalten z.B. durch zwei Elastizitätskonstanten kennzeichnen. Das Bruchverhalten, und zwar sowohl die Bruchfestigkeit als auch die gebildete Bruchfläche, hängt, wie wir sanen, von Fehlstellenstrukturen ab. Deren Wirkung ist im einzelnen zu wenig bekannt, als daß man die notwendige und hinreichende Anzahl der maßgeblichen Einflußgrößen angeben könnte. Wir müssen deshalb die Stoffart als Einflußgröße eliminieren und als weitere Voraussetzung annehmen, daß

(c) *Die Teilchen aus dem gleichen Stoff bestehen*

Es bleiben zwei willkürliche Einflußgrößen: die Beanspruchungsgeschwindigkeit und die Teilchengröße. Führt man beispielsweise bei *festgelegter* Beanspruchungsgeschwindigkeit *und* Teilchengröße einen Druckversuch aus, so bricht der Körper, sobald seine Bruchfestigkeit erreicht ist. Die Arbeitsaufnahme und Oberflächenbildung sind damit festgelegt, sofern der Versuch so geführt wird, daß nach dem Bruch keine weitere Beanspruchung ausgelöst wird. Selbstverständlich erhält man auch bei genauer Einhaltung der Ähnlichkeitsbedingungen statistische Schwankungen der Versuchswerte, weil die maßgeblichen Stoffeigenschaften nicht konstant gehalten werden können, sondern von Versuchskörper zu Versuchskörper schwanken. Die Aussagen gelten nur für die Mittelwerte aus einer jeweils größeren Zahl von Versuchen.

Variiert man bei dem Druckversuch die Beanspruchungsgeschwindigkeit, so verändert sich auch die Festigkeit und damit die erreichbare Arbeitsaufnahme und Oberflächenbildung. Mit der Beanspruchungsgeschwindigkeit läßt sich die realisierbare Beanspruchungsintensität beeinflussen.

Beim Prallversuch ist man nicht an eine Festigkeitsgrenze gebunden. Die spez. Arbeitsaufnahme ist dem Quadrat der Aufprallgeschwindigkeit proportional:

$$A_m = \tfrac{1}{2}\, v^2$$

Nach den Ähnlichkeitsgesetzen der Prallbeanspruchung sind die entstehenden Spannungen nicht von der Teilchengröße, sondern nur von der Aufprallgeschwindigkeit abhängig. Mit ihr wird die Beanspruchungsintensität eingestellt.

In allen Fällen müssen wir damit rechnen, daß die Festigkeit von der Teilchengröße abhängt, da die Anzahl und Wirksamkeit bruchauslösender Fehlstellen und Anrisse mit der Teilchengröße variiert. Ferner ist zu erwarten, daß auch der Bruchflächenverlauf von der Teilchengröße abhängt, also bei gleicher Festigkeit und gleicher spez. Arbeitsaufnahme nicht notwendig ähnlich ist. Diese Erwartung gründet sich darauf, daß

(1) Das Verhältnis der gesamten Bruchlänge zur Griffithlänge und damit der Anteil der verschiedenen Bruchphasen sich mit der Teilchengröße ändern und

(2) Die von elastischen Wellen herrührende Sekundärbruchbildung wahrscheinlich nicht ähnlich verläuft.

Einzelkornversuche sollten also so ausgeführt werden, daß man bei definierter Teilchenform und Beanspruchungsart die Beanspruchungsgeschwindigkeit und die Teilchengröße unabhängig voneinander verändern kann. Weitere unabhängige Varianten sind selbstverständlich die Teilchenform und Beanspruchungsart.

In der Zerkleinerungswissenschaft und Zerkleinerungstechnik spielen die sogenannten Zerkleinerungsgesetze eine große Rolle.

Das Rittingersche Gesetz besagt, daß die Oberflächenbildung der Arbeitsaufnahme proportional sei. Dann ist der Wirkungsgrad konstant.

$$\eta' = \text{konst} \quad \text{(Rittinger)} \quad . \quad . \quad . \quad (5).$$

Das Kicksche Gesetz sagt erstens aus, daß bei den Ähnlichkeits-voraussetzungen a und b die Arbeitsaufnahme dem Volumen proportional, d.h. der spez. Arbeitsaufwand konstant sei. Dann ist der Wirkungsgrad dem Zuwachs an spez. Oberfläche ΔO_v proportional:

$$A_v = \text{konst}; \quad \eta' \sim \Delta O_v \quad \text{(1. Aussage Kick)} \quad . \quad (6).$$

Die zweite These des Kickschen Gesetzes postuliert ähnlichen Bruchflächenverlauf. Dann ist der Wirkungsgrad der Teilchen-größe umgekehrt proportional:

$$\Delta O_v \cdot x_1 = \text{konst}; \quad \eta' \sim \frac{1}{x_1} \quad \text{(2. Aussage Kick)} \quad . \quad (7).$$

Wir können ein einfaches Potenzgesetz als Ähnlichkeitsgesetz aufstellen, wenn wir zu der *Voraussetzung* a–c die weiteren Annahmen machen, daß

(*d*) die Beanspruchungsgeschwindigkeit konstant gehalten werde und

(*e*) die Bruchspannung σ konstant, d.h. unabhängig von der Teilchengröße sei.

Dann ist wie bie der ersten Aussage des Kickschen Gesetzes

$$A_v = \text{konst}.$$

Wir können bei linearelastischem Verhalten analog zu den Formeln des Zugversuches eine Griffithlänge formulieren, die ein Maß für die Zerreißspannung σ ist und substituieren

$$A_v \sim \frac{\sigma^2}{E} \sim \frac{\gamma_0}{l_{griff}}$$

$$\eta' \sim \Delta O_v \cdot l_{griff} = \Delta O_v \cdot x_1 \cdot \frac{l_{griff}}{x_1}$$

Bei ähnlicher Oberflächenbildung ist $\Delta O_v \cdot x_1 = \text{konst}$. Nach dem oben gesagten können wir erwarten, daß $\Delta O_v \cdot x_1$ eine Funktion de Korngröße ist. Mit dem Potenzansatz

$$\Delta O_v \cdot x_1 = \left(\frac{x_1}{l_{griff}}\right)^k \quad 0 < k < 1$$

wird

$$\eta' \sim \left(\frac{l_{griff}}{x_1}\right)^{1-k} = \left(\frac{l_{griff}}{x_1}\right)^n \quad 1 > n > 0 \quad . \quad . \quad (8)$$

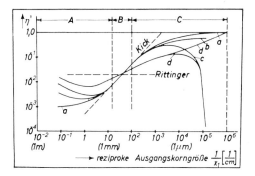

ABB. 4.—Wirkungsgrad η' der stufenweisen Einzelkornzerkleinerung

Dieses Potenzgesetz enthält die beiden extremen Möglichkeiten

Kick: $\eta' \sim \dfrac{1}{x_1}$ $k = 0$ $n = 1$

Rittinger: $\eta' = \text{konst}$ $k = 1$ $n = 0$

In Abbildung 4 sind einige hypothetische Kurven der Stufen-wirkungsgrade η' über der reziproken Korngröße $\dfrac{1}{x_1}$ in logarith-mischem Maßstab aufgetragen.

Es ist angenommen, daß es einen Korngrößenbereich B gebe, in dem das Potenzgesetz [8] erfüllt sei. Damit erhält man für η' eine Gerade mit der Neigung n. Dem Kickschen Gesetz entspricht die 45°-Gerade, dem Rittingerschen Gesetz die Horizontale. In dem rechts anschließenden Bereich C sei die Feinstruktur maßgeblich, die Festigkeit nimmt dort wegen der Verarmung bruchauslösender Inhomogenitätsstellen zu. Die Wirkungsgradkurve wird sich nicht geradlinig fortsetzen, sondern gegenüber der Geraden abfallen. Der maximale Wirkungsgrad $\eta' = 1$ muß theoretisch bei molekularen Abmessungen erreicht werden. Allerdings ist zu prüfen, ob ein Einzelteilchen bei immer kleiner werdender Teilchengröße über-haupt zerteilt werden kann. Dies hängt von der Beanspruchungs-weise ab. SMEKAL [14, 15] hat mit Mikroritzversuchen gezeigt, daß auch spröde, harte Stoffe, wie Diamant, Korund, Quarz, Glas plas-tisch reagieren, wenn eine Druckbeanspruchung bis zur Größenord-nung der molekularen Festigkeit auf kleine Stoffbereiche unter etwa 1 μm Ausdehnung beschränkt bleibt. Demnach müsste man es für möglich halten, daß kleine Teilchen unter 1 μm Korngröße sich bei Druckbeanspruchung plastisch zusammenpressen lassen. Der Wirkungsgrad würde dann auf Null absinken (Kurve c). Erst der

Versuch kann zeigen, ob sich spröde Stoffe tatsächlich derart verhalten. Unsere Druckversuche mit Glaskugeln bis herab zu 11 μm Durchmesser ergaben immer spröde Stoffreaktionen.

Bei großen Teilchen im Bereich A können Grobstrukturen die Festigkeit und den Bruchablauf beeinflussen, beispielsweise die Korngrenzen eines Gesteins. Dann sinkt die Festigkeit und die Wirkungsgrade werden vermutlich über der Geraden des Bereiches B liegen.

Es sind mehrere hypothetische Kurven dargestellt. Nur das Experiment kann zeigen, wie die Energieausbeute bei den angegebenen Variationsmöglichkeiten verlaufen wird.

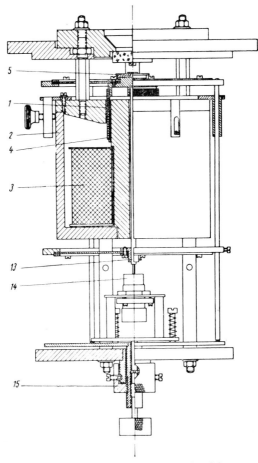

ABB. 5.—Beanspruchungsgerät, Schnittzeichnung

4. BRUCHPHÄNOMENE BEI DER DRUCKZERKLEINERUNG

Aus einer großen Zahl von Messungen der Druckzerkleinerung kleiner Teilchen seien einige Versuche ausgewählt. Die Meßeinrichtung [16] (Abb. 5) gestattet die Aufnahme der Kraft-Weg-Kurve bei gleichzeitiger mikroskopischer Betrachtung. Die Teilchen wurden zwischen zwei Saphirplatten beansprucht. Die untere Platte wird elektromagnetisch nach oben verschoben. Die Kraft ist dem Strom proportional. Die Verformungswege werden induktiv gemessen. Sie können im empfindlichsten Meßbereich bis zu einer Genauigkeit von $1/20$ μm gemessen werden. Die sehr feinfühlige Aufzeichnung der Verformungswege ist notwendig, wenn man das tatsächliche Geschehen erkennen will.

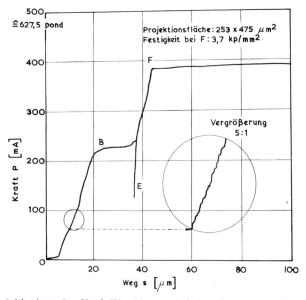

ABB. 6 bis ABB. 9.—Kraft-Weg-Kurven bei der Einzelkornzerkleinerung

Abbildung 6 zeigt den Ablauf der Druckzerkleinerung eines Kalksteinteilchens von etwa 450 μm Größe.

Folgende Phänomene treten auf:

(1) *Abbröckeln (B)*. An den Kanten brechen kleine Bruchstücke ab. Oft folgen einander eine große Zahl solcher Abbröckelungen, so daß bei geringerer Wegauflösung ein kontinuierlicher Verformungsprozess vorgetäuscht würde.

(2) *Elastische Verformung* (*E*). Die elastische Verformung verläuft längs einer steilen glatten Linie, wie sie z.B. bei der Entlastung angezeigt wird. Man sieht, daß die vorherige und nachfolgende Belastung mit Abbröckelungen verbunden sind. Zuweilen sind auch im Belastungsverlauf größere elastische Strecken zu beobachten. Wahrscheinlich liegt das Teilchen auf Flächen auf.

(3) *Zerteilen* (*T*). Größere Bruchwege, die aber in einen erneuten Kraftanstieg übergehen, zeigen an, daß das Teilchen in größere Bruchstücke zerteilt wurde, bzw. daß große Bruchstücke ausbrechen. Wir nennen diese Erscheinung Zerteilen. An der waagerechten Verschiebung kann man die Korngrößenreduktionen ablesen.

(4) *Zertrümmern* (*F*) und (*P*). Am Ende der Belastungskurve steht oft eine Zertrümmerung in kleine Teilchen. Bei der mikroskopischen Beobachtung kann man zwei Abläufe deutlich unterscheiden.

(*a*) *Zerfallen* (*F*).

Das Korn zerfällt zwischen den Druckplatten in viele kleine Bruchstücke.

(*b*) *Zerplatzen* (*P*)

Die Bruchstücke fliegen weg. Sie besitzen nach dem Bruch noch erhebliche kinetische Energie. Diese Brucherscheinung beobachtet man bei hohen Bruckfestigkeiten. Sie trat bei Kalkstein nicht auf.

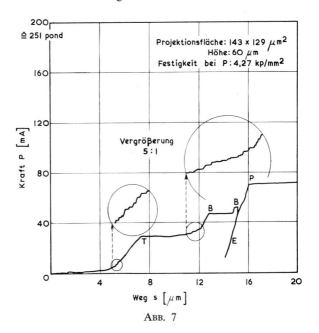

ABB. 7

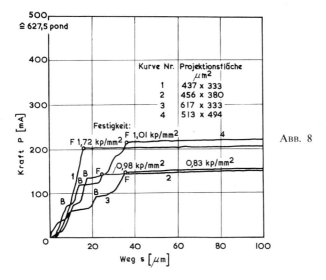

ABB. 8

Bei der in Abb. 7 wiedergegebenen Druckzerkleinerung eines Quarzteilchens von rund 130 μm Größe erkennen wir die gleichen Erscheinungen des Abbröckelns (*B*), elastischen Verformens (*E*) beim Entspannen und längs kurzer Belastungswege und des Zer-

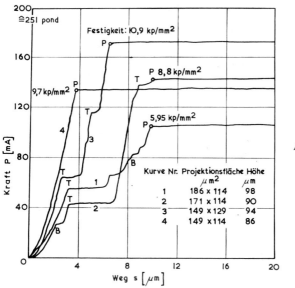

ABB. 9

teilens (*T*), während die endgültige Zertrümmerung in Form des Zerplatzens (*P*) verlief.

Weitere Beispiele der Druckzerkleinerung von Kalkstein und Quarz sind in den Abbildungen 8 und 9 zusammengestellt.

Abbildung 10 zeigt Mikrofotos eines Quarzteilchens und der Bruchstücke in verschiedenen Stadien des Druckversuches. In der zweiten Aufnahme sieht man einen Schleier feiner Teilchen, der nach

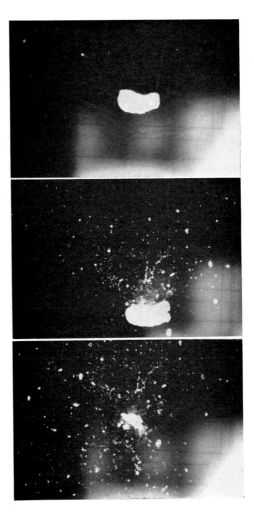

ABB. 10—Bruchsplitterfeld eines Quarzteilchens (Ausgangskorngröße ca. 1 mm)

einer Richtung hin von dem beanspruchten Teilchen weggeflogen ist. Er entstand beim Abbröckeln.

Die Bruchphänomene sind sehr vielfältig und von der jeweiligen Teilchenlage abhängig. Sie weichen von der Vorstellung ab, daß das ganze Bruchgeschehen bei Überschreitung einer bestimmten Festigkeitsgrenze ablaufe und dann abgeschlossen sei. Eine Auswertung ist nur statistisch, bei einer großen Teilchenzahl möglich.

5. ENERGIEAUSBEUTE BEI DER EINZELKORNZERKLEINERUNG

Die Abhängigkeit der erzeugten Oberfläche von der Arbeitsaufnahme zeigt Abb. 11 für die Druckbeanspruchung von Glaszylindern. Die Versuchswerte sind der Veröffentlichung von KENNY und PIRET [17] entnommen. Die 45°-Geraden geben die Linien gleicher Wirkungsgrade an. Die spez. Grenzflächenenergie von Glas wurde mit $\gamma_0 = 500$ erg/cm² angesetzt. Kenny und Piret haben die spez. Oberflächen mit der BET-Methode bestimmt.

Die Beanspruchungsrichtung—auf Stirnseite oder Mantellinie—und Größe der Zylinder ist aus der Tabelle ersichtlich. Die Arbeitsaufnahme ist bei den stirnseitig beanspruchten Zylindern

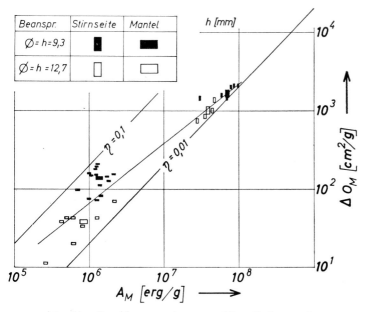

ABB. 11.—Druckbeanspruchung von Glaszylindern nach KENNY und PIRET (1961)

wesentlich größer als bei den mantelseitig beanspruchten. Die
Unterschiede zwischen den 12,7 und 9,3 mm großen Zylindern sind,
wie die Korrelationsrechnung zeigt, innerhalb der 90% Wahrschein-
lichkeitsschranke nicht signifikant. Die Versuche sind somit in
erster Linie als Beispiel für die Variation der Beanspruchungsweise
zu werten. Die den Mittelwerten der Versuche zugeordnete Re-
gressionsgerade ist flächer als die 45°-Linie, der Wirkungsgrad
nimmt also mit zunehmender Energieaufnahme ab. Dieser Befund
ist nochmals in Abb. 12 für die gleichen Versuchswerte in der
Auftragung $\eta' = f(A_m)$ dargestellt. Man findet $\eta' \sim A_m - 0,3$.

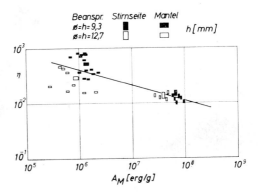

ABB. 12.—Druckbeanspruchung von Glaszylindern nach
KENNY und PIRET (1961)

Abbildung 13 enthält verschiedene Versuchsergebnisse mit Glaskugeln, in der Auftragung $\Delta O_m = f(A_m)$. Mit Kugeln von 12,7 mm
ϕ erhielten Kenny und Piret Energieausbeutewerte, die bei
$\gamma_0 = 500$ erg/cm² einem Wirkungsgrad von ca. 1% entsprechen.
Die spez. Oberfläche war mit der BET-Methode bestimmt worden.
Die in meinem Institut mit der in Abb. 5 gezeigten Mikro-
druckapparatur an 38–270 μm-Teilchen und einer zweiten Apparatur
an 1000 μm-Teilchen ausgeführten Messungen zeigen einen ge-
krümmten Verlauf. Die Punkte sind Mittelwerte aus je etwa 10 Versuchen. Bei der kleinen Substanzmenge der einzelnen Kugel war
eine BET-Oberflächenmessung der Bruchstücke nicht auszuführen.
Die Oberflächenwerte wurden auf Grund einer Auszählung bestimmt
und mit dem auf Grund von Vergleichswerten geschätzten Ober-
flächenfaktor 6 umgerechnet. Die so entstandene gestrichelte
Kurve ist in der absoluten Lage zu ungenau zum Vergleich mit den
Messungen von Kenny und Piret, die überdies mit einer anderen
Glassorte ausgeführt wurden. Der gekrümmte Kurvenverlauf läßt

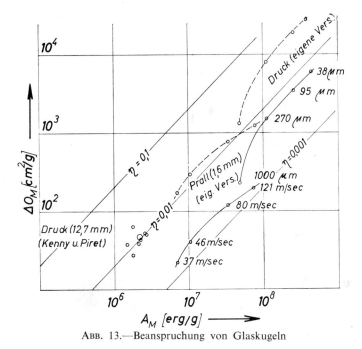

ABB. 13.—Beanspruchung von Glaskugeln

zwei Tendenzen erkennen: Von 270 μm zu kleineren Kugeln nimmt die Arbeitsaufnahme auf Grund der steigenden Festigkeit zu. Nach größeren Teilchengrößen hin scheint die Arbeitszunahme einem konstanten Wert, also konstanter Festigkeit zuzustreben. Für eine genauere Aussage fehlen noch Versuchspunkte oberhalb 1000 μm.

Weiter sind die Ergebnisse von Prallversuchen mit Glaskugeln von 1,6 mm Durchmesser und zwischen 37 und 121 m/sec variierten Prallgeschwindigkeiten dargestellt. Die Versuchsmethode erlaubt die Beanspruchung einer Teilchenfolge, so daß die Oberflächenwerte auf Grund einer Photosedimentations-Analyse bestimmt werden konnten. Die Aufprallgeschwindigkeit wurde mit elektronischer Zeitmessung bei der Passage der Teilchen zwischen zwei Lichtstrahlen mit Streuung festgestellt. Abbildung 14 gibt die gleichen Versuche in der Auftragung $\eta' = f(A_m)$ wieder. Bei dieser Auftragung entspricht dem Kickschen Gesetz eine vertikale und dem Rittingerschen Gesetz eine horizontale Gerade. Die Druckversuche mit feinen Glaskugeln lassen im Bereich zwischen 1000 und 270 μm einen Übergang von der einen zur anderen Tendenz erkennen. Hier ist es nicht zulässig, die Energieausbeutefunktion durch ein Potenzgesetz darzustellen.

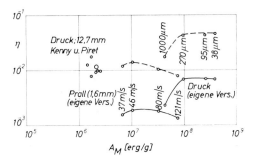

ABB. 14.—Beanspruchung von Glaskugeln

Die Wirkungsgrade der Prallzerkleinerungsversuche haben ein flaches Maximum zwischen 46 und 80 m/sec. Der Abfall nach kleineren Geschwindigkeiten zu ist durch die Annäherung an eine Festigkeitsgrenze erklärlich. Das Experiment zeigt, daß oberhalb eines gewissen Geschwindigkeitsbereiches die Energieverluste prozentual zunehmen.

Die Prallzerkleinerung von unregelmäßig geformten Quarzteilchen der Korngröße $x_1 = 5,5$ mm und $x_1 = 1,8$ mm und drei Geschwindigkeitsstufen 50 m/sec, 100 m/sec und 150 m/sec führt zu den in Abb. 15 dargestellten Ergebnissen. Die Punkte sind jeweils Mittelwerte aus Versuchen mit etwa 50 Teilchen die Korngrösse 5,5 mm und 100 Teilchen die Korngrösse 1,8 mm. Es ist η' als Funktion der reziproken Ausgangskorngröße $1/x_1$ dargestellt. Deutlich ausgeprägt ist die Abnahme des Wirkungsgrades mit

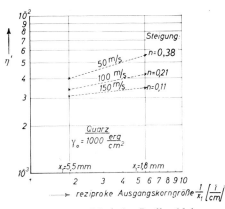

ABB. 15.—Stufenwirkungsgrad bei der Prallzerkleinerung von Quarz

zunehmender Prallgeschwindigkeit. Für die Feststellung der funktionalen Abhängigkeit $\eta' = f\left(\dfrac{1}{x_1}\right)$ reichen zwei Versuchspunkte noch nicht aus. Die an der gestrichelten Verbindungsgeraden je zweier Punkte ablesbare Tendenz läßt darauf schließen, daß mit zunehmender Geschwindigkeit die Steigung abnimmt und formal eine Annäherung an die Rittingersche Hypothese erfolgt. Es sei darauf hingewiesen, daß die Versuchswerte aus laufenden Arbeiten im Rahmen eines umfassenden Versuchsprogrammes stammen.* Sie sollen hier nur als ein Beleg dafür mitgeteilt werden, daß die Abhängigkeit der Arbeitsaufnahme, der Oberflächenerzeugung und des daraus zu errechnenden Wirkungsgrades von der Beanspruchungsgeschwindigkeit einerseits und der Korngröße andererseits in den verschiedenen Bereichen unterschiedliche Funktionsabläufe zeigt, so daß ihre Darstellung durch generelle Potenzgesetze zu irreführenden Schlüssen und Interpretationen führen kann.

6. MASCHINELLE ZERKLEINERUNG

Die Einzelkornzerkleinerung liefert die Maßstäbe für die maschinelle Zerkleinerung, sowohl hinsichtlich der herstellbaren Kornverteilungen als auch der günstigenfalls erforderlichen Energieausbeute. Solange die Optimalwerte der Einzelkornzerkleinerung nicht bekannt sind, läßt sich, da eine theoretische Vorausberechnung nicht möglich ist, keine Aussage darüber machen, welche Chancen einer weiteren Verbesserung der maschinellen Verfahren offenstehen.

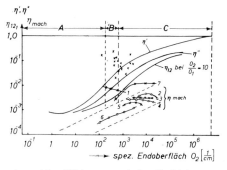

ABB. 16.—Wirkungsgrad der Zerkleinerung

* Für die experimentelle Ausführung der Untersuchungen und weitere Mithilfe danke ich den Herren Dipl. phys. K. Schönert, Dipl.-Ing. D. Behrens, Dipl.-Ing. J. Priemer, Dipl.-Ing. R. Faulhaber und Dipl. phys. H. Umhauer.

Abbildung 16 gibt eine Zusammenstellung einiger experimenteller Werte der maschinellen Zerkleinerung von Quarz. Die Wirkungsgrade wurden unter der Annahme $\gamma_0 = 1000$ erg/cm² errechnet. Die Kurven stammen aus folgenden Arbeiten:

Kurve 1: KWONG, ADAMS, JOHNSON, PIRET [18]: Kollektive Zerkleinerung in der Mörser- und Fallgewichtsapparatur von Gross und Zimmerley.

Kurve 2: ZEISEL [19]: Mahlbarkeitsprüfer der Forschungsinstitute der Zementindustrie.

Kurve 3: PAPADAKIS und ZEISEL [20]: Mörser.

Kurve 4: MORTSELL und SVENSSON [21]: Kugelmühle.

Kurve 5: PIRET [22]: Kollektivzerkleinerung in der Druckapparatur nach Gross und Zimmerley.

Kurve 6: BATEL [23]: Schwingmühle.

Jede Maschine hat einen begrenzten optimalen Einstellbereich. Würde man für einen bestimmten Stoff, z.B. Quarz, alle derzeit erreichten Optimalbereiche der Wirkungsgradkurven in das Diagramm eintragen, so würde die Hüllkurve dieser Kurven die augenblicklich gültige empirische Optimalbeziehung der maschinellen Zerkleinerung von Quarz liefern. Jeder weitere Fortschritt verschiebt die Kurve nach oben, näher zu der Einzelkornzerkleinerungskurve η_{12}. Die Kurve für den stufenweisen Einzelkornwirkungsgrad η' ist in dem Diagramm in Anlehnung an einige von ACHSELSON und PIRET [24] veröffentlichte Versuchswerte hypothetisch eingezeichnet.

Die beiden anderen hypothetischen Kurven für η'' und η_{12} gelten für Teilchenkollektive unter der Annahme, daß die Einzelteilchen unter den gleichen energetischen Bedingungen wie bei der Einzelkornzerkleinerung, d.h. verlustfrei beansprucht werden, und zwar η'' für einen differentiellen und η_{12} für einen endlichen Zerkleinerungsschritt.[25]

Der maschinellen Beanspruchungsmöglichkeit sind bei sehr kleinen Teilchengrößen Grenzen gesetzt. Sie hängen von der Beanspruchungsmethode ab. Bei der Trockenmahlung ist es vor allem die Agglomeration, der Wandansatz und die damit zusammenhängende Plättchenbildung, die bei einem größeren Anteil von feinen Teilchen, unter ca. 5 μm, vor allem unter 2 μm Teilchengröße die Energieausbeute sehr reduzieren. Im Extremfall schlägt der Zerkleinerungsprozeß in einen Kornvergrößerungsprozeß um, bei dem die vorher erzeugten feinen Teilchen wieder agglomeriert werden. Eine weitere Grenze stellt die Einbettung härterer Teilchen in beanspruchende metallische Flächen dar. Der Vergleich mit der Vickers-Mikrohärte ermöglicht eine Abschätzung dieser Beanspruchungen (s. Abb. 17). Die im Einzelkornversuch ermittelte Druckfestigkeit der Teilchen $Pd = \dfrac{P}{d^2\pi/4}$ ist mit der Vickershärte $H_v = 1,85 \cdot \dfrac{P}{a^2}$ der beanspruchenden Fläche durch die Formel

$$P_d \approx H_v \cdot \left(\frac{a}{d}\right)^2 \qquad \text{verknüpft.}$$

Fur $P_d \approx H_v$ ist also größenordnungsmäßig $a \approx d$. Noch festere Teilchen werden vollkommen eingebettet, ehe sie zu Bruch gehen und sind dann der Bruchbeanspruchung weitgehend entzogen. Bei Glaskugeln, die zwischen Flächen aus weichen Stahl von 42 kp/cm² beansprucht werden, ist die Bedingung $P_d \approx H_v$ bei etwa 30 μm Teilchen erfüllt. Spitze, mehr pyramidenähnlich geformte Teilchen größerer Festigkeit werden eingebettet.

Bei der Prallbeanspruchung ist eine Beanspruchungsgrenze erreicht, wenn die Gutteilchen zwischen zwei Wandstößen oder Zusammenstößen durch die Luftströmung soweit abgebremst werden, daß die Aufprallgeschwindigkeit nicht mehr zur Bruchauslösung ausreicht. Dies ist der Fall, wenn der Abbremsweg der Teilchen kleiner wird als ihre mittlere freie Weglänge zwischen zwei Stößen. Beide Größen lassen sich überschlägig berechnen.

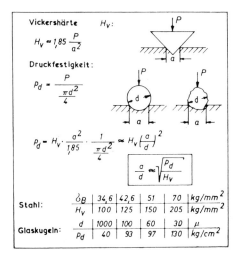

ABB. 17.—Vergleich der Vickers-Mikrohärte mit der Druckfestigkeit

Bei üblichen Gutkonzentrationen der Trockenmahlung liegt die Beanspruchungsgrenze im Korngrößenbereich um 0,1 μm – 1 μm. Beansprucht man Kugeln im Schergeschwindigkeitsfeld einer Flüssigkeit lediglich durch die Kräfte, die von der Flüssigkeit auf die Oberfläche der Teilchen ausgeübt werden, so ist der erzielbare max. Spannung

$$\sigma \approx 2,5 \cdot \tau = 2,5 \cdot \eta \cdot \frac{du}{dy}$$

der Schubspannung τ proportional, die dem Schergefälle zugeordnet ist. Die Beanspruchung ist unabhängig von der Korngröße und deshalb für feinste Teilchen geeignet. Maximale Werte erhält man beim Kneten hochviscoser Massen. Sie liegen in der Größenordnung 1–10 kp/cm², reichen also nicht zur Zerkleinerung fester Substanzen aus. Zum Aufteilen von Agglomeraten kann man diese Beanspruchungsart technisch ausnutzen.

LITERATURVERZEICHNIS

1. Gilman, J. J., " Cleavage, Ductility and Tenacity in Crystals." In: Fracture, Hrsg. Averbach, B. L., Felbeck, D. K., Hahn, G. T., und Thomas, D. A. (New York/London, 1959, S. 193/224).
2. Irwin, G. R., *Materialprüfung*, **4**, 1, 1962.
3. Schardin, H., und Struth, W., *Glastechn. Berichte*, **16**, 219, 1938.
4. Berry, J. P., " Fracture Processes in Polymeric Materials. 1. The Surface Energy of Poly-Methyl Methacrylate ", *General Electric Res. Lab. Rep. No. 60-RL-2519 C,* September 1960.
5. Berry, J. P., " Fracture Processes in Glassy Polymers II. The Tensile Strength of Polystyrene," *General Electric Res. Lab. Rep. No. 60-RL-2526 C,* October 1960.
6. Cottrell, A. H., " Theoretical Aspects of Fracture." In: Fracture, Hhrgs. Averbach, B. L., Felbeck, D. K., Hahn, G. T., und Thomas, D. A. (New York/London 1959, S 20/53).
7. Stroh, A. N., *Advances in Physics,* **6**, 418, 1957.
8. Kochendörfer, A., *Materialprüfung,* **3**, 266, 1961 (darin umfangreiche Literaturangaben).
9. Charles, R. J., " The Strength of Silicate Glasses and Some Crystalline Oxides." In: Fracture, Hrsg. Auerbach, B. L., Felbeck, D. K., Hahn, G. T., und Thomas, D. A. (New York/London, 1959) S 225-249.
10. Anderegg, F. O., *Ind. Engng. Chem.,* **31**, 290, 1939.
11. Emrick, J. R., " Apparatus in procedures for determining tensile properties of iron whiskers." Instrument Society of America (ISA). Preprint number 147/LA61.
12. Schönert, K., und Rumpf, H., in Symposium Zerkleinern, Verlag Chemie GmbH. Weinheim/Bergstr. und VDI-Verlag Düsseldorf 1962.
13. Hillig, W. B., in: " The Factors Affecting the Ultimate Strength of Bulk Fused Silica." Symposium sur la résistance mécanique du verre et les moyens de l'améliorer. Florence 1961, S. 296/325. (Union Scientifique continentale du Verre: Charleroi/Belgien.)

14. Smekal, A. G., Warmfeste und korrosionsbeständige Sinterwerkstoffe. 2. Plansee-Seminar, 19. bis 23.6.1956 in Reutte/Tirol. Metallwerke Plansee GmbH Reutte 1956, S. 28/40.
15. Smekal, A. G., Mikroplastizitäts-Vergleich zwischen Kristall und Glas. Anzeiger der math.-naturw. Klasse der Oesterreichischen Akademie der Wissenschaften (1955) S. 72/74.
16. Schönert, K., und Rumpf, H., in Symposion Zerkleinern, Verlag Chemie G.m.b.H., Weinheim Bergstr. und VDI-Verlag Düsseldorf, 1962.
17. Kenny, J., und Piret, E. L., *Amer. Inst. Chem. Engng.*, **2**, 199, 199, 1961.
18. Kwong, J. N. S., Adams, J. T., Johnson, J. F., and Piret, E. L., *Chem. Engng. Progress*, **45**, 508, 1949.
19. Zeisel, H. G., " Schriftenreihe der Zementindustrie," Heft 14.
20. Zeisel, H. G., *Z. Ver. dtsch. Ing.*, **101**, 483, 1959.
21. Mortsell, S., und Svensson, J., *Min. Engng.*, **3**, 981, 1951. *Trans. Amer. Inst. Chem. Engr.*, **190**, 981, 1951.
22. Piret, E. L., *Chem. Engng. Progr.*, **49**, (2) 56, 1953.
23. Batel, W., TVF Ingenjörsvetenskapsakademien (Stockholm), **30**, (6), 246, 1959.
24. Axelson, J. W., und Piret, E. L., *Ind. Engng. Chem.*, **42**, 665, 1950.
25. Rumpf, H., *Chemie-Ing. Techn.*, **34**, (11), 731, 1962

8—Compaction of Dry Ceramic Powders

By G. J. OUDEMANS

Philips Research Laboratories
N.V. Philips' Gloeilampenfabrieken,
Eindhoven, Netherlands

ABSTRACT
C32—D422

It is argued that the problems of powder compaction are increased when the particle size falls in the sub-micron range. In a cylindrical die, one-sided compaction experiments were carried out with very fine α-Fe$_2$O$_3$, α-Al$_2$O$_3$ and γ-Al$_2$O$_3$ powders. The internal volume of the compact was measured as a function of the compacting force. The force transmitted to the stationary punch was also measured. Other variables were: particle size, initial height of the powder filling, humidity of the powder, and die-wall lubrication. The specific compaction behaviour of these fine powders is discussed and compared with that of coarser powders.

Compactage de poudres céramiques sèches

On démontre que la densification des poudres pose de plus grands problèmes quand la dimension des particules s'abaisse au-dessous du micron. Des essais de densification par pressage exercé sur seul un côté sont effectués dans une matrice cylindrique avec des poudres très fines de Fe$_2$O$_3$-α, Al$_2$O$_3$-α et Al$_2$O$_3$-γ. Le volume interne du produit pressé est mesuré en fonction de la force appliquée. On mesure également la force transmise au poinçon stationnaire. Les autres variables sont: la dimension des particules, la hauteur initiale de remplissage avec la poudre, l'humidité de la poudre et le degré de lubrification des parois de la matrice. Le comportement spécifique à la densification de ces poudres fines est examiné et comparé avec celui des poudres à grains grossiers.

Verdichtung von trockenen keramischen Pulvern

Es wird darauf hingewiesen, dass die Probleme bei der Verdichtung von Pulvern zunehmen, wenn die Teilchengrösse in den Submikronbereich fällt. Mit einem zylindrischen Presswerkzeug mit einseitig beweglichem Stempel wurden Untersuchungen mit sehr feinen α-Fe$_2$O$_3$-, α-Al$_2$O$_3$- und γ-Al$_2$O$_3$-Pulvern durchgeführt. Die Raumdichte des Presslings wurde in Abhängigkeit vom Pressdruck gemessen. Die auf den feststehenden Gegenstempel übertragene Kraft wurde ebenfalls gemessen. Die anderen Variablen waren Teilchengrösse, Anfangshöhe des eingefüllten Pulvers, Feuchtigkeit des Pulvers und Schmierung der Presswerkzeugwand. Das spezifische Pressverhalten dieser feinen Pulver wird erörtert und mit dem von groberen Pulvern verglichen.

1. INTRODUCTION

There is a trend today towards raising demands on the size tolerance of ceramic products used in electronic and nuclear applications.

By the very nature of the ceramic production process it is difficult to fulfil these demands. The powdered dry materials are compacted in a classical die and punch assembly into a shape similar to that of the final product, which is obtained by firing the compacts. The linear shrinkage due to firing usually ranges between 10 and 30%, and causes discrepancies between compact and fired product in size as well as in shape.

There are two obvious ways in which an exact size requirement can be met. First, within the compact the mass of powder should be evenly distributed, i.e. the compact should be of homogeneous density. If this condition is not fulfilled, the less dense regions of the compact will shrink more than the denser ones during firing, and the shape of the products will not be similar to the original shape of die and compact. It is well known that compaction by the classical method of die and punch does not generally yield compacts of homogeneous density.

Secondly, the density of the powder compact, which should be homogeneous, should also be as high as possible. The firing conditions of ceramic ware will not be the same everywhere within one and the same furnace, and in addition may not be reproducible in different firings. Thus the sintering and shrinkage of some compacts may be different from those of other compacts of the same batch. This differential behaviour has less noticeable effect on the size of the products, the less the powder compact has to shrink.

However, the recent demand for products of extremely dense materials with porosities of less than 1%, or even less than 0.1%, complicates the application of the simple view outlined above. These materials include, for instance, ferrites, translucent alumina, and ceramic nuclear fuel elements. In order to sinter products to a high density, the initial material has to be a very fine powder consisting of particles of submicron size. In general, these fine powders show relatively low pressed densities. During compaction the punch also has a longer travel because of the extremely low bulk density of fine powders, which tends to increase the inhomogeneity of the density distribution within the compact.

Because of the poor flow properties of fine powders, granulation techniques must be applied in order to facilitate production. Granules do not permit a homogeneous development of the sintering process on a microscale in the compact,[1] and the resulting inhomogeneous crystal and pore-size distributions inhibit densification beyond a few percent porosity. Other compaction techniques, like hydrostatic pressing, may overcome some of the problems for fine powders, but not all of them.

Up till now, difficulties accompanying compaction, such as capping and the occurrence of cracks and stresses in the compact, etc., have always been solved by trial and error. However, it is obvious that, with increasing demands, improvement of the compaction process by classical methods must be preceded by the acquisition of more accurate knowledge of the mechanism of this process, of which little is known.

2. PREVIOUS INVESTIGATIONS

Hardly anything is known about how compaction proceeds within a die, and what forces operate on the individual powder particles and determine their movements individually or in small assemblages.

Owing to the complexities of the experimental problem, there are not many publications in which the compaction of dry ceramic powders has been an object of research. Within the thick walls of a die, high pressures are built up and consequently the process is inaccessible to conventional observation and measuring techniques. Most investigations have been carried out on compacts after they have been ejected from the die. These compacts yield only limited, and possibly even veiled, information about the final stationary state of the compaction process. Among these investigations must be mentioned the experiments of TRAIN [2, 3] on the density distribution in compacts of magnesium carbonate, and of KUCZINSKY and ZAPLATYNSKY [4] and of UNCKEL [5] on the hardness and the related density distribution within compacts of metal powders. RUMPF and TURBA [6] investigated the strength of barium sulphate compacts and the underlying bonding mechanism.

Measurements inside a die during compaction have been carried out by DUWEZ and ZWELL,[7] who placed dynamometers in the bottom and wall of the die to measure the force distribution on the inside surface of the die during the compaction of metal powders. LONG [8] measured the average radial pressure on a cylindrical die wall during compaction of powders of metals and inorganic salts. KAMM, STEINBERG and WULFF [9] traced with X-rays the deformation of a lead grid placed inside a metal-powder filling of an aluminium die. During the course of compaction TRAIN [3] measured pressures—regardless of direction—at a great number of points within a compact of magnesium carbonate with manganin resistance gauges.

Up to now, no studies of this kind have been made on fine powders of hard crystalline materials. Though such studies certainly seem feasible for these materials, an attempt has first been made to learn something about powder compaction by the more practicable experiment of measuring the average density of several iron oxide and alumina powders as a function of the applied compaction force. Simultaneously the average force transmitted to the stationary bottom punch of the cylindrical die was measured.

3. EXPERIMENTAL

The arrangement of die and punches is shown in Fig. 1. The upper punch A moves down in a cylindrical die B by the upward movement of the lower platen F of the hydraulic press G. The

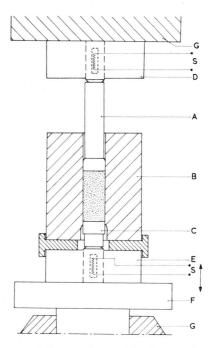

FIG. 1.—Arrangement of die, punches and load-gauges between the platens of the press. For letters see text.

spacing between punch and die is between 4 and 30 μ. The diameter of the die cavity is 20 mm. The roughness due to grooves in the die wall perpendicular to the axis is 0·3 μ as measured by a Taylor–Hobson apparatus. In Fig. 1 only the die and punches are drawn to scale. The die material is a hard Stellite alloy.

The load on the compacting punch A is measured with load gauge D, the transmitted load on the stationary punch C likewise with gauge E. Both load gauges incorporate strain gauges S. The displacement of the upper punch is measured with a dial-gauge reading to an accuracy of 5 μ. The height of the powder column is calculated from the dial-gauge readings, with a correction for the elastic compression of punches and gauges. This elastic compression can be determined as a function of the load by experiments without a powder filling.

The plunger movement was relatively slow and was interrupted at frequent intervals to enable the instruments to be read. The height to pressure relationship of the compact was measured at initial heights of 11, 33 and 66 mm for each powder under two conditions of lubrication.

Two alumina and five iron-oxide powders were selected. The particle size and tap density are given in Table 1. The par-

Table 1

Powder	Particle size (μ)	Tap density (g/cm^3)
α -Al$_2$O$_3$ (Linde)	0·3	0·301
γ -Al$_2$O$_3$ (Baikowski)	1·0 (*)	0·169
α -Fe$_2$O$_3$ Technical grade	0·1–3	0·768
α -Fe$_2$O$_3$ Chemically pure	0·05	0·580
α -Fe$_2$O$_3$,, ,,	0·1	0·613
α -Fe$_2$O$_3$,, ,,	0·3	0·667
α -Fe$_2$O$_3$,, ,,	1·0	1·428

* Possibly the size of agglomerates.

ticle size was determined from electron micrographs of the powders. Three iron-oxide powders, of average particle size 0·1 μ, 0·3 μ and 1 μ respectively, were prepared by heating chemically pure iron oxide with a particle diameter of 0·05 μ at 600°, 750° and 900° respectively in a furnace for 1 h. After the heat treatment the powders were disagglomerated in a ball mill. These powders had a relatively small spread of particle size, whereas the technical grade iron oxide had a wide spread of particle size.

Initially the results of the experiments were not reproducible over periods of more than one day. It was then realized that the compaction behaviour of the powder depends on the varying humidity of the surrounding atmosphere. It was therefore decided to carry out the experiments under two conditions: with dry powder in a die with a non-lubricated wall, and with a humidified powder and a lubricated wall. Both conditions could be controlled easily, and proved to yield relatively reproducible results. The powder was assumed to be dry after having been in a drying-stove at 120°C.

138 OUDEMANS:

for 48 h, because its weight no longer changed significantly. For the same reason a powder was considered humid after exposure in a closed vessel to saturated water vapour at 20°C. for 48 h. The increase in weight by water absorption amounted to 2 to 4% for the alumina powders, to 2% for the finest iron-oxide powder, and to between 0·1 and 0·5% for the less fine powders. The die-wall lubricant applied was stearic acid.

The powder was distributed in the die as equally as possible by tapping the die and vibrating it moderately at 100 c/s while it was being filled. A circular filter paper of 20 mm diam. was placed between powder and punch to prevent the powder particles from slipping into the space between punch and die. A correction was applied for the thickness of the paper.

4. RESULTS

When the results are plotted as the logarithm of the applied force on the upper punch (in kilograms) against the internal height of the compact (in millimeters), two types of curves are found. In most cases a linear relationship exists between both variables, and the plots for dry γ-Al$_2$O$_3$ of Fig. 2 are typical. In other cases the

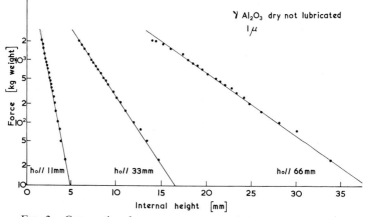

Fig. 2.—Compaction force *versus* compact height for dry γ-Al$_2$O$_3$

relationship is a curved line convex to the abscissa, and the results for dry α-Fe$_2$O$_3$ with a particle size of 0·3 μ, as shown in Fig. 3, are typical of this behaviour.

For the initial heights of 11 and 33 mm of powder filling in the die the linear relationship prevails, whereas for the initial height of 66 mm, half the curves are straight, the other half are curved.

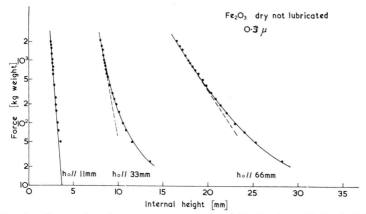

FIG. 3.—Compaction force *versus* compact height for dry α-Fe$_2$O$_3$ (solid curves).

The shape of the curves for the humidified powders in the lubricated die differs only slightly from that for the dry powders in the unlubricated die. Under the same compaction force the densities of the former are generally higher than those of the latter.

The graphs in Fig. 2 and Fig. 3 present the striking evidence that, under a load of 10 kg, i.e. a pressure of about 3 kg/cm^2, the powder has already been considerably consolidated, as indicated by the reduced height of the filling. In most cases this initial displacement amounts to more than one-third of the initial height of the powder filling.

In all cases where the plotted data gave curved lines, the part corresponding to loads between 200 and 2,000 kg could be represented by a straight line, as indicated by the dotted lines in Fig. 3. These straight parts were used to compare the compaction behaviour of the different iron-oxide powders in the higher pressure range. This was done to investigate whether a specific uniformity or similarity between these lines would show up due to the constant material factor, regardless of the variables such as the particle size and the initial height of filling. In order to compare the specific effect of the latter, a relative volume is introduced:

$$\text{Relative volume} \equiv \frac{V - V_x}{V_x} = \frac{P}{1 - P} = \frac{h - h_x}{h_x}$$

where h and V are the height and volume taken up by the powder in the die, and P is the porosity. The subscript x refers to the height or volume that the mass of powder would have taken up as a solid of maximum density.

The equality between relative height and relative volume only holds when it is assumed that the diameter of the die remains practically constant during compaction. For one substance the relative volume is then a quantity proportional to the pore volume per unit of mass.

The lines in Fig. 4 represent the logarithm of the compaction force versus the relative volume for the data on four dry iron-oxide powders compacted in an unlubricated die. The data on dry α-Al_2O_3 were added because both substances possess the corundum crystal structure.

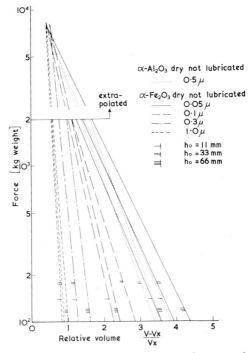

FIG. 4.—Compaction force *versus* relative volume of compact for dry α-Fe_2O_3 and α-Al_2O_3 powders. Note that not all extrapolated lines intersect at one point.

The graphs show that, for one powder under equal forces of compaction, compacts of larger initial height are generally—but not always—less compressed than compacts of smaller initial height. When compared under an equal force of compaction and with an equal initial height of filling, one finds that the density of a compact is greater the larger the powder particles. However, the change of compaction height (or the change of density) with force compared at equal forces of compaction is smaller for compacts consisting of larger particles and having the same initial height. But if this change of compaction height (or change of density) with force is compared at equal reduced heights, i.e. at equal relative densities, then it is larger for compacts consisting of larger particles and having the same initial height.

The force transmitted to the bottom punch was measured simultaneously with the applied compaction force and compact height. The ratios of this transmitted force to the applied force corresponding to the points of Figs. 2 and 3 are shown in Figs. 5 and 6 respectively as a function of the applied force.

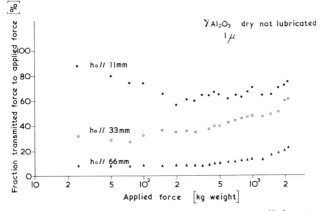

Fig. 5.—Ratio of transmitted to applied force *versus* applied compaction force. Data correspond to those in Fig. 2.

For the dry iron-oxide powders there was no evident relationship between these curves with regards to particle size. In comparison with their dry counterparts the ratios for the humidified and lubricated powders were higher, especially for the compacts with initial heights of 33 and 66 mm. In general, the ratios for a lubricated powder compact of initial height of 66 mm ran equal with the ratios for the dry compact of the same powder with an initial height of 33 mm.

There was no significant difference in ratios for the different humidified and lubricated iron-oxide powders and alumina powders with the same initial height of compaction. For an initial height of 11 mm the ratios fluctuated between 80 and 100%; for an initial

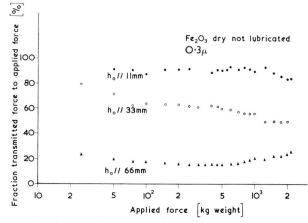

FIG. 6.—Ratio of transmitted to applied force *versus* applied compaction
force. Data correspond to those in Fig. 3.

height of 33 mm the ratios fluctuated between 60 and 90%; for an
initial height of 66 mm the ratios fluctuated between 30 and 70%.

With allowance for some scatter, the series of the ratios of transmitted force to applied force for one compact versus the compaction
force could be represented by a straight line. For the humidified
and lubricated powders the slope of this line was zero or slightly
positive.

5. DISCUSSION

It would be interesting to compare the compaction curves of
Figs. 2 and 3 with data from literature on other materials.

TRAIN[2] measured the compaction curve of a magnesium carbonate
powder with a particle size of approximately 70 μ. The average of
his results is shown schematically in Fig. 7; the curve runs concave
to the abscissa. Only under a force greater than 50 kg/cm² does
the degree of compaction become appreciable. The initial degree of
compaction is small because presumably there was not much room
left for the particles to slip past each other under a small force.*
The large compaction under higher pressures must have taken place
by simultaneous fracture or plastic deformation of the crystals with
a calcite structure. This structure has planes of easy cleavage and
parting that allow for these effects.

Our apparatus was too heavy to measure forces less than 10 kg,
but it would be interesting to see what would happen under a much

---

* It must be remarked that TRAIN applied " hand tamping to ensure a
constant initial condition of packing of the particles ".

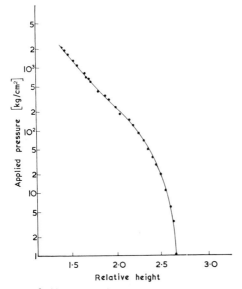

Fig. 7.—Average of 10 compaction curves of magnesium carbonate as measured by TRAIN.[2] Here the relative height is the actual height divided by the theoretical height at 100% density

lower compaction force. During the large initial displacement of the powder under a small force, the basis may already be laid for the particle configuration that exists under greater forces.

One can hardly assume that particle fracture or plastic deformation occurs during this initial phase of compaction. This compaction must be established by the slipping of particles past each other into denser arrangements. Such a large initial compaction from a loose state of packing under a small force does not occur to the same degree with powders of particles size well over 10 μ without particle fracture or plastic deformation. It is impossible to think of any model consisting of much coarser particles that behaves similarly.

It must be supposed that the loose packing in systems of submicron particles is caused by interparticle forces which have a much smaller effect in systems consisting of coarser particles. These forces must be at least of a magnitude to counteract the force of gravity of one particle or of a small assemblage of particles, but they cannot be so large as to prevent movement under applied forces of a few kg/cm². The effectiveness of these forces can also be attributed to the presence of a high surface area to mass ratio in submicron particle systems. Two types of interparticle forces—both of

an electric nature—may be considered: the electric force due to the
irregular electrostatic charge distribution of the crystalline surface
of the particles, and the London–van der Waals forces. Under
specified conditions of shape and mass the latter forces may depend
on distance according to an inverse cube law.[10]

We found no agreement with the relationship proposed for metal
powders by BAL'SHIN.[11] Recently COOPER and EATON[12] have developed a formula that expresses compaction as the sum of two
distinct effects. Each effect corresponds to a particular compaction
mechanism, which is allowed to occur according to a statistical
probability dependent on the applied compaction pressure P only.
They plot the inverse of P against the logarithm of the relative
volume compaction V^*, which is the fraction of volume decrease
to the total of the initially present void volume. This is expressed
as follows

$$V^* = a_1 \exp(-k_1/P) + a_2 \exp(-k_2/P)$$

where a_1 and a_2 are the maximum possible fractional volume com-
pactions each associated with one particular densification mechanism. a_1 is associated with the mechanism of the particles slipping past each other, which fills a category of large holes. a
is associated with a mechanism by which smaller holes are filled,
for instance by fragmentation or plastic flow of the particles.
k_1 and k_2 are approximately the respective pressures under
which both mechanisms are most likely to occur. From the
above-mentioned plot the values for a_1, a_2, k_1 and k_2 can be derived.
If we plot our data in the same way for one powder with three
different initial heights we obtain three different curves. The constants a_1, associated with the compaction mechanism at lower
pressures, differ considerably. This is not easy to understand in
terms of the model used by Cooper and Eaton. However, their
experimental work was done with powders consisting of particles
much coarser than the ones used in our experiments.

It must be noted that in Fig. 4 most lines, when extrapolated to
higher forces, intersect each other in a small area between 6 and
8.10^3 kg and at a relative volume between 0·6 and 0·7. For humidified powders of $\alpha\text{-Fe}_2\text{O}_3$ in a lubricated die the extrapolated lines
show a similar behaviour, but they intersect each other in a wider
area lying between 4.10^3 and 1.10^4 kg force and between relative
volume values of 0·3 and 0.75.

The significance of this intersection is not clear. It might be that
the powder is compacted according to an equation of state, giving
as a lower limit of attainable reduced height the value of 0·6–0·7 for
dry powders of $\alpha\text{-Fe}_2\text{O}_3$, i.e. a lower limit of porosity between 3

and 41%. It is assumed that up to 10^4 kg the substance would continue to behave as it does up to 2.10^3 kg. Experiments with higher compaction forces have still to be carried out.

As Fig. 8 shows, the powders of α-Al_2O_3 and γ-Al_2O_3 do not fit into this description. We are not sure if the particles of γ-Al_2O_3, as visible on electron micrographs, consist in reality of a large number of much smaller particles, all arranged in open sponge-like structures. The high values for the relative volume as compared with α-Al_2O_3 point in that direction.

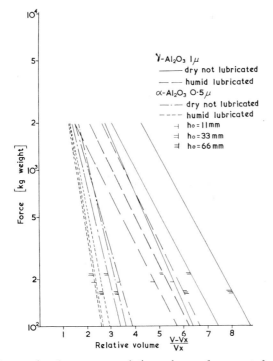

FIG. 8.—Compaction force *versus* relative volume of compact for dry and humidified α-Al_2O_3 and γ-Al_2O_3 powders

The ratios of transmitted to applied force, as given in Figs. 5 and 6 and observed for the other powders, have a tendency to remain roughly constant as a function of the applied force. The same behaviour was observed by STEINHARTZ [13] for powders of stainless steel, iron and copper, and by SPENCER and others [14] for a polystyrene powder.

6. CONCLUSION

The compaction behaviour of powders consisting of particles of submicron diameter is different from that of powders usually described in the arts of powder metallurgy and ceramics. The small initial bulk density of these powders is striking and also the large change of volume under a small force. Under higher pressures up to 700 kg/cm^2 the decrease of compact height goes linearly with the logarithm of the pressure.

REFERENCES

1. Stuijts, A. L., *Philips tech. Rev.,* **26,** 1965. Stuijts, A. L., and Kooy, C., " Science of Ceramics " (this volume) pp. 231-242.
2. Train, D., *J. Pharm. Pharmac.,* **8,** 745, 1956.
3. Train, D., *Trans. Inst. Chem. Eng.,* **35,** 258, 1957.
4. Kuczinsky, G. C., and Zaplatynsky, I., *J. Metals,* **8,** 215, 1956.
5. Unckel, H., *Arch. Eisenhüttenw.,* **18,** 161, 1945.
6. Rumpf, H., and Turba, E., *Ber. dtsch. keram. Ges.,* **41,** 78, 1964; Turba, E. Thesis, Technische Hochschule, Karlsruhe, 1963.
7. Duwez, P., and Zwell, L., *J. Metals (Trans.),* **185,** 137, 1949.
8. Long, W. M., *Powder Met.,* **6,** 73, 1960.
9. Kamm, R., Steinberg, M.. and Wulff, J., *Trans. A.I.M.E. (Met. div.),* **171,** 439, 1947.
10. Hamaker, H. C., *Physica,* **4,** 1058, 1937.
11. See Jones, W. D., " Fundamental Principles of Powder Metallurgy " (Edward Arnold Ltd., London, 1960), pp. 282-283.
12. Cooper, A. R., jr., and Eaton, L. E., *J. Amer. Ceram. Soc.,* **45,** 97, 1962.
13. Sheinhartz, I., McCullough, M. H., and Zambrow, J. L., *J. Metals,* **6,** 515, 1954.
14. Spencer, R. S., Gilmore, G. D., and Wiley, R. M., *J. Appl. Phys.,* **21,** 527, 1950.

9—Torsional Hysteresis in Plastic Clay

By N. F. ASTBURY and F. MOORE

British Ceramic Research Association

ABSTRACT D42—D444

An account is given of some experimental studies on the behaviour of plastic clay under symmetrical cyclic torsional strain. Characteristic hysteresis is observed and a model is proposed to explain the behaviour. The limitations of the model are discussed in terms of the observed results and the relevance of the work to the concept of technical plasticity is briefly noted.

Hystérésis torsionnelle dans l'argile plastique

Rapport relatif à des études expérimentales concernant le comportement de l'argile plastique soumise à une déformation torsionnelle cyclique symétrique. Une hystérésis caractéristique est observée et un modèle expliquant ce comportement, est proposé. Les limitations du modèle sont étudiées en fonction des résultats observés et l'applicabilité du concept de plasticité technique au cas étudié est signalée.

Torsionshysterese in plastischen Tonen

Es wird eine Übersicht über experimentelle Untersuchungen betr. das Verhalten von plastischen Tonen unter symmetrischem Torsionsspannungswechsel gegeben. Eine charakteristische Hysterese wird beobachtet und es wird ein Modell zur Erklärung dieses Verhaltens vorgeschlagen. Die Grenzen dieses Modells werden anhand der beobachteten Ergebnisse erörtert, und die Beziehung dieser Arbeit zur Vorstellung über die technische Plastizität wird kurz besprochen.

1. INTRODUCTION

The study of the behaviour of materials under alternating stresses has proved to be rewarding in various fields of physics, and the authors [1] have recently shown that this type of technique when applied to plastic clay produces certain characteristic effects that promise to give a deeper understanding of the nature of plastic deformation in bodies containing clay.

The experimental technique, now considerably improved, has been fully described elsewhere.[2] Basically, it consists in imposing a sinusoidal torsional strain of prescribed amplitude and frequency on one end of a cylindrical rod specimen (the other end being fixed), and measuring the resultant stress. In effect, two electrical signals, proportional respectively to the strain (or angular displacement) and the stress (or torque), after suitable amplification are fed into an *xy*-recorder where the stress–strain relationship is recorded automatically as a succession of hysteresis loops.

Most specimens of clay initially produce a series of loops of gradually decreasing widths until, after 10–20 cycles, a reproducible closed loop of characteristic shape (Fig. 1) is obtained, representing a stable plastic condition of the material. This loop is then repeated

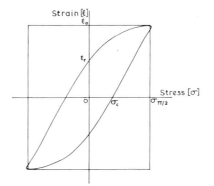

FIG. 1.—Comparison of typical clay hysteresis loop with ideal plastic rectangular loop. (σ_c = coercive stress; ϵ_r = remanent strain; $\sigma_{\pi/2}$ = value of stress at maximum strain, ϵ_0)

until failure of the specimen begins. The obvious resemblance of the clay hysteresis loop to the hysteresis loops of ferro-magnetic materials has led the authors to borrow some of the nomenclature from this field. Thus, the value of the intercept of the loop on the stress axis has been called the "coercive stress", and that on the strain axis the "remanent strain" or "remanence". The area of the loop is a measure of the energy absorbed by the specimen during the cycle. The ratios of these three quantities to their respective maximum values (defined by the rectangle through the points of maximum strain) provide a convenient means of characterizing the shape of the loop for purposes of comparison.

2. A PLASTICITY MODEL

The literature of rheology contains many examples of the use of models composed of particular arrangements of purely elastic and viscous elements (springs and dashpots) to represent the behaviour of real materials. It can be shown [3] that, no matter how complex the series–parallel arrangement of these elements, any such fixed combination will inevitably produce an elliptical hysteresis loop when the model is subjected to sinusoidal stress or strain. Consideration of this fact leads to the conclusion that, excluding the use of other types of element of doubtful validity, the shape of the clay hysteresis loop can arise only if the relative proportions of elastic and viscous elements are not fixed but vary through the stress cycle, and this led one of the authors [4] to put forward a new model based on this concept.

It is the purpose of the present paper to examine this model critically in terms of the considerable amount of experimental data that has now been obtained, and it is convenient to re-state here the main features of the model.

It is assumed that:

(i) the material contains at a given time n_e elastic elements and n_v viscous elements within a given volume:

(ii) the elastic elements obey a law $g_1 x = F$ and the viscous elements a law $g_2 \dfrac{dx}{dt} = F$, where x is displacement, F is force and the g's are appropriate moduli:

(iii) the elastic elements are disposed so that they all sustain the same force and the viscous elements are disposed so that each sustains a displacement equal to the total displacement of the elastic elements:

(iv) a breakdown mechanism operates under which, as more and more energy is stored in the model, the elastic elements begin to break down and become converted into viscous elements.

It then follows, from (i), (ii) and (iii), whatever the nature of the breakdown mechanism assumed in (iv) that, if F and x are respectively the total force and displacement for the model,

$$F = \frac{g_1 x}{n_e} + n_v g_2 \frac{dx}{dt} \; . \qquad . \quad . \quad . \quad . \quad . \quad (1)$$

and, for a sinusoidal displacement, $x = x_0 \sin \omega t$,

$$F = \frac{g_1 x_0}{n_e} \sin \omega t + n_v g_2 x_0 \, \omega \cos \omega t \quad . \quad . \quad (2).$$

The model can be illustrated by a number of springs in series, in parallel with a number of dashpots in parallel, as shown in Fig. 2, with the breakdown mechanism indicated by the arrow.

The particular breakdown mechanism used in the model in its present form rests on the concept that the disruption of the elastic elements is determined by the amount of stored energy. It is assumed that an increase δU in the stored energy produces a decrease, $-\delta n_e$, in the number of elastic elements and an increase, δn_v, in the number of viscous elements, and that the number of

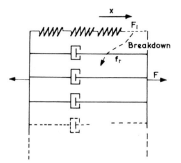

FIG. 2.—Representation of model depicting breakdown of elastic elements.

elements breaking down is proportional to the number existing at that time and to the energy change. We can therefore write

$$-\delta n_e = \delta n_v = n_e \frac{\delta U}{U_c} . \qquad . \qquad . \qquad . \qquad (3)$$

where U_c is a constant characterizing the rate of breakdown and which can be regarded as a critical strain energy.

Since an increase, δx, in displacement, is associated with an increase in stored energy, δU, given by

$$\delta U = g_1 x \delta x / n_e$$

it follows from (2) and (3) that

$$c = c_0 (1 - \lambda \sin^2 \theta) \qquad . \qquad . \qquad . \qquad . \qquad (4)$$

and

$$F = \frac{x_0}{K_1} \frac{\sin \theta}{1 - \lambda \sin^2 \theta} + \frac{x_0}{K_2} \left(1 + \frac{c_0 \lambda}{1 - c_0} \sin^2 \theta \right) \cos \theta . \qquad (5)$$

where

$$\left. \begin{array}{c} \theta = \omega t \\[2mm] c = \dfrac{n_e}{n_e + n_v} = \dfrac{n_e}{N} \\[2mm] \lambda = \dfrac{g_1 x_0^2}{2 N c_0 U_c} \\[2mm] K_1 = \dfrac{N c_0}{g_1} \end{array} \right\} \qquad (6)$$

and

$$K_2 = \frac{1}{\omega g_2 N (1 - c_0)}$$

N is the total number of elements, c is the proportion of elastic elements, and c_0 the initial value of c.

Equation (5) gives an expression for F consisting of two terms, the first in phase with the displacement and the second in quadrature with it.   The in-phase term may be obtained experimentally as the median curve of the hysteresis loop, and from it λ and K_1 may be calculated.   The quadrature term is numerically equal to half the width of the loop and is used to calculate c_0 and K_2. U_c is obtained from the product λK_1.

With our cylindrical specimens in torsion, x is replaced by ε, the value of shear strain at the surface of the specimen ($=r\phi/l$), and F by σ, the corresponding shear stress ($=2T/\pi r^3$, where r, $l=$ radius and length of specimen, $T=$ torque and $\phi=$ angular displacement).

3. EXPERIMENTAL INVESTIGATION OF THE MODEL

3.1 General Features

Perhaps the most striking feature of the model outlined above is its ability to fit the experimental hysteresis loops with considerable accuracy.   In Fig. 3 are plotted four experimental loops of differing

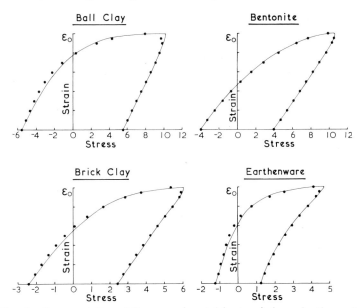

FIG. 3.—Representation of four experimental hysteresis loops by the model. The full lines are the experimental loops and the points are values calculated from the model. (1 unit of stress $\equiv 2\cdot18 \times 10^4$ dyn/cm^2; maximum strain $=2\%$)

shape with, in each case, a number of points computed from Equa
tion (5) after selecting appropriate values of λ, c_0, K_1 and K
(Table 1).

Table 1

Values of Constants used in Calculating Curves in Fig. 3

	λ	c_0	K_1	K_2
Ball clay	0·44	0·58	$2·18 \times 10^{-7}$	$1·75 \times 10^{-7}$
Bentonite	0·26	0·37	1·32	2·44
Brick clay	0·36	0·57	2·85	4·02
Earthenware	0·55	0·75	5·26	7·85

3.2 Constancy of Total Number of Elements

The proposed breakdown mechanism whereby one viscous ele
ment is formed as each elastic element breaks down implies a con
stancy in the total number of elastic and viscous elements. Reference
to Equation (2) indicates that, during any cycle, the in-phase com
ponent of stress, i.e. the coefficient of $\sin \omega t$, is inversely proportiona
to the number of elastic elements, whereas the quadrature componen
of stress, the coefficient of $\cos \omega t$, is directly proportional to the
number of viscous elements present. We should therefore expec
that, if our hypothesis regarding the constancy of the total numbe

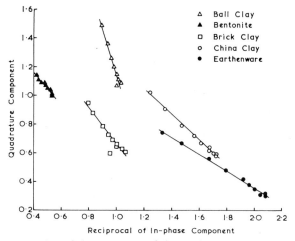

Fig. 4.—Illustration of the constancy of the total number of elements. The
value of the abscissa is proportional to the number of elastic element:
and the value of the ordinate to the number of viscous elements.

of elements is valid, a plot of the reciprocal of the in-phase component against the quadrature component should be a straight line of negative slope. Furthermore, this should apply whatever the exact breakdown mechanism, provided the gain of viscous elements equals the loss of elastic ones. Figure 4 shows that this is indeed so for a number of materials.

3.3 Effect of Strain Amplitude, ε_0

An experimental study of the effect on the hysteresis loop of altering the maximum strain amplitude has been made by subjecting single specimens to cycles of different amplitude. For each change of amplitude the specimen was allowed to give a stable loop before a recording was made. In most cases the order of testing was randomized to avoid bias from the small amount of drying inevitable in a long experiment.

Table 2 lists the effect of strain amplitude on three of the hysteresis parameters. The analysis of the model predicts that U_c and c_0, being material constants, should be independent of the experimental variable, ε_0. While this holds approximately for c_0, the value of U_c

Table 2

Effect of Strain Amplitude on Hysteresis Parameters

Material	Maximum strain (%)	U_c (10^3 erg/cm^3)	λ	c_0
Ball Clay	1	1·3	0·37	0·58
	2	2·8	0·26	0·72
	3	5·0	0·25	0·73
China Clay	1	1·8	0·37	0·61
	2	4·6	0·30	0·70
	3	8·4	0·29	0·69
Etruria Marl	1	0·9	0·26	0·58
	2	1·8	0·24	0·67
	3	3·1	0·29	0·64
Bentonite	1	3·7	0·12	—
	2	4·7	0·24	0·36
	3	11·2	0·24	0·37
Earthenware	0·5	0·10	0·42	0·42
	1	0·22	0·44	0·62
	1·5	0·35	0·49	0·68
	2	0·42	0·55	0·75
	2·5	0·61	0·54	0·76
	3	0·93	0·51	0·75

increases roughly in proportion to ε_0. On the other hand, the definition of λ (Equation (6)) predicts that it should increase markedly with increase in ε_0, whereas in practice it is almost independent of ε_0.

3.4 Effect of Frequency, ω

The experimental set-up at present is restricted to a narrow frequency range and almost all the tests have been made at either 0·01 or 0·04 c/s. A very large number of specimens have, however, been tested at both these frequencies and certain trends have become apparent in the effect of frequency on the various hysteresis parameters. Table 3 summarizes these trends and compares them with the predictions from the model. As in the previous section, the lack of constancy of U_c is conspicuous, and the model in its present form is clearly unable to predict the effects of change of frequency satisfactorily.

Table 3

Comparison of Predicted and Actual Effects of a Fourfold Increase in ω

Effect on	Predicted	Actual
λ	None	None
c_0	None	None
U_c	None	20% decrease
$\sigma_c/\sigma_{\pi/2}$	Increase	5% decrease
ϵ_r/ϵ_0	Increase	5% decrease
W/W_0	Increase	5% decrease
$\sigma_{\pi/2}/\epsilon_0$	None	15% decrease

3.5 Effect of Moisture Content of Specimen, M

The effects of varying the moisture content of a brick clay on several of the hysteresis ratios are listed in Table 4. The ratio of the stress at maximum strain to the strain amplitude $(\sigma_{\pi/2}/\varepsilon_0)$ is essentially a measure of the " stiffness " of the material and naturally decreases as M increases, approximately in proportion to $M^{-7.2}$. Here the value of the exponent of M indicates the degree of sensitivity of the brick clay to change in moisture content.

In contrast, the values of the three dimensionless ratios, i.e. the ratios of the stress and strain intercepts and loop area W to their respective maximum values defined by the rectangle through the points of maximum strain, are remarkably insensitive to change in moisture content. Insofar as the circumscribing rectangle is itself the hysteresis loop that might be expected for an ideal plastic

Table 4

Effect of Moisture Content on Hysteresis Ratios
(Etruria marl; 1·6% max. strain)

Moisture content (%)	$\sigma_{\pi/2}/\epsilon_0$ $(10^6 \ dyn/cm^2)$	$\dfrac{\sigma_c}{\sigma_{\pi/2}}$	$\dfrac{\epsilon_r}{\epsilon_0}$	$\dfrac{W}{W_0}$
23·4	41·2	0·47	0·59	0·39
24·5	29·4	0·46	0·58	0·38
26·3	16·7	0·46	0·59	0·38
26·9	13·6	0·46	0·56	0·38
28·2	11·1	0·46	0·57	0·40
29·7	8·1	0·46	0·56	0·38
30·8	6·0	0·46	0·56	0·38
33·3	3·1	0·42	0·54	0·36

material (one showing no recovery whatsoever on removal of stress), these ratios may be considered as empirical indices of plasticity, since the greater their values, the more nearly does the loop resemble the ideal plastic loop. Furthermore, since the ratios are independent of moisture content they may be regarded as measuring the "intrinsic plasticity" of the material.

Table 5 lists the effects of moisture content on the hysteresis parameters U_c, λ and c_0 for the same series of tests. It is difficult to predict *a priori* what these effects should be. Understandably, the intrinsic energy term U_c decreases markedly with increasing moisture-content, varying approximately as M^{-7}. On the other hand, λ and c_0 appear to be independent of moisture content, whereas one might have expected intuitively to have found a higher proportion of elastic elements in the drier specimens.

Table 5

Effect of Moisture Content on Hysteresis Parameters
(Etruria marl; 1·6% max. strain)

Moisture content (%)	U_c $(10^3 \ erg/cm^3)$	λ	c_0
23·4	10·0	0·26	0·51
24·5	7·4	0·28	0·48
26·3	3·9	0·27	0·53
26·9	3·6	0·26	0·53
28·2	2·8	0·26	0·51
29·7	2·3	0·25	0·50
30·8	1·7	0·26	0·47
33·3	0·7	0·28	0·52

F

3.6 Comparison of Various Materials

Representative values of the hysteresis parameters U_c, λ and c_0 and of the three dimensionless ratios are listed in Table 6 for a number of materials made up to their normal consistencies.

Table 6
Typical Values of Hysteresis Parameters

	U_c	c_0	λ	$\dfrac{\sigma_c}{\sigma_{\pi/2}}$	$\dfrac{\epsilon_r}{\epsilon_0}$	$\dfrac{W}{W_0}$
Bentonite	45·4	†	0·08	0·22	0·31	0·18
Sepiolite	6·0	†	0·17	0·44	0·47	0·35
Ball clay	5·2	0·77	0·23	0·55	0·80	0·51
Ball clay + flint:						
80% 20%	7·9	0·68	0·31	0·44	0·65	0·39
60% 40%	3·7	0·70	0·35	0·40	0·62	0·37
40% 60%	1·6	0·73	0·46	0·29	0·58	0·30
China clay:						
A (most plastic)	2·5	0·63	0·32	0·56	0·76	0·49
B	2·8	0·61	0·30	0·58	0·76	0·52
C	0·9	0·68	0·30	0·53	0·77	0·46
D (least plastic)	0·4	0·75	0·29	0·43	0·65	0·39
Brick clay	2·5	0·47	0·26	0·45	0·57	0·38
Earthenware body	1·3	0·76	0·43	0·29	0·68	0·31
Bone china body	0·7	0·68	0·34	0·42	0·64	0·38
Plasticine	5·3	0·56	0·36	0·36	0·51	0·31

U_c is expressed in 10^3 erg/cm^3.   † values indeterminate.

The progressive additions of non-plastic flint to a plastic ball clay result in progressive reductions in the values of the three dimensionless ratios as expected, i.e. progressively greater divergences from the ideal plastic rectangular loop. Associated with this sequence also are a decrease in U_c and an increase in λ.

The four china-clay samples used are generally recognized, on the basis of their particle size and strength, to be in the designated order of plasticity. Although the results are not quite as clear-cut as those for the ball clay and flint mixtures, these clays provide some confirmation for associating high plasticity with high values of U_c and the three dimensionless ratios.

The position of bentonite is unique among ceramic materials of our experience in giving an almost purely elliptical hysteresis loop with a correspondingly low value of λ. (We note that for $\lambda=0$ the model degenerates into linear viscoelastic behaviour with a hysteresis loop in the form of an ellipse.) It has been suggested that the three-layer crystal structure of the clay mineral montmorillonite, present in bentonite, as compared with the two-layer structure of kaolinite is responsible for the unique behaviour of bentonite, but we have no direct evidence on this point.

It appears from the experiments just reported that a high " technical " plasticity is characterized by a high value of U_c. For bentonite U_2 is very high, and on this basis bentonite would be classed as highly plastic. But the low values of the three dimensionless ratios for this material suggest low plasticity. This contradiction is not without some foundation in fact. Although bentonite is usually regarded as an efficient plasticizer, there is evidence that addition of bentonite to some bodies of low plasticity does in fact worsen their working properties, presumably because of the highly elastic component it adds to their behaviour.

4. A RE-APPRAISAL OF THE MODEL

The evidence presented in the preceding sections shows that some features of the model are in good agreement with experiment whilst others are definitely unsatisfactory in their present form. The model can account well for the observed shape of any particular hysteresis loop if suitable values are assigned to the parameters. Furthermore the notion that the numbers of elastic elements and viscous elements are complementary to one another during a stress cycle is supported well by experiment. This in turn supports the hypothesis of a breakdown mechanism involving a one-for-one conversion of elastic elements into viscous elements and vice versa.

One of the main difficulties lies in the lack of constancy of the parameters U_c and c_0. If the breakdown process is to be completely characterized by the constant U_c, we should expect that U_c would be independent of the experimental variables of strain amplitude and frequency. In fact, as defined at present it depends markedly on these.

Similar remarks apply to c_0, the initial proportion of elastic elements, which would also be expected to be independent of strain amplitude and frequency. In this case, the experimental evidence does not entirely disprove the supposition. Frequency variation in the range investigated has no obvious effect on c_0, and though some results suggest that c_0 increases as the maximum strain increases (see Table 2), the increase is often small and occasionally reversed. The values of c_0, depending as they do on certain subtle features of the shape of the loop, are liable to considerable uncertainty.

Perhaps the greatest divergence between the model and experiment arises in relation to the effects of the strain frequency, ω. Equation (2) predicts that, if n_e and n_v were independent of ω, the in-phase component of stress $(g_1 x_0 / n_e)$ would be independent of ω whereas the quadrature stress component $(n_v g_2 x_0 \omega)$ would increase in proportion to ω. The situation is similar to that of internal friction in certain types of solid, notably ceramics and some glasses. In these materials, the ratio of the quadrature component of stress to the in-phase stress, which is a measure of the internal friction, is found to be substantially independent of ω over very wide ranges. But, if the effect is interpreted in terms of a model such as a Kelvin solid or a standard linear solid, in which only one relaxation time or viscosity coefficient is involved, then we would expect the quadrature term or internal friction to depend linearly, or nearly linearly, upon frequency. In our present model we have, in effect, assumed a single relaxation time to describe the viscous behaviour, and we have been confronted with the same situation. We should therefore more properly base our analysis not upon a single term of the form ωg_2 but upon a summation or integral covering a wide range of g_2 values—a summation or integral which, as in the theory of internal friction, may be substantially invariant with ω over a very wide range.

We believe that this should be considered in any further development of the theory, together with a critical re-examination of the breakdown hypothesis.

ACKNOWLEDGMENTS

The authors gratefully acknowledge the permission to publish this paper given by the Council of the British Ceramic Research Association. Their thanks are also due to Mr. J. A. Lockett who carried out the experimental work.

REFERENCES

1. Astbury N. F., and Moore, F., *Trans. 8th Internat. Ceram. Cong.* (Copenhagen, 1962), p. 3.
2. Moore, F., *J. Sci. Instrum.,* **40**, 228, 1963.
3. Astbury, N. F., and Davis, W. R., " The A.T. Green Book " (Stoke-on-Trent, The British Ceramic Research Association, 1960), p. 189.
4. Astbury, N. F., *Trans. Brit. Ceram Soc.,* **62**, 1, 1963.

10—Rheologie des Gieszschlickers

P. HAGEMAN und H. M. R. OP DEN CAMP

N.V. Kon. Sphinx-Céramique, Maastricht, Netherlands

INHALT A72—C33

Im Rahmen des Strebens nach einem Gieszschlicker mit konstantem Verhalten in der Giesserei, wird ein Übersicht gegeben über die rheologischen Eigenschaften derselben, besonders im Zusammenhang mit der Thixotropie des Materials. Es werden Versuche gemacht die thixotropen Eigenschaften formelmässig zu fassen und auf anderen Kennzahlen und Umstände zu beziehen.

Rheology of casting-slip

With the aim of producing a casting-slip with constant behaviour in the casting-shop, the rheological properties of slips are reviewed, especially the thixotropic properties. Attempts are made to derive a mathematical expression of the thixotropic properties and to relate them to other characteristic values and conditions.

Rhéologie des barbotines de coulage

Etude critique des propriétés rhéologiques des barbotines de coulage, en particulier des propriétés thixotropes, en vue de la production d'une barbotine de coulage dont le comportement reste constant dans l'atelier de coulage. Une expression mathématique des propriétés thixotropes est calculée et un essai est tenté pour établir une corrélation entre elles et certaines valeurs et circonstances caractéristiques.

1. EINLEITUNG

Für die übliche Formgebung keramischer Ware unterscheidet man die Trockenpressung, das plastische Formen und das Gieszverfahren. Letzteres wird insbesondere gebraucht für Ware von verwickelter Form, so dass z.B. Sanitär praktisch völlig nach dem Gieszverfahren hergestellt wird. Die technische Ausführung des Gieszprozesses ist abhängig von den Trocknungsumständen im Gieszraum, vom Gips als Formenmaterial und vom Gieszschlicker selbst. Die Eigenschaften des Gieszschlickers werden bestimmt von der Rezeptur, dem Peptisationsmittel und dem Peptisationsgrad. Angenommen dass die obenerwähnten Umstände und die Gipsformen als konstant zu betrachten sind, dann ist die Produktion abhängig von den Eigenschaften des Schlickers, welche man so konstant wie möglich gestalten soll. Das ist um so mehr notwendig, da man immer weniger fachgeschulte Arbeiter bekommen kann und trotzdem eine steigernde Produktion erfordert wird.

In dieser Situation versteht sich die zunehmende Tendenz nach Mechanisierung. Die Realisierung eines Gieszbandes ist aber völlig abhängig von der Möglichkeit Tag aus Tag ein einen Gieszschlicker mit konstanten Eigenschaften herzustellen, damit die erwünschte Reproduzierbarkeit unter Betriebsbedingungen gewährleistet werden kann. Deshalb wurde versucht die Eigenschaften des Schlickers in eindeutig bestimmten Kennzahlen festzulegen.

Als solche kann man an erster Stelle die Scherbendicke messen unter den herrschenden Betriebsbedingungen, z.B. in einem Gipstopf mit flachen Wänden, zusammen mit dem Feuchtigkeitsgehalt des Scherbens im Entleerungszustande. Um unabhängig zu sein von den Gipseigenschaften (Wassergehalt der Gipsform, Gips/Wasser Verhältnis u.s.w.), kann man den Schlicker abfiltrieren auf Papier unter einen Ueberdruck von 0,90–1,10 Atm, damit man einen Scherben bekommt von gleicher Zusammendrückbarkeit.

Zugleich kann man die Permeabilität des Scherbens bestimmen, ein Masz für das Verhalten während der Trocknung. Weil das Gieszverfahren selbst Schlicker in Strömung impliziert (ein- und ausgiessen der Form, Zirkulation in Röhrleitungen, pumpen des Schlickers u.s.w.) sind die rheologischen Eigenschaften besonders wichtig und zugleich insbesondere geeignet zur Charakterisierung. Versucht man aber den Zähigkeitskoeffizient eines Schlickers zu bestimmen, dann zeigt sich dieser gar nicht viskos im Sinne Newtons. Man hat gelernt neben den Newtonschen Flüssigkeiten, welche dem einfachen Ansatz $\tau = \eta D$ gehorchen, einige andere rheologische Grundformen zu unterscheiden durch Studierung vieler Modellsubstanzen, wie strukturviskoses, dilatantes und plastisches Fliessen. Diese Formen können nicht mehr durch eine einzige Zahl charakterisiert werden, nur durch eine Kurve im $D-\tau$ Diagram. Diese Begriffe sind alle dadurch gekennzeichnet, dass die Zeit darin keine Rolle spielt. Daneben ist schon 1929 der Begriff Thixotropie von Freundlich geprägt worden.

Er definierte ihn als die reversible, isotherme, Sol-Gel Unwandlung durch Anwendung mechanischer Kräfte wie Rühren und Schütteln auf die kolloidale Lösungen.

Für Modellsubstanzen verwendete er Fe_2O_3-Sol mit NaCl und Wyoming-Bentonit mit NaCl. Die Messung geschah reichlich primitiv durch die Zeit, welche verstreichen muss um die Flasche umkehren zu können, ohne dass der Inhalt herausfliesst. Weil die festgewordene Substanz eine unendlich hohe Zähigkeit bekommt, hat man vielfach versucht die thixotrope Suspension zu charakterisieren durch die Hysteresis-Schleife, die man bekommt, wenn man die Rotationsgeschwindigkeit des Drehkörpers im Viskosimeter fortwährend erhöht und dann erniedrigt. Diese Schleife ist aber Apparat—bedingt und deshalb ungeeignet.

Der Gieszschlicker zeigt im allgemeinen all diese Begriffe zugleich, hat also eine Fliessgrenze, fängt an wie eine strukturviskose Substanz und zeigt Dilatanz bei hohen Rotationsgeschwindigkeiten des Drehkörpers. Schliesslich tritt auch eine Art Thixotropie auf, welche aber meistens eine stundenlange Erstarrungszeit zeigt. Deshalb ist es fraglich ob man wirklich mit Thixotropie zu tun hat und man kann die Erscheinung besser bezeichnen mit dem allgemeinen und nicht streng definierten Worte " Ersteifung ".

Es hat sich gezeigt, dass diese Zeitabhängigkeit der " Viskosität " wohl der wichtigste Faktor ist, für das Verhalten eines Gieszschlickers in der Praxis.

Die heutige Untersuchung hat deshalb zum Zweck eine Methodik zu schaffen um die scheinbare Viskosität und die Ersteifung reproduzierbar zu messen.

2. DAS RÜHREN DES SCHLICKERS

Es ist sowohl experimentell wie im Laufe der Betriebsproduktion möglich einen Schlicker mit vernachlässigbarer Zeitabhängigkeit der scheinbaren Viskosität herzustellen. Dieser Zustand des Schlickers wird erreicht durch Zugabe einer solchen Menge eines peptisierenden Elektrolyts oder ein Gemisch verschiedener Salze und Kolloide, dass die scheinbare Zähigkeit minimal ist. Man nennt den Schlicker dann optimal peptisiert.

Rheologisch ist der völlig peptisierter Gieszschlicker charakterisiert durch die Abwesenheit einer Flieszgrenze und durch Dilatanz. Ein daraus formierter Scherben ist dünner und dichter als derselbe aus einem Betriebsschlicker unter gleiche Umstände. Für die normale Betriebspraxis hat ein solcher Schlicker zu viel Nachteile. Die Verarbeitbarkeit im grünen Zustand ist schwer durch das sehr schnelle Austrocknen, m.a.W. die Plastizität ist zu weit zurückgedrängt worden. Ausserdem klebt der Gieszling in der Form, wegen der sehr kleinen Trockenschwindung. Eine peptisierte Suspension wird betrachtet als eine Sammlung einander abstoszende Einzelteilchen und eine koagulierte Suspension dagegen enthält mehr oder weniger grosse Aggregate. Angezeigt worden ist, dass die Peptisation einer ganz verdünnten Tonsuspension nur möglich ist durch Kombination von Peptisator und Rührenergie.

Deshalb kann man annehmen, dass eine koagulierte Suspension durch Rühren zeitlich und stellenweise in Einzelteilchen zerfällt, wenn die verwendete Energie genügend hoch ist. Im selben

Moment, wo das Rühren aufhört, nimmt die Suspension wieder den koagulierten Zustand an.

Ersteifung im Gieszschlicker tritt auf, wenn man als Elektrolyt-Zusatz mehr oder vor allem weniger als das optimale Quantum verwendet. Man kann also die Erscheinung der Ersteifung auffassen wie eine ganz allmählige Koagulation.

Um ein normaler Betriebsschlicker zu charakterisieren, ist die erste Frage, wie man ein reproduzierbarer Ausgangszustand herbeiführen kann. In Anlehnung an das Obenstehende kann die Antwort scheinbar ganz einfach lauten: Rühren! Aber da kann man einen Unterschied machen zwischen das Rühren von der Hand mit einem Holzstäbchen und intensive Rührung wie etwa mit einem Ultraturrax oder Ultrasonor.

Es hat sich inzwischen gezeigt, dass ein Schlicker irreversibel geändert wird, wenn man eine relativ grosse Menge Rührenergie hineinführt (Cady-Mill). Anderseits hat sich auch gezeigt, dass das Rühren mit einem Holzstäbchen nicht zu reproduzierbare Werte führt. Das ist um so merkwürdiger, da die aussterbende Rasse der alten Werkmeister die Gieszschlicker herstellten und korrigierten durch langsam und schnell rühren mit einem Stäbchen.

Allerhand Sorten Rühr- und Vibrationsapparate wurden versucht, als auch ultrasonore Vibration, bis am letzten ein einfacher Rührer in der Form eines Gabels, der durch den Schlicker schneidet, die beste lösung ergab. Aber auch mit dem Gabelrührer kann man nur unter bestimmte Zeitbedingungen reproduzierbare Ergebnisse bekommen. Beim Drehzahl des Rührers von 500 pro Minute darf man nicht länger als 1,5 und nicht kürzer als 0,5 Minute rühren um den maximalen Peptisationsgrad zu erreichen.

Die Wiederholung einer Bestimmung soll immer wieder an frischen Proben stattfinden, sonst bekommt man eine Erhöhung der gemessenen Werte.

3. MESSUNG DER ZÄHIGKEIT UND DER ERSTEIFUNG

Die Zähigkeit wird verursacht durch die innere Reibung eines Stoffes und kann daher nur dynamisch gemessen werden. Abgesehen von Apparate, die auf dem Gesetz von Hagen–Poiseuille beruhen, also die Viskosität errechnen lassen aus der Strömung des Stoffes durch eine Kapillare, sind die Rotationsviskosimeter die besten Apparate, weil sie direkt auf dem Ansatz von Newton beruhen. Um die Berechnung einfacher zu gestalten, nimmt man immer einen ganz engen Spalt zwischen Rotor und Stator. Obwohl diese Apparate ausgezeichnet sind zur Messung des wirklichen Zähigkeitskoeffizienten und aller nicht-zeitabhängigen verwickelteren Strömungszustände, sind sie leider nicht geeignet zur Messung der Ersteifung, weil das Geschwindigkeitsgefälle im Spalt so gross ist, dass die Ersteifung bald vernichtet wird. Zur Messung der Ersteifung sind deshalb nur Apparate geeignet, welche die Suspension frei die Möglichkeit bieten im koagulierten Zustand zu gelangen, d.h. eine Struktur zu bilden. Tatsächlich versucht man dann den Widerstand der Suspension zu messen in nächster Umgebung des Rotors im Vergleich zu einer umgebenden Suspensionsmenge im Ruhezustand.

Von der uns zur Verfügung stehende Apparate war der Brookfield Viskosimeter und der Gallenkamp Torsionsviskosimeter zu diesem Zweck gut geeignet. Aber auch der Brookfield Viskosimeter bedingt eine Rotationszeit von 20–30 Sekunden um ein Gleichgewicht zwischen rotierendem Drehkörper und umgebender Suspension herbeizuführen. Diese Bedingung gilt nur im Falle eines ersteifenden Schlickers, sonst spielt die Rotationszeit fast keine Rolle.

Um mit den genannten Viskosimetern gute und zuverlässige Ergebnisse zu erreichen, ist ein genau Anhalten der Zeitdauer und des Zeitpunktes der Messung notwendig, weil die Ersteifung anfängt, sobald man den Rührer hält. Die Ersteifung wurde nicht ernsthaft beeinflusst durch vorsichtiges Uebergiessen des Schlickers oder Einführen des Drehkörpers in das Messgefäss. Es ist also notwendig alle Handlungen zur Ausführung einer Messung zu normalisieren. Etwa 3/4 L. Schlicker in einem 1 L.-Gefäss wird mit dem Gabelrührer mit 500 Umdrehungen pro Minute gerührt während 45 Sekunden.

Der Rührer wird herausgenommen, das Gefäss unter den Viskosimeter gestellt und dieser gesenkt, bis der Drehkörper richtig im Schlicker steht. Diese Handlung dauert etwa 10 Sekunden. 15 Sekunden nach dem Aufhören des Vorrührens wird der Motor des Viskosimeters in Gang gesetzt mit der gewünschten Rotationszahl des Drehkörpers. Nach 25 Sekunden drehen, also auf dem Zeitpunkt 40″, wird der Widerstandswert in Skalenteile abgelesen.

Für die Bestimmung der scheinbaren Viskosität wird die Drehzahl 50 gewählt und nachher die ganze Bestimmung wiederholt mit einer neuen Probe und Drehzahl 20 pro Minute. Die scheinbare Viskosität wird errechnet aus der Differenz beider Messwerte, multipliziert mit dem Apparatfaktor. Die Ersteifung wird bestimmt durch Ablesung des Skalenwertes 40 Sekunden nach Ende des Rührens bei irgendeiner Rotationszahl des Drehkörpers (meistens wird 50 gewählt). Dann wird der Motor abgestellt, nach 95 Sekunden wieder in Gang gesetzt und nach 120 Sekunden abermals abgelesen.

Als praktischer Wert der Ersteifung wird gestellt die Differenz beider Skalenwerte dividiert durch 2, d.h. die Schubspannungszunahme pro Minute. Dieser Arbeitsvorschrift ist schon ziemlich lange im Betrieb verwendet worden.

4. MESSERGEBNISSE

In Bild 1 sind die Ergebnisse von Rührversuchen mit dem Gabelrührer bei 500 Umdrehungen pro Minute zusammengestellt. Jede Probe aus einem Betriebsbehälter mit Rahmenrührwerk wurde eine bestimmte Zeit, schwankend zwischen 10″ und 5′ gerührt und dann sofort gemessen bei den möglichen Umdrehungsgeschwindigkeiten von 10, 20, 50 und 100 pro Minute des Drehkörpers. Die Messung nahm allerdings 40 Sekunden in Anspruch.

Aus der graphischen Darstellung ist zu ersehen, dass erst eine jähe Abnahme der Schubspannung (Skalenwerte) auftritt, von dem hohen Wert im Behälter zum minimalen Wert, gefolgt von einem allmähligen Ansteigen. Das Minimum tritt bei den gegebenen Rührbedingungen auf bei 40–50″ Rührzeit.

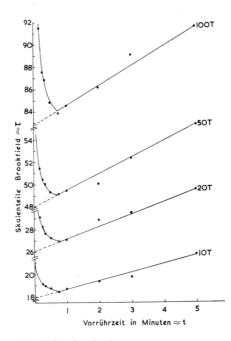

BILD 1.—Einfluss der Rührzeit mit einem Gabelrührer (500 Umdr / Min) auf den sofort gemessenen Widerstand des Schlickers

Die Messgenauigkeit und die relativ kurze Zeit von 5′ in Betracht ziehend, ist es möglich durch die Messpunkte der zweiten Ast eine Gerade zu ziehen, die sich extrapolieren lässt bis Rührzeit = 0. Diese 4 extrapolierten Skalenwerte stellen die Strömungswiderstande bzw. Schubspannungen dar, die auftreten bei den zugehörigen aufgeprägten Rotationsgeschwindigkeiten des Drehkörpers. In Bild 2 sind die Messergebnisse bei den Rührzeiten 0 und 5 Minute und die Messwerte sofort aus dem Behälter in einer D—τ Kurve zusammengetragen. Daraus ersieht man, dass die Fliessgrenze von 13,5 bis auf 9,5 Skalenteile erniedrigt wird durch die zugeführte Rührenergie um dann wieder auf 12,0 anzusteigen nach 5′ rühren. Wenn man also in Bild 1 die Umdrehungsgeschwindigkeit des Drehkörpers extrapoliert auf Null, dann bekommt man eine Gerade zwischen die beiden Fliessgrenzen, also mit dem Tangenten = 0,5. Zum Schluss kann man noch die Richtungskoeffizienten bestimmen der 4 Geraden durch die Messpunkte. Diese Tangente werden grösser um so schneller die Rotation ist. Aus der ebenfalls in Bild 2 gezeichnete Kurve der Tangentenwerte gegen die zugehörigen

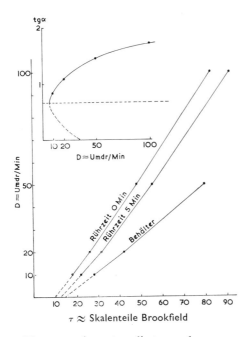

BILD 2.—D—τ Diagramm der extrapolierten und gemesenen Werte nach 5 Minuten Rührzeit, nebst die parabolische Beziehung zwischen Richtungskoeffizienten und Umdrehungsgeschwindigkeiten

Umdrehungsgeschwindigkeiten des Drehkörpers, folgt, dass die 4 Messwerte Punkte eines Parabels sind, was sofort folgt aus einer gleichen Kurve auf logarithmischem Papier.

Die allgemeine Gleichung des Parabels $x = ay^2 + by + c$ hat laut einer Berechnung folgende Werte für die Konstanten $a = 70,63$, $b = 90,16$, $c = 35,60$.

Die Achse des Parabels liegt auf $y = +0,638$ und der Scheitel auf $x = +6,72$. Diese Berechnung hat den Zweck zu zeigen, dass der Parabel keine reelle Schnittpunkte hat mit der Y-Achse, d.h. wenn man die Umdrehungsgeschwindigkeit des Drehkörpers extrapoliert auf Null, bekommt man keine Gerade mit definierter Richtung. Es gibt also einen scheinbaren Widerspruch, indem einerseits aus den extrapolierten Tangenten eine Gerade unmöglich ist, anderseits nach zweifacher Extrapolation eine Gerade resultiert, die bei der Fliessgrenze anfängt. Im letzten Falle entsteht die Fliessgrenze aber als Ergebnis von Messungen, die 40 Sekunden Zeit brauchen. Wenn man in Uebereinstimmung mit dem ersten Fall annimmt, dass der zweifach extrapolierte Wert von 9,5 ausschliesslich entstanden ist während der 40″ Messzeit, dann ist im Minimum noch eine Fliessgrenze von 9,9–9,5 = 0,4 anwesend.

Zusammenfassend folgt aus dieser Untersuchung, dass der Gieszschlicker im Behälter eine gewisse Struktur hat, z.B. gekennzeichnet durch die Anwesenheit einer Bingham'schen Fliessgrenze von 13,5 Skt.

Durch den Gabelrührer wird diese Fliessgrenze vernichtet, aber nicht ganz, weil während der Rührzeit eine andere oder eine gleiche erneute Struktur entsteht, welche linear in der Zeit zunimmt, offenbar nach einer Gerade parallel an die Kurve durch die Fliessgrenzwerte und gehend durch den Nullpunkt. Schliesslich folgt aus den Kurven, dass diese neue Struktur beschleunigt entsteht durch das laminare Rühren der Suspension verursacht durch den Drehkörper (Freundlich Rheopexie). Eine Wiederholung dieser Messungen mit einer neuen Schlickermenge führte im Grossen und Ganzen zum selben Ergebnis.

Weil die Messungen ausgeführt wurden mit Rührzeiten bis 12 Minuten und Rührgeschwindigkeiten des Gabels von 500, 300 und 100 U/Min. verwendet wurden, zeigte sich, dass das Minimum in der Kurve Skalenteile—Rührzeit sich auf längere Zeit verschiebt, wenn die Rührgeschwindigkeit abnimmt, was übrigens zu erwarten war. Leider konnte keine Konstante, wie z.B. die gesamte Rührenergie herausgeschält werden. Auch war die Schubspannung im Minimum etwas höher bei den niedrigeren Rührgeschwindigkeiten. Dies deutet darauf hin, dass die Rührenergie

ungenügend war um die Struktur zu vernichten, obwohl die Ein-
wirkungsdauer viel länger war.

Schliesslich zeigte sich, dass der zweite Ast nach dem Minimum
sich mehr einem Parabel wie einer Gerade ähnelt.

Im Wesentlichen macht das nicht viel aus, weil alle extrapolierte
Werte dann etwas kleiner werden. Die Messungenauigkeit macht
es aber unmöglich die Gleichung dieses Parabels zu errechnen und
damit den exakten Wert der Extrapolation.

5. MESSUNG DER ERSTEIFUNG

Die zweite Untersuchung umfasst die Messungen der Ersteifung
aber in mehr ausgedehnter Form als für den Betriebspraxis notwendig und üblich ist.

Nach 45″ rühren mit dem Gabelrührer wurde für die fortgesetzten
Messungen der Viskosimeter sofort in Gang gestellt mit einer
bestimmten Umdrehungszahl (10, 20 und 50) und abgelesen auf
1/2, 1, 2, 4 . . . bis 32 Minuten nach dem Halten des Gabelrührers.
Diese Messungen ergeben also eine kontinuierliche Kurve des
Schubspannung-Zeitverhältnisses.

Eine neue Probe wurde abgelesen nach 2, 4, 6 . . . bis 32
Minuten nach dem Halten des Gabelrührers, wobei aber der Viskosimeter erst 25″ vor dem Ablesezeitpunkt in Gang gesetzt und
nach der Ablesung abgestellt wurde bis zum nächsten Messungszeit-
punkt. In dieser Weise entsteht eine unterbrochene Kurve. Die
Ergebnisse sind zusammengefasst worden in den Bildern 3 und 4,
worin die Beziehung zwischen Zeit, Schubspannung und Geschwindigkeitsgefälle in zwei von den drei möglichen Projektionen
gezeichnet wurden. In Bild 3 sieht man aus dem Verlauf aller
Kurven, dass diese wahrscheinlich einen asymptotischen Grenzwert
anstreben, nämlich den Widerstandswert des völlig ertsteiften
Gieszschlickers.

Die Ersteifung ist definitionsmässig $= \dfrac{d\tau}{dt}$ und kann bestimmt
werden von einem Tangenten an jeder Kurve in jedem bestimmten
Zeitpunkt. Der Wert des Tangenten wird kleiner nachdem die
Zeitdauer vom Anfang der Messungen grösser wird, aber auch zeigt
sich, dass die Tangenten z.B. im Zeitpunkt 32′ an den kontinuierlichen Kurven bedeutend kleiner sind als die entsprechenden an
den intermittierenden Kurven. Die kontinuierliche Messung
erreicht also schneller den Grenzwert, aber bei kleinerer Schubspannung wie die unterbrochene Messung. Deshalb werden in die
intermittierend gemessenen Suspensionen im Laufe der Zeit
grössere Aggregate gebildet, während durch die laminare Strömung,

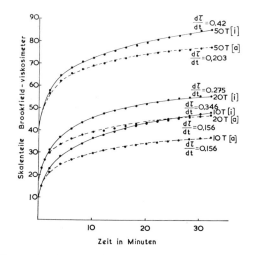

BILD 3.—Widerstand-Zeitkurven bei intermittierende und anhaltende Rotation des Viskosimeters bei verschiedenen Drehzahlen

verursacht von dem kontinuierlich bewegenden Drehkörper, die Struktur einerseits beschleunigt geformt und anderseits auch wieder teilweise abgebrochen wird, bis ein stationärer Zustand entstanden ist. Während der intermittierenden Messung wird die Strukturbildung jede 2 Minuten 25″ unterbrochen bzw. geändert.

Nach Bild 4 kann man die Messwerte extrapolieren nach der Rota-

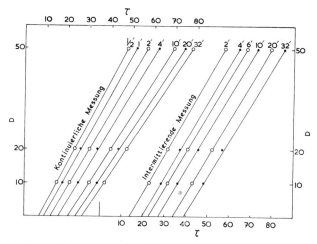

BILD 4.—D—τ Diagrammen des Widerstandes in Beziehung zu der Zeit

tionsgeschwindigkeit des Drehkörpers gleich Null und bekommt also Werte, welche man erhalten würde, wenn die Suspension ungestört durch die Messung ersteifen konnte. Diese extrapolierten Grenzwerte sind identisch mit der Bingham'sche Fliessgrenze, wodurch abermals das enge Verhältnis zwischen Koagulation und Thixotropie, oder plastisches und ersteifendes Verhalten gezeigt worden ist. Auch die scheinbare Zähigkeit kann man aus dieser Kurvenschar errechnen. Diese sind in Bild 5 dargestellt. Im Falle der intermittierenden Messung wird sie schon nach 4 Minuten fast vollständig Konstant, weil sie während der kontinuierlichen Messung erst schnell ansteigt, aber auch nach 4 Minuten wächst zu grösseren Werten, wie bei der intermittierenden Messung geschieht.

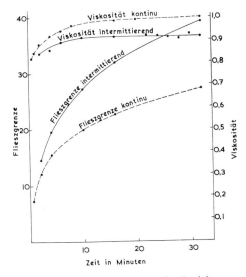

BILD 5.—Viskosität und Flieszgrenze in Beziehung zur Zeit

Im selben Bilde sind die Fliessgrenzwerte als Funktion der Zeit dargestellt. Nach unendlicher Zeit soll die Suspension völlig fest sein, mit einer bestimmten Fliessgrenze (wie auch Stahl zeigt), die asymptotisch genähert wird, obgleich davon in diesem Bilde noch nichts zu ersehen ist.

Selbstverständlich wurde versucht die Schubspannungskurven, die Ersteifung und die Grenzwertkurven mathematisch zu erfassen, um die Ersteifung im Betrieb nach bestimmter Zeit vorhersagen zu können.

Theoretisch sollte es möglich sein, die Koagulationstheorie von

Smoluchowski zu verwenden, nachdem die Anzahl aller zusammengesetzten Teilchen pro ml. $\sum\limits_{1}^{\infty} Z_K$ von der Zeit abhängig ist

nach der Formel $\sum\limits_{1}^{\infty} Z_K = \dfrac{Z_0}{1 + t/t^{\frac{1}{2}}}$, worin $t^{\frac{1}{2}}$ die Halbwertzeit ist.

Annehmend dass die Ersteifung proportional ist mit dem Verhältnis der ständig abnehmenden aber auch grösser werdenden Teilchen zur ursprünglichen Anzahl: $\dfrac{\sum Z_K}{Z_0}$, dann ist

$$\frac{d\tau}{dt} = C\,\frac{\sum Z_k}{Z_0} = \frac{C}{1 + t/t^{\frac{1}{2}}} = \frac{C}{1 + at}$$

Die Integration ergibt dann: $\tau = \tau_0 + \dfrac{C}{a}\ln(1 + at)$.

In Bild 6 sind die Messergebnisse abermals gezeichnet worden als Funktion der log Zeit und wie man sieht bekommt man recht gute Gerade, besonders wenn man die zweifellos grosse Messfehler in Betracht nimmt.

Damit ist sowohl der Proportionalitätsfaktor $C \equiv \left(\dfrac{d\tau}{dt}\right)_{t=0}$ und die Halbwertzeit $t^{\frac{1}{2}}$ eines bestimmten Gieszschlickers zu errechnen und die Ersteifung und Fliessgrenze bestimmt worden.

Deshalb ist der Weg gebahnt worden für die praktischen Untersuchungen auf diesem Gebiet, die für den Betrieb so ausserordentlich wichtig und wesentlich sind.

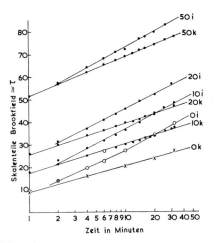

BILD 6.—Halblogarithmische Darstellung der Widerstandskurven

11—Die Eigenschaften von Gipsformen und die Bildung des Scherbens

By W. J. H. BERDEN and P. H. DAL

Laboratory N.V. Kon. Sphinx-Ceramique,
Maastricht, Netherlands

INHALT   C33—C753

Die Bildung eines Scherbens beim Schlickergiessen an einer Gipsober-fläche steht in direkter Beziehung zu den Eigenschaften der Poren und hängt von den feinsten Poren ab. Wenn der sich bildende Scherben eine niedrige Permeabilität hat, sind nur die Poren der Gipsform mit einem hydraulischen Radius von 30 Å aktiv und der Kapillardruck beträgt schätzungsweise 230 Atm. Wenn der sich bildende Scherben eine höhere Permeabilität hat, ist die Scher-benbildungsgeschwindigkeit grösser und die Poren des Gipses mit einem hydraulischen Radius von 40 bis 45 Å sind aktiv, wobei der Kapillardruck ungefähr 170 Atm. beträgt. Da die Bildung des Scherbens nur durch die feinen Poren verursacht wird, benimmt sich die Form wie ein poröses Medium mit niedriger Permeabilität. Die Druckabnahme infolge Scherbenbildung ist nur geringfügig und erreicht etwa 1 Atm. Infolgedessen bildet sich in der trockenen Gipsform der Scherben so als ob der Schlicker bei einer Druck-differenz von 1 Atm. gefiltert würde.

The properties of plaster moulds and the formation of casts

The formation of a cast from casting-slip on a plaster surface is directly related to the properties of the pores, and depends on the finest pores only. When the cast formed has very low permeability, only pores of the plaster mould with a hydraulic radius of about 30Å are active, and the capillary pressure is estimated at 230 atm. When the cast formed has a higher per-meability, the casting-rate is greater and pores in the plaster with a hydraulic radius up to 40–45 Å are active; the capillary pressure is then about 170 atm. Since the formation of the cast is caused only by the fine pores, the mould behaves as a porous medium with low permeability, and so the decrease in pressure through the forming cast is only small, and attains about 1 atm. Consequently in dry plaster moulds the cast forms as if the slip were being filtered at a pressure difference of 1 atm.

Les propriétés des moulds en plâtre et la formation des pièces coulées

La formation d'une pièce coulée sur une surface de plâtre à partir d'une barbotine de coulage est en relation directe avec les propriétés des pores et dépend seulement de leur finesse. Quand la pièce coulée à une très faible perméabilité, seuls sont actifs les pores du moule de plâtre d'un rayon hydraulique d'environ 30 Å et la pression capillaire est estimée à 230 atmo-sphères. Quand la pièce coulée qui a été formée possède une perméabilité plus élevée, la vitesse de coulage est plus grande et les pores du plâtre d'un rayon hydraulique pouvant atteindre 40–45 Å sont actifs; la pression capillaire est alors d'environ 170 atm. Puisque ce sont seulement les pores fins qui

171

sont responsables de la formation de la pièce coulée, le moule se comporte comme un milieu poreux à faible perméabilité et il n'y a ainsi qu'une diminution de pression de faible importance atteignant environ 1 atm., dans la pièce en formation. En conséquence, dans les moules en plâtre sec la pièce coulée se forme comme si la barbotine était filtrée à une différence de pression de 1 atm.

1. EINLEITUNG

Bei der Herstellung keramischer Ware nach dem Gieszverfahren muss dem Gieszschlicker Wasser entzogen werden um einen formfesten Scherben zu bekommen. Ausser der prinzipiellen Möglichkeit, die Feststoffkonzentration zu erhöhen durch Anwendung der Elektroforese-erscheinung,[1] bildet das Filtrationsprinzip[2] die einfachste und bis heute die meist normale Methode um dem Gieszschlicker Wasser zu entziehen.

Der Filtrationsprozess ist mit kapillar-porösen Formen am einfachsten durchzuführen. Die Gipsform hat sich dazu am besten bewährt.

Vor einigen Jahren konnten DEEN und einer unser[2] zeigen, dass die Scherbenbildung an einer Gipsoberfläche mit dem Gesetz von Darcy zu beschreiben ist. Daraus geht hervor, dass man mit einer Filtrationserscheinung zu tun hat. Aus dieser Theorie folgt, dass der Scherbenanwuchs unmittelbar zusammenhängt mit den Hohlraumeigenschaften der Gipsform, nämlich dem Porenanteil, ihrer Permeabilität und dem damit verbundenen Kapillardruck. Weiter wird der Scherbenanwuchs durch bestimmte Eigenschaften des Gieszschlickers und des sich bildenden Scherbens beëinflüsst.

Es folgt jetzt eine Untersuchung über den Einfluss der Gipskörpereigenschaften auf die Scherbenbildung. Dazu wurden Gipskörper hergestellt, mit Eigenschaften, die sehr weit auseinander lagen. Weiter wurde dann versucht fest zu stellen, wie die, bei diesen Gipskörpern gemessenen Hohlraumeigenschaften sich bei der Scherbenbildung aus dem Gieszschlicker auswirken.

2. HERSTELLUNG DER GIPSBREIE

Die Körpereigenschaften der Gipsformen sind wesentlich abhängig von den Aufbereitungsbedingungen des verwendeten Gipshalbhydrates. In erster Linie gilt dieses für den Gipswasserfaktor, also das Verhältnis worin Gips mit Wasser aufbereitet wird, aber auch für die übrigen Aufbereitungbedingungen, namentlich die Einstreu und Sumpfdauer und weiter die Zeit und Intensität des Rührens. Für die Herstellung der verschiedenen Gipsbreie, die in diese Untersuchung herangezogen waren, wurde nur der Gipswasserfaktor und die Zeit des Rührens variiert.

Die Aufbereitung der Gipsbreie wurde in einem speziell dazu konstruierten Vacuumgipsmischer in Mengen von je 5 kg durchgeführt. Für die Einstreu- und die Sumpdauer wurden insgesamt zwei Minuten gewählt. Das Rühren wurde im Vacuum vorgenommen mit immer gleichbleibender Drehgeschwindigkeit des Quirls.

Die Gipsbreie wurden hergestellt aus einem typischen Formengips, der überwiegend aus β Halbhydratgips besteht.

Bei Halbhydratgips sind zwei Sorten zu unterscheiden, die obwohl sie röntgenografisch eine identische Kristallstruktur aufweisen, verschieden in ihren physikalischen Eigenschaften sind.

Zum Vergleich wurde darum auch ein α Halbhydratgips mit herangezogen. Folgende Gipsbreie wurden aufbereitet:

Halbhydratgips	Gipswasser-faktor	Rührdauer (Minuten)	Kodierung
Formengips F	0,9	6	F 0,9/6
,,	1,3	6	F 1,3/6
,,	1,3	4	F 1,3/4
,,	1,3	2	F 1,3/2
,,	1,7	2	F 1,7/2
α Halbhydratgips	1,3	12	α 1,3/12
,,	1,3	6	α 1,3/6
,,	2,5	4	α 2,5/4

Bei dem Formengips wurde der Gipswasserfaktor variiert von 0,9 bis 1,7, womit also ein grösseres Gebiet als in der Praxis gebräuchlich umfasst wurde. Weiter wurde, was auch aus der Praxis wohlbekannt ist, festgestellt dass der Gipsbrei längere Zeit gerührt werden soll, wenn der Gipswasserfaktor erniedrigt wird. Die eigentlichen Rührzeiten, wobei der Gipsbrei eine gute Gieszkonsistenz bekam, betrugen 6, 4 und 2 Minuten für die Gipswasserfaktoren 0,9–1,3 und 1,7. Daneben wurde für den Gipswasserfaktor 1,3 auch 6 und 2 Minuten Rührdauer angewandt, um einen Vergleich zu haben mit den Gipsformen angefertigt mit den Gipswasserfaktoren 0,9 und 1,7 bei gleichen Rührzeiten, und weiter um zu untersuchen wie die Gipskörpereigenschaften sich ändern, wenn zu kurz oder zu lang gerührt wird.

Der α Halbhydratgips, der im allgemeinen mit sehr hohen Gipswasserfaktoren aufbereitet werden kann, brauchte für einen Gipswasserfaktor von 1,3 eine dreimal längere Rührzeit um einen guten giessfähigen Gipsbrei zu bekommen, und eine Rührzeit von 12 Minuten war dann auch notwendig. Die Rührzeit von 6 Minuten war für α Halbhydratgips zu kurz, und ist in dieser Hinsicht einigermassen vergleichbar mit der Rührzeit von 2 Minuten die für den Formengips mit dem Gipswasserfaktor 1,3 gebraucht wurde.

Weiter wurde ein Gipsbrei mit dem Gipswasserfaktor 2,5 auf bereitet. Dafür lässt sich nur noch der α Halbhydratgips verwenden

3. GIPSKÖRPEREIGENSCHAFTEN

An den aus diesen Gipsbreie hergestellten und völlig getrockneten Probekörpern wurden verschiedene Eigenschaften gemessen.
Die Ergebnissen dieser Messungen sind in Tabelle 1 zusammenge fasst.

3.1 Scheinbare und wahre Porosität

Die scheinbare und die wahre Porosität wurden bestimmt mit den üblichen Methoden der freiwilligen und erzwungenen Wasserauf nahme. Aus Tabelle 1 ist ersichtlich, dass die wahre Porosität sich praktisch nur ändert, wenn der Gipswasserfaktor bei der Aufbereitung abgeändert wird, während die scheinbare Porosität auch noch einigermassen abhängig ist von der Rührdauer und der Art des verwendeten Gipses.

Tabelle 1

	Gipskörper							
	F 0,9|6	F 1,3|6	F 1,3|4	F 1,3|2	F 1,7|2	a1,3|12	a1,3|6	a2
Scheinbare Porosität (cm³/cm³ Masse)	0,537	0,408	0,411	0,430	0,343	0,378	0,375	0,
Wahre Porosität (cm³/cm³ Masse)	0,650	0,549	0,550	0,548	0,465	0,549	0,528	0,
Unterer Kapillardruck bestimmt nach Beskow (Atm.)	0,46	0,87	0,68	0,67	0,79	0,65	0,40	>
Luftpermeabilität (cm².10¹⁰)	16,7	3,3	7,8	9,2	3,5	6,2	13,6	0,
Spezifische Oberfläche (cm²/cm³ Feststoff)	17700	26400	16200	14600	16400	18300	10700	41
Aus der Luftpermeabilität berechneter Kapillardruck für Wasser (Atm.)	0,68	1,55	0,96	0,87	1,35	1,08	0,68	5,
L^2/t-Wert für Wasser 20°C (cm²/sec.)	0,081	0,031	0,042	0,055	0,036	0,038	0,058	0,
Aus dem L^2/t-Wert berechneter Kapillardruck (Atm.)	2,6	6,8	5,0	3,8	5,9	5,6	3,6	3

3.2 Wasseransaugefähigkeit

Die Wasseransaugefähigkeit ist einfach zu bestimmen an senk recht aufgestellten zylindrischen Stäben, deren untere Oberflächen mit Wasser in Berührung gebracht wird. Bei diesen Messungen, die bis zu 16 cm Steighöhe ausgeführt wurden, konnte eine streng lineare Beziehung zwischen dem Quadrat der Steighöhe und der Zeit festgestellt werden.

Die Wasseransaugung in einem vertikal aufgestellten porösen Stab ist mit dem Gesetz von Darcy zu beschreiben.

$$\frac{1}{O}\frac{dQ}{dt} = \frac{K(P - \gamma g L)}{\eta L}$$

$$dQ = O\, n_e\, dL$$

$dQ/dt =$ Menge Wasser pro Zeiteinheit (cm³/sec)
$\gamma g L =$ Hydrostatischer Druck des aufgestiegenen Wassers dyn/cm²)
$\quad\gamma =$ Dichte des Wassers (g/cm³)
$\quad g =$ Gravitätskonstante (981 cm/sec²)
$\quad L =$ Steighöhe des Wassers (cm)
$P =$ Kapillardruck (dyn/cm²)
$\eta =$ Viskosität des Wassers (dyn sec/cm²)
$O =$ Querschnitt des Stabes (cm²)
$n_e =$ Effektiver durch Wasser gefüllten Porenanteil
$K =$ Proportionalitätskonstante, Permeabilität genannt (cm²)

Lösung dieser Gleichung gibt:

$$t = \frac{\eta n_e}{K\gamma^2 g^2}\left(-\gamma g L + P\ln\frac{P}{P - \gamma g L}\right)$$

Wird der hydrostatische Druck des aufgestiegenen Wassers vernachlässigt, dann ergibt sich:

$$t = \frac{\eta\, n_e}{2KP} L^2$$

also eine proportionale Beziehung zwischen L^2 und t, wie auch experimentell festgestellt wurde. Hieraus folgt schon, dass man einen bedeutenden Kapillardruck erwarten kann.

Die Wasseransaugefähigkeit kann ohne weiteres in den L^2/t-Wert ausgedrückt werden. Aus den in Tabelle 1 gesammelten Werten ist ersichtlich, dass der L^2/t-Wert abnimmt, wenn der Gipsbrei woraus die Gipskörper hergestellt waren, mit höherem Gipswasserfaktor oder mit längerer Rührzeit aufbereitet wurde. Weiter ist zu bemerken dass mit α Halbhydratgips bei einer dreimal längere Rührzeit etwa der L^2/t-Wert des Formengipses erreicht wird. Auch in den noch weiter zu besprechenden Eigenschaften macht sich diese Erscheinung mehr oder weniger deutlich bemerkbar.

3.3 Kapillardruck

Wie schon erwähnt, soll das Saugvermögen der Gipsformen abhängig sein vom Kapillardruck der Poren.

In erster Linie wurde der Kapillardruck gemessen nach der Methode von Beskow (siehe Tabelle 1).

Diese Bestimmung wurde folgendermassen durchgeführt. Zylindrische Probekörper (1 cm Höhe and 4 cm Durchmesser) wurden völlig mit Wasser gesättigt (mit der Methode der gezwungenen Wasseraufnahme). Die Gipsscheiben wurden dann in eine Büchse zwischen zwei Gummiringen festgeklemmt. Auf einer Seite der Gipsscheibe wurde dann Wasser angebracht und weiter ein Unterdruck angelegt, der jede zwei Minuten um 1 cm Hg gesteigert wurde, bis sich eine Luftblase durch die Gipsscheibe drückte.

Es ist deutlich, dass mit dieser Methode nur der untere Kapillardruck, nämlich der, der gröbsten Kapillare gemessen wird. Es ergibt sich jedenfalls kein richtiges Masz für den wirksamen Kapillardruck der Gipsform, wie sich dieses bei der Scherbenbildung bemerkbar macht.

Deswegen wurde in zweiter Linie versucht den Kapillardruck annährend zu errechnen aus der mittleren Porengrösse.

Dazu wurde die Luftpermeabilität gemessen. Hieraus ist dann die innere Oberfläche des Porenraums zu berechnen, woraus dann weiter der Kapillardruck hervorgeht.

Die Luftpermeabilität wurde bestimmt an zylindrischen Probestückchen (5 cm Höhe und 4 cm Durchmesser). Die zylindrische Wand wurde abgedichtet mit Quecksilber. Auf eine Seite wurde ein Unterdruck von etwa 0,1 Atm. angelegt. Die Menge durchströmender Luft wurde mit einem Rotameter bestimmt. Die Permeabilität ist dann zu berechnen mit dem Gesetz von Darcy.

$$\frac{O}{t} = \frac{OK\,\Delta P}{\eta L}\left(1 - \frac{\Delta P}{2P}\right)$$

$Q/t =$ Menge Luft pro Zeiteinheit (cm^3/sec), gemessen bei dem Druck P

$\Delta P =$ Angelegter Druckdifferenz (dyn/cm^2)

O und $L =$ Querschnitt (cm^2) und Höhe (cm) des Prüfkörpers

$\eta =$ Viskosität der Luft (188 . 10^{-6} poises)

$K =$ Luftpermeabilität (cm^2)

Mit der Luftpermeabilität wird die Permeabilität des gesammten durchfliessbaren Porenraums umfasst. Bei der Wasseransaugefähigkeit wird nur ein Teil der Poren mit Wasser gefüllt (effektiver Porenanteil), wofür eine andere Permeabilität zu berücksichtigen ist. Deswegen kann man die Luftpermeabilität nicht einsetzen bei der Berechnung des Kapillardruckes aus der Wasseransaugefähigkeit. Ausserdem soll nach dem Gesetz von Darcy bei der Wasseransaugung eine scharf begrenzte Wasserfront zu erwarten sein. Es wurde aber festgestellt, dass die Wasserkonzentration in der Nähe der Scheidungsfläche "nass-trocken" mit der Zunahme der Steighöhe abnimmt (siehe Bild 1), was auch hervorgeht aus der Abschwächung der Scheidungslinie "nass-trocken" beim weiteren Anstieg des Wassers. Wie der Wassertransport vor sich geht ist schwer festzustellen. Jedenfalls steht fest, dass die Kapillaren im Gips aus einer Sammlung von grösseren und kleineren mit einander verbundener Hohlräume besteht. Die gröberen Poren haben den geringsten Widerstand und in diesen Poren steigt das Wasser am schnellsten. Der L^2/t-Wert sollte dann auch bestimmt sein durch die gröberen Kapillaren mit dem niedrigsten Kapillardruck. Es wird aber auch die Auffassung vertreten, dass die Wasserströmung durch die feineren Poren im Stande gehalten wird. DEEN,[3] der diesem Gedankengang vorsteht, geht vom Standpunkt aus, dass die Kapillaren aus Hohlräumen isotroper Abmessungen bestehen. Er konnte zeigen, dass eine völlige Abfüllung mit Wasser am schnellsten bei den kleineren Hohlräume erreicht wird. Demzufolge werden die gröberen Poren schon abgeschlossen, wenn sie nur zum Teil mit Wasser gefüllt sind, wodurch die Strömung des Wassers dann durch die feineren Poren im Stande gehalten werden.

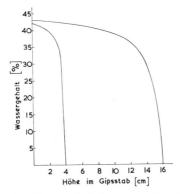

BILD 1.—Verteilung des Wassers bei Ansaugeproben für die Zeitpunkten von 4 cm und 16 cm Steighöhe.

Aus der Luftpermeabilität ist die spezifische Oberfläche des Gipses zu berechnen mit der Formel:

$$K = \frac{1}{5S^2} \cdot \frac{n^3}{(1-n)^2} + \frac{ZF}{5S} \cdot \frac{n^2}{1-n}$$

$S=$ Spezifische Oberfläche (cm²/cm³ Feststoff)
$n=$ Porenanteil (cm³/cm³ Masse)

Das erste Glied ist die Formel von Kozeny und Carman für die Berechnung der spezifischen Oberfläche. Im zweiten Glied ist eine Korrektur aufgenommen für die molekuläre Diffusion, die bei der Strömung von Luft in den sehr feinen Poren stattfindet. F ist die freie Weglänge der Luftmolekülen (6.10^{-6} cm) und Z der sogenannte " Slipfaktor " ($Z=3$).

Der Gesamtporenraum ist weiter zu ersetzen durch eine Kapillare mit dem Volumen n cm³/cm³ Masse $= \dfrac{n}{1-n}$ cm³/cm³ Feststoff, mit innerer Oberfläche S cm²/cm³ Feststoff. Für den Quotient der beiden Werte findet man:

$$m = \frac{n}{(1-n)S} = \frac{\text{Volumen}}{\text{Oberfläche}} = \frac{\text{Querschnitt}}{\text{Umfang}}$$

Die Grösse m ist also der hydraulischen Radius der Kapillar. Für den Kapillardruck ergibt sich:

$$P = \frac{\sigma}{m}\cos \psi$$

$\sigma = $ Oberflächenspannung der Flüssigkeit (dyn/cm)
$\psi = $ der Randwinkel

Für Gips darf man annehmen, dass es völlig durch Wasser benetzt wird ($\cos \psi = 1$). Der Kapillardruck für Wasser beträgt dann:

$$P = \frac{1-n}{n} S \sigma \qquad (\sigma = 73 \text{ dyn/cm bei } 20°\text{C.})$$

In erster Linie fällt jetzt auf, dass zwischen den aus den Luftpermeabilitäten berechneten Kapillardrucken und die reziproken L^2/t-Werte fast eine proportionale Beziehung besteht (siehe Bild 2).

Auch aus dem L^2/t-Wert ist der Kapillardruck zu berechnen, wie dieses aus dem Gesetz von Poiseuille abzuleiten ist.

Für eine zylindrische Kapillar gilt:

$$\frac{\mathrm{d}L}{\mathrm{d}t} = \frac{m^2 P}{2\eta L}$$

Für eine Kapillar mit beliebiger Querschnittsform soll noch ein Faktor a eingesetzt werden:

$$\frac{\mathrm{d}L}{\mathrm{d}t} = \frac{am^2 P}{2\eta L}$$

Mit $P = \dfrac{\sigma}{m}$ folgt dann:

$$P = \frac{a\sigma^2}{\eta} \cdot \frac{t}{L^2}$$

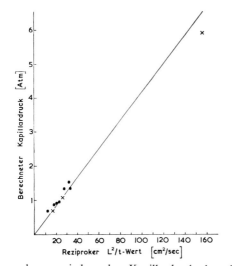

BILD 2.—Zusammenhang zwischen den Kapillardruck, berechnet aus der Luftpermeabilität, und den L^2/t-Wert
● Formengips F,
× Gips aus α Halbhydrat.

Die Werte σ (Oberflächenspannung des Wassers) und η (Viskosität des Wassers) sind konstant. Der Faktor a ändert sich mit der Form des Porenquerschnittes. Nehmen wir an, dass dieser Faktor für die verschiedenen Gipskörper gleich geblieben ist, dann ist der Kapillardruck umgekehrt proportional mit dem L^2/t-Wert.

Wird der Faktor $a = 2/5$ gestellt, wie dieses allgemein für poröse Körper nach Kozeny und Carman angegeben wird, dann folgt:

$$\frac{L^2}{t} = \frac{2\sigma^2}{5\eta P}$$

Man bekommt dann Werte, wechselnd von 2,6 Atm. bis 33 Atm. (siehe Tabelle 1) die in diesem Fall bezogen sind auf die sich freiwillig mit Wasser füllenden Poren, während die aus der Luftpermeabilität berechneten Kapillardrucke von 0,7 Atm. bis 6 Atm. variieren.

An einem Gipskörper sind also verschiedene Kapillardrucke zu messen, abhängig von der Art der Poren, auf welche die Messung bezogen ist.

Aus Tabelle 1 ist weiter zu sehen dass, welchen Kapillardruck man auch betrachtet, immer eine Ansteigung hervorgerufen wird, nachdem der Gipsbrei mit höheren Gipswasserfaktor oder/und mit längerer Rührzeit aufbereitet wurde.

Bei Gipskörpern, hergestellt aus Gipsbreie die nur längere Zeit gerührt wurden, ist die Porosität gleich geblieben und deswegen kann das Ansteigen der Kapillardrucke nur auf das Entstehen von einer grösseren Menge feinere Poren zurückgeführt werden. Beim längeren Rühren werden mehr Keimkristalle gebildet. Dadurch wird der Anwuchs grösserer Gipskristalle behindert und so entsteht ein feinkörniges Gefüge von kleinen Gipskristallen mit feinen Poren.

Man kann die Keimbildung bei gleichbleibender Rührzeit noch beschleunigen oder verzögern, was denselben Effekt hat wie längere oder kürzere Zeit rühren. Beschleunigung der Keimbildung kann hervorgerufen werden durch eine geringe Menge Dihydratgips in der Halbhydratgips. Mit Natriummmetaphosphat zum Beispiel wird die Keimbildung verzögert (siehe Tabelle 2).

Tabelle 2

Gipskorper angefertigt aus:	L^2/t (cm²/sec)	P gemessen nach Beskow (Atm.)	P berechnet aus der Luftpermeabilität (Atm.)
F 1,3/2 ⎫	0,055	0,67	0,87
F 1,3/4 ⎬ ohne Zufügung	0,042	0,68	0,96
F 1,3/6 ⎭	0,031	0,87	1,55
F 1,3/4 + 0,1 % Dihydratgips < 150 μ	0,030	0,76	1,35
F 1,3/4 + 0,03 % NaPO₃	0,049	0,62	0,91

4. DIE SCHERBENBILDUNG

Im vorgehenden Teil wurden die Hohlraumeigenschaften der verschiedenen Gipskörper besprochen. Die wichtigste Frage ist jetzt wie die Aenderung dieser Eigenschaften sich bei der Scherbenbildung bemerkbar machen. An sich ist diese Frage nicht so einfach zu beantworten, da auch die Eigenschaften des Gieszschlickers den Scherbenanwuchs massgebend beeinflüssen. Demzufolge kann der Einfluss der Gipskörpereigenschaften auf die Scherbenbildung nur vergleichmässig festgestellt werden an einem Gieszschlicker der in seinen rheologischen Eigenschaften möglichst konstant gehalten werden kann. Für diesen Zweck wurde ein völlig peptisierter Sanitärgieszschlicker hergestellt, der mit der Zeit praktisch keine Thixotropie aufwies.

Versuche über die Scherbenbildung wurden durchgeführt in viereckigen Gipsformen gleicher Abmessungen, die aus den schon besprochenen Gipsbreien hergestellt worden waren. Die völlig

rockenen Gipsformen wurden bis zum oberen Rand mit Giesz-
chlicker gefüllt und dann wurde zwei Stunden gewartet um den
cherben sich bilden zu lassen. Nach dem Ausgiessen des über-
üssigen Gieszschlickers wurden die Giesslinge sofort aus den
jipsformen genommen und eine halbe Stunde umgekehrt auf-
estellt um den noch anhaftende Gieszschlicker völlig austropfen zu
assen.

Vom Boden der Giesslinge wurde dann die Scherbendicke und
ie Feuchtigkeit gemessen. Die Ergebnisse sind in Tabelle 3
usammengefasst.

Tabelle 3

	Gipsform							
	F 0,9/6	F 1,3/6	F 1,3/4	F 1,3/2	F 1,7/2	a1,3/12	a1,3/6	a2,5/4
bendicke (mm)	4,4	4,8	4,7	4,9	4,8	4,6	4,4	5,0
tigkeit (%)	17,3	17,5	17,2	17,2	17,1	17,2	17,3	17,1

Es sind nur sehr geringe Unterschiede in der Scherbendicke fest-
ustellen, obwohl die Gipskörpereigenschaften stark von einander
verschieden waren.

Nur in zwei Fällen kann man sprechen von einem etwas kleineren
Scherbenanwuchs. Dies konnte beobachtet werden bei den Gips-
ormen, mit dem aus der Berechnung hervor gegangenen niedrigsten
Kapillardruck.

Eine ähnliche Erscheinung wurde schon früher von LORE
LEHMANN[4] aufgemerkt, wobei sie eine geringe Zunahme des Scher-
bengewichtes beobachten konnte bei starker Verringerung des
L^2/t-Wertes.

Mit einem Gieszschlicker aus dem Betrieb konnte dieser Zusammenhang nochmals bestätigt werden (siehe Bild 3). Diese Proben
waren den Betriebsbedingungen angepasst. Es wurde nämlich nicht
allein Zeit gegeben für die Scherbenbildung, sondern es wurde wie
in der Praxis üblich eine Zeit gewartet, bevor der Scherben aus der
Form genommen wurde.

Im folgenden wird jetzt versucht den Zusammenhang zwischen
Hohlraumeigenschaften und Scherbenbildung näher zu begründen.

Nach der Filtrationstheorie, die von Deen und einem von uns[2]
ausgearbeitet wurde, ist der Scherbenanwuchs an einer ebenen
Gipswand mit dem Gesetz von Darcy zu beschreiben:

$$\frac{1}{O}\frac{dQ}{dt} = \frac{P}{\eta\left(\dfrac{L_s}{K_s} + \dfrac{L_g}{K_g}\right)}$$

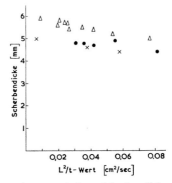

BILD 3.—Zusammenhang zwischen Scherbendicke und L^2/t-Wert.
Mit völlig peptisierten Gieszschlicker innerhalb 2 Stunden in Gipsformen aus
● Formengips F,
x Gips aus α Halbhydrat.
Mit Betriebsgieszschlicker in Gipsformen aus einem anderen Formengips
△ { Zeit für Scherbenbildung 1½ Stunde;
    { Lösen aus der Gipsform 1½ Stunde später.

Einführung der Ergebnisse der Materialbilanz:

$$dQ = \alpha\, O\, dL_s = n_g\, O\, dL_g \qquad \left(\alpha = \frac{1 - c - n_s}{c} \right)$$

gibt:

$$L_s = \frac{1}{\alpha} \sqrt{ \frac{2Pt}{ \eta\left(\dfrac{1}{\alpha K_s} + \dfrac{1}{n_g K_g} \right) } }$$

L_s und $L_g =$ Scherbenanwuchs und Steighöhe des Wassers im Gips
$P =$ Kapillardruck der Gipsform
$t =$ Zeit der Scherbenbildung
$\eta =$ Viskosität des abfiltrierten Wassers
K_s und $K_g =$ Permeabilität des Scherbens und des Gipses
$c =$ Volumenkonzentration des Festoffes im Giesz-schlicker
n_s und $n_g =$ Volumenporosität des Scherbens und effektiver Porenanteil des Gipses

Wenn man in erster Linie voraussetzt, dass $K_s \ll K_g$, kann eine Vereinfachung angebracht werden, wobei die normal gebräuchliche Filtrationsformel entsteht.

$$L_s = \sqrt{ \frac{2PK_s c t}{\eta(1 - c - n_s)} }$$

Hieraus ist ersichtlich, dass der Scherbenanwuchs, was die Gipskörpereigenschaften anbelangt vom Kapillardruck abhängig ist. Die
aus den Luftpermeabilität berechneten Kapillardrucke zum Beispiel,
ergeben dass für die verschiedenen Gipsformen Unterschiede
bestehen von 0,7 Atm. bis 6 Atm. Auch die aus den L^2/t-Werte
berechneten Kapillardrucke variieren mit einem Faktor von etwa
0. Bei der Aenderung des Druckes ändert sich ebenfalls die Permeabilität des Scherbens. Aus einzelnen Versuchen konnte gezeigt
werden, dass bei Druckerhöhung von 0,25 Atm. bis 4 Atm. die
durchschnittliche Permeabilität des Scherbens um etwa 100% ab-
inkt. Anderseits ändert sich die Volumenporosität des Scherbens,
die aus der durchschnittlichen Feuchtigkeit zu berechnen ist, nur
wenig. Wenn man die Unterschiede im Kapillardruck der Gipsformen und die damit fluktuierenden Permeabilitäten des Scherbens
berücksichtigt, sollte man allerdings bei den Scherbendicken Unterschiede mit einem Faktor 2 erwarten können.

Jedenfalls sind derartige Unterschiede nicht festgestellt worden,
und es hat den Anschein dass der Mechanismus der Scherbenbildung mehr verwickelt ist als sich anfangs ansehen liess.

Um eine Uebersicht zu bekommen, wie die Scherbendicke sich
ändern sollte mit dem angewandten Druck, wurden einzelne Filtra-
tionsversuche ausgeführt. Das Filtrieren des Gieszschlickers wurde
unter Benützung von Filtrierpapier bei verschiedenen Ueberdrücken
vorgenommen. Genau wie bei den Scherbenanwuchsproben in den
Gipsformen wurde zwei Stunden abfiltriert, dann wurde der über-
flüssige Gieszschlicker ausgegossen und eine halbe Stunde gewartet
um das Probestückchen austropfen zu lassen.

Bestimmt wurden Dicke und Feuchtigkeit der Filterkuchen und
weiter wurden die Permeabilitäten dieser Filterkuchen errechnet
(siehe Tabelle 4).

Tabelle 4

	Ueberdrucke (Atm.)				
	$\frac{1}{4}$	$\frac{1}{2}$	1	2	4
Dicke des Filterkuchens (mm)	2,6	3,4	4,6	6,0	8,2
Feuchtigkeit (%)	18,1	18,0	17,6	17,5	17,1
Permeabilität (cm² × 10¹⁴)	6,0	5,1	4,5	3,8	3,4

Für die Scherbendicke in den Gipsformen wurden Werte gefunden,
die lagen zwischen 4,4 mm und 5,0 mm. Aus einer Interpolation
findet man, dass diese Scherbendicken zu Stande kommen bei einem
Druck wechselnd von 0,9 Atm. bis 1,25 Atm. (siehe Bild 4).

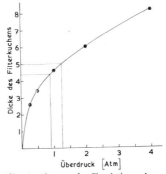

BILD 4.—Dicke des Filterkuchens als Funktion des angewanten Druckes

Hieraus geht hervor, dass die Scherbenbildung in trockenen Gips formen zu Stande kommt, als ob der Gieszschlicker mit einem Druc rund 1 Atm. abfiltriert wird. In erster Linie bekommt man dam auch den Eindruck, dass die Scherbenbildung nicht ohne weitere vom Kapillardruck abhängt. Darum wurde weiter untersucht o der Wassertransport in der Gipsform noch eine Rolle spielt. E wurde schon festgestellt, dass die Gipsformen mit dem höchste Kapillardruck das Wasser am langsamsten ansaugen. Anderseits i die Menge Wasser, die dem Gieszschlicker entzogen wird im al gemeinen gering im Vergleich mit der Menge Wasser, die bei eine Wasseransaugeprobe aufgenommen wird. So konnte berechne werden, dass bei einem Scherbenanwuchs von 5 mm in zwei Stunde noch nicht vollständig 0,2 cm^3 Wasser pro cm^2 Gipsoberfläch aufgenommen wird, während sogar die Gipsform aufbereitet m dem Gipswasserfaktor 2,5 bei einer freiwillige Wasseraufnahm noch immer 1,5 cm^3 Wasser in dieser Zeit ansaugen kann.

Nun wurde bei den Scherbenanwuchsproben bemerkt, dass scho nach kurzer Zeit eine makrohomogene Verteilung des Wassers i der Gipsform stattfindet. Das bedeutet, dass die kleine Meng Wasser in den feinsten Poren mit dem höchsten Kapillardruck au genommen wird. Weiter konnte gezeigt werden, dass die Wassera saugung auch bei der Scherbenbildung mit einem L^2/t-Verband v sich geht.

Diese Proben wurden wie folgt ausgeführt. Zylindrische Scheibe aus den verschiedenen Gipskörpern wurden mit ihrer Unterseite m Gieszschlicker in Berührung gebracht. Die Steighöhe des Wasse kann visuell nicht beobachtet werden. Darum wurden auf ve schiedenen Höhen Ringe mit spitzenförmigen Nadeln um d Zylinderwand geklemmt. Zwischen jedem Ring und einer i Gieszschlicker angebrachte Elektrode wurde eine Spannung v

15 Volt gelegt. In dem Moment wo das Wasser bis zu einen Ring aufgestiegen ist, wird der Stromkreis geschlossen, was jeweils ersichtlich ist auf einem dem Stromkreis angeschlossenen Milliamperemeter.

Dieser L^2/t-Wert war für die verschiedenen Gipsformen praktisch gleich, nämlich $0,0009 \pm 0,0002$ cm²/sec. Es wurde schon gezeigt, dass an einem Gipskörper verschiedene Kapillardrucke zu messen sind, abhängig von der Art der Poren, worauf die Messung bezogen ist. Ein L^2/t-Wert von $0,0009$ cm²/sec gehört also wieder einem anderen Teil der im Gips vorhandenen Poren.

Aus der Beziehung

$$\frac{L^2}{t} = \frac{2\sigma^2}{5\eta P} = \frac{2m^2 P}{5\eta}$$

folgt, dass der Kapillardruck dieser Poren $2,37 \cdot 10^8$ dyn/cm² $= 230$ Atm. sein soll, verursacht durch Kapillaren mit einem hydraulischen Radius von 30 Å. Aus dem L^2/t-Wert folgt weiter, dass innerhalb 2 Stunden, das Wasser 2,54 cm tief in die Gipsform gedrungen ist.

Aus den Daten des Gieszschlickers und des gebildenden Scherbens:

$c = 0,485$, $n_s = 0,354$ und $\alpha = \dfrac{1 - c - n_s}{c} = 0,332$ (Litergewicht 1795,

Dichte des Feststoffes 2,64) folgt dass bei einem Scherbenanwuchs von 0,44 cm bis 0,50 cm respektivlich 0,146 cm³ und 0,166 cm³ Wasser pro cm² Oberfläche im Gips aufgenommen ist.

Für den effektiven sich mit Wasser füllenden Porenanteil (n_g) folgt dann:

$$\frac{0,146}{2,54} = 0,0575 \quad \text{und} \quad \frac{0,166}{2,54} = 0,0653$$

Nach der Filtrationstheorie [2] ist der Scherbenanwuchs, wie schon erwähnt, mit folgender Formel aus zu drücken:

$$L_s = \frac{1}{\alpha} \sqrt{\frac{2Pt}{\eta\left(\dfrac{1}{\alpha K_s} + \dfrac{1}{n_g K_g}\right)}}$$

oder:

$$L_s = \sqrt{\frac{2t}{\eta\left(\dfrac{\alpha}{P K_s} + \dfrac{5\alpha^2 P}{n_g^2 \sigma^2}\right)}}$$

Nehmen wir vorläufig an, dass der Druckabfall im Scherben im Vergleich mit dem Druckabfall in der Gipsform äusserst gering ist, dann bleibt der Gesamtdruckabfall 230 Atm. $(2{,}37 \cdot 10^8 \text{ dyn/cm}^2)$. Für den innerhalb 2 Stunden gebildenden Scherben, mit einer durchschnittlichen Permeabilität $K = 4{,}6 \cdot 10^{-14} \text{ cm}^2$ folgt dann:

für $n_g = 0{,}0575$: $L_s = 0{,}44$ cm; $\alpha K_s / n_g K_g = 243$
Druckabfall im Scherben: 0,95 Atm.

für $n_g = 0{,}0653$: $L_s = 0{,}50$ cm; $\alpha K_s / n_g K_g = 188$
Druckabfall im Scherben: 1,22 Atm.

Tatsächlich ist der Druckabfall im Scherben vergleichsmässig sehr gering. Sowohl der Scherbenanwuchs als der Druckabfall im Scherben stimmen praktisch quantitativ überein mit den bei den verschiedenen Messungen gefundenen Werten. Weiter ist zu sehen, dass die Permeabilität der Gipsform nicht ausgeschaltet werden darf und genau wie der Kapillardruck abhängig ist von der Art der Poren, worauf diese bezogen ist.

Ein ähnlicher Versuch wurde ausgeführt mit einem Gieszschlicker aus grobkörnigen Kaolin und Quarzmehl, mit welchem in kürzerer Zeit der Scherben gebildet wurde.

Daten: Gieszschlicker: Litergewicht 1815, $c = 0{,}495$.
Scherben: L_s in 15 Minuten 0,42 cm, $n_s = 0{,}394$, $K_s = 20 \cdot 10^{-14} \text{ cm}^2$.
L^2/t-Wert bei der Scherbenbildung: 0,00125 cm²/sec

Aus diesen Daten folgt:

Kapillardruck 170 Atm.
Effektiver Porenanteil der Gipsform $n_g = 0{,}0888$.
Berechnete Scherbendicke: 0,42 cm.
Druckabfall im Scherben 1,10 Atm.

Bei einem sich bildenden Scherben mit höherer Permeabilität wird das Wasser dem Gieszschlicker schneller entzogen. Der aus dem L^2/t-Wert folgende Kapillardruck besagt, dass in diesem Fall das Gebiet der aktiven Poren sich ausgebreitet hat bis zu einem hydraulischen Radius von 43 Å.

Hiermit ist gezeigt, dass der Mechanismus der Scherbenbildung mit der Filtrationstheorie völlig zu erklären ist. Weiter ist gezeigt dass die Scherbenbildung in trockenen Gipsformen durch den sehr hohen Kapillardruck der feinsten Poren verursacht wird. Im Scherben entsteht dabei ein Druckabfall von etwa 1 Atm.

Zum Schluss folgt noch eine kurze Angabe über die Scherben bildung in nassen Gipsformen. Wenn der Gieszschlicker mit de

rockenen Gipsoberfläche in Berührung kommt, wird dem Giesz-
chlicker Wasser entzogen und solange die Wasserfront die Aussen-
eite der Gipsform noch nicht erreicht hat, bleibt der Kapillardruck
öllig bestehen.

Ist die Aussenseite einmal erreicht, wobei auch die feinsten Poren
nit Wasser gefüllt sind, dann soll der Scherbenanwuchs weiter durch
mmer gröbere Poren mit niedrigeren Kapillardrucken unterhalten
verden. Demzufolge nimmt der Scherbenanwuchs auch noch mit
ler Zunahme des Wassergehaltes im Gipsform almählich ab (siehe
3ild 5).

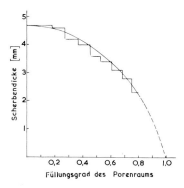

ILD 5.—Abnahme der Scherbenanwuchs mit dem Wasserfüllungsgrad des
Porenraums (Gipsform F 1,3/4).

5. ZUSAMMENFASSUNG

Aus diesen Untersuchungen kann konkludiert werden, dass die
:herbenbildung in trockenen Gipsformen nur sehr wenig beëin-
lisst wird, wenn man die Gipskörpereigenschaften weitgehendst
ıdert. Die Unterschiede im Scherbenanwuchs sind jedenfalls so
ein, dass sie für die Praxis keinerlei Bedeutung haben. Was die
erstellung der Gipsformen anbelangt, so müssen doch gewissen
ɔrderungen eingehalten werden. In erster Linie muss der auf-
:reitete Gipsbrei eine gute Gieszfähigkeit haben, welche nur zu
reichen ist, wenn für jeden Gipswasserfaktor die dazu geëigneten
ufbereitungsumstände gewählt werden. In zweiter Linie muss das
erhalten der Gipsformen beim längeren Gebrauch berücksichtigt
:rden. Die Anwendung eines zu hohen Gipswasserfaktors gibt
ınn den Nachteil, dass die Gipsformen zu wenig Porenraum
kommen. Demzufolge nimmt der Wassergehalt der Poren bald
und sinkt der Druck bei der Scherbenbildung schnell ab. Ein
niedriger Gipswasserfaktor wird die mechanische Festigkeit der

Gipsformen ungünstig beëinflüssen. Weiter wird die mit dem Gieszschlicker in Berührung kommende Gipsoberfläche dann zu schnell abgenutzt. Die Erfahrungen von einem Jahrhundert Arbeiten mit Formengips haben ausgewiesen, dass die Herstellung von Gipsformen mit dem Gipswasserfaktoren 1,3 bis 1,5 am besten ist. Es wurde dann auch der Eindruck gewonnen, dass die Gipskörpereigenschaften in bezug auf die Scherbenbildung keiner kritischer Abstimmung brauchen.

LITERATUR

1. Kocatopcu, S. S., *Bull. Amer. Ceram. Soc.*, **25**, 51, 1946.
2. Dal, P. H., and Deen, W., *Klei*, **9**, 59, 1959; VI Intern. Keram. Kongr. Wiesbaden 1958. " Die Scherbenbildung beim keramischen Gieszverfahren ".
3. Deen, W., *Ber. Dtsch. Keram. Ges.*, **38**, 107, 1961.
4. Lehmann, L., *Ber. Dtsch. Keram. Ges.*, **34**, 232, 1957; **35**, 273, 1958.

Part Three

BEHAVIOUR DURING FIRING

12—Dynamic Properties of Grain Boundaries

By J. HORNSTRA

Philips Research Laboratories
N.V. Philips' Gloeilampenfabrieken,
Eindhoven, Netherlands

ABSTRACT A7

Dynamic properties relate to the motion of grain boundaries with respect to the grains or of the grains with respect to each other. The most important process in Nabarro-Herring creep is grain-boundary squeezing—the motion of grains towards each other accompanied by material transport. The rate of grain-boundary sliding, the motion of grains parallel to the boundary, largely depends on the smoothness of the boundary. These two processes are important in sintering. Grain-boundary migration, the displacement of the boundary with respect to the grains, is the basic process in recrystallization and grain growth and is very sensitive to the presence of impurities.

Propriétés dynamiques des joints de grains

Les propriétés dynamiques concernent le mouvement des joints de grains par rapport aux grains ou le mouvement des grains les uns par rapport aux autres. Le processus le plus important dans la déformation plastique du type Nabarro-Herring est le pressurage des joints de grains, c'est-à-dire le mouvement des grains les uns vers les autres accompagné d'un transport de matière. La vitesse de glissement le long du joint, le mouvement des grains parallèlement à leur joint, dépend largement de la régularité du joint. Ces deux processus sont importants pour le frittage. La migration du joint de grains, c'est-à-dire le déplacement du joint par rapport aux grains, est le processus fondamental de la recristallisation et de la croissance des grains, et elle est très sensible à la présence d'impuretés.

Dynamische Eigenschaften von Korngrenzen

Unter dynamische Eigenschaften versteht man hier eine Verschiebung der Korngrenzflächen in bezug auf die Lage der Körner oder eine Verschiebung der Körner gegenseitig. Der wichtigste Vorgang beim Nabarro-Herring Kriech ist die Bewegung der Körner nach einander, begleitet von Materialtransport. Die Geschwindigkeit womit die Körner längs einander gleiten wird hauptsächlich bestimmt durch die Glätte der Grenzebenen. Diese beiden Vorgänge sind wichtig bei der Zusammensinterung. Wanderung der Korngrenzen, dass heisst die Verschiebung in bezug auf die Körner, bestimmt die Rekristallisation und das Wachsen der Körner und ist sehr empfindlich für die Anwesenheit von Verunreinigungen.

1. INTRODUCTION

Grain boundaries have been studied for many years, especially in metals.[1, 2] The properties of grain boundaries can be divided into two kinds, those of static boundaries and those of moving boundaries. To the properties of static boundaries belong segregation of impurities at the boundary, diffusion along the boundary, and the structure of the boundary. In this paper the behaviour of moving boundaries is considered.

Looking at two grains separated by one straight boundary, we can distinguish three types of motion:

(1) The grains do not move with respect to each other, only the boundary moves sideways. This process is called migration.

(2) The grains move with respect to each other in a direction parallel to the boundary. This type of motion is called grain boundary sliding.

(3) The grains move relative to each other in a direction perpendicular to the boundary. This process is called grain-boundary squeezing; it is always accompanied by material transport, e.g. diffusion of vacancies or interstitials.

These three types of motion cannot always be separated. Often two processes occur at the same time with the same boundary or with adjacent boundaries and there may be a strong interaction between the two processes. On the other hand, it will be clear that the dynamic properties of grain boundaries cannot be understood without knowledge of the properties of static boundaries.

2. LOW-ANGLE GRAIN BOUNDARIES

A well-known example of two types of motion occurring necessarily together are sliding and migration of a low-angle tilt-boundary. Such a boundary can be described as an array of edge dislocations. These edge dislocations may be all of the same type (Fig. 1) or of two or more different types (Fig. 2). When a shear stress

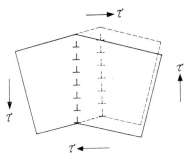

Fig. 1.—Combined sliding and migration of a one-dislocation grain boundary under the action of a shear stress τ.

acts on a one-dislocation boundary (Fig. 1) the dislocations begin to glide. This causes a migration of the boundary and at the same time a sliding of the grains. This phenomenon has been observed by PARKER and WASHBURN [3] and by BAINBRIDGE, LI, and EDWARDS.[4]

If a tilt boundary is a two-dislocation boundary, the coupling between migration and sliding is much less.[5] Figure 2 shows the dislocation mechanism of the three fundamental types of grain boundary motion and one combination of two types. Except migration, all types of motion are connected with diffusion of vacancies. In the case of sliding, only diffusion of vacancies from one type of dislocation to dislocations of the other type occurs. Migration can occur without sliding and without diffusion of vacancies. It will do so if the dislocation paths can cross without difficulty.

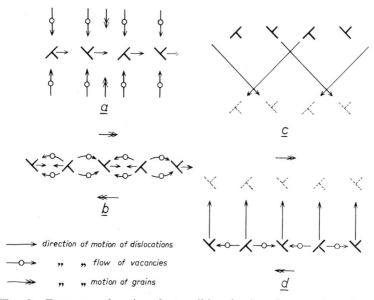

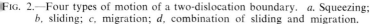

FIG. 2.—Four types of motion of a two-dislocation boundary. *a*, Squeezing; *b*, sliding; *c*, migration; *d*, combination of sliding and migration.

Hence, coupling between different types of motion of low-angle grain boundaries depends greatly on boundary structure. This type of coupling will be absent in high-angle grain boundaries, which cannot be considered as arrays of dislocations. However, the phenomenon of deformation twinning shows that stress may cause migration of twin boundaries, which means that in this case a coupling exists between sliding and migration. Whenever this coupling is present, the boundaries will not migrate easily in recrystallization, because the surrounding grains will hinder the necessary sliding.

3. NABARRO-HERRING CREEP

Creep is a slow deformation caused by low stress at high temperature. In metals, dislocations are so mobile that creep is mainly caused by slip of dislocations and the contribution by grain boundaries is negligible. In non-metals, slip of dislocations may be so difficult that creep of polycrystals is essentially a grain-boundary process. This process has been analysed by NABARRO [6] and HERRING [7] and is therefore called Nabarro-Herring creep. The process consists in squeezing of most of the grain boundaries and sliding along other boundaries. The processes occurring at adjacent boundaries are strongly connected with each other. This connection is brought about by secondary stresses built up during the process. The creep velocity is determined by the velocity of the slower of the two processes.

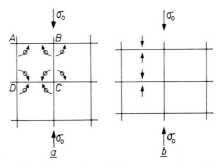

FIG. 3.—Compression of a polycrystalline aggregate with squeezing boundaries only. *a,* Initial state; *b,* after some deformation. σ_0, compressive stress; the curved arrows show the diffusion of vacancies.

We shall assume that squeezing is the slower process and come back to this point in the next section.

The behaviour of two simple boundary arrays under compression is shown in Figs. 3 and 4. In Fig. 3 the boundaries of orientation AB and CD are compressed and will tend to absorb vacancies. These vacancies have to be emitted by the boundaries of orientation AD and BC, although there is no stress present across these boundaries. In this case, only squeezing occurs and no sliding. The reverse is true for the arrangement in Fig. 4, where initially only sliding occurs by the shear stresses across the grain boundaries. Very soon new boundaries are formed, which have to be squeezed in order to keep the deformation going. These two simple cases suffice to show the connection between processes at neighbouring boundaries.

It is worth deriving the relation between stress and deformation velocity for the configuration in Fig. 3, because this derivation clearly shows how the dynamic properties of grain boundaries depend on static properties. Moreover, several steps of this derivation occur also in the discussion of other dynamic properties of grain boundaries.

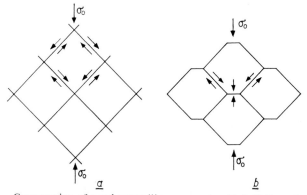

FIG. 4.—Compression of a polycrystalline aggregate with initially only sliding boundaries. σ_0, compressive stress. a, Initial state; b, after some deformation squeezing boundaries are formed.

The first step of the derivation of the relation between stress and strain rate is the calculation of the change of vacancy concentration induced by stress. In the neighbourhood of grain boundaries the vacancy concentration will soon attain its equilibrium value, because grain boundaries can act as a source or a sink for vacancies. If the grain boundary is perpendicular to the direction of the compressive stress σ, the energy of formation of a vacancy is raised by an amount $\sigma\Omega$ where Ω is the volume of one atom. Therefore the equilibrium concentration of vacancies, which is C_0 in the neighbourhood of a stress-free boundary, is lowered by a Boltzmann factor $\exp(-\sigma\Omega/kT)$ near a boundary normal to a compressive stress σ. Here, k is Boltzmann's constant and T is absolute temperature. Generally $\sigma\Omega \ll kT$ and the exponential can be replaced by $(1 - \sigma\Omega/kT)$, so that the difference in the equilibrium concentration of vacancies between boundary AB and boundary BC is equal to

$$\Delta C = \frac{C_0 \, \sigma\Omega}{kT}. \qquad . \qquad . \qquad . \qquad (1)$$

It is impossible that the equilibrium concentration along BC is everywhere C_0 and along AB everywhere $C_0 - \Delta C_0$, because any difference in these concentrations in the neighbourhood of B would give rise to a rapid diffusion of vacancies from boundary BC to boundary AB. By this diffusion process the compressive stress across AB is lowered near the edges of the grains, and a compressive stress across BC is built up near the edges. The pattern of secondary stresses adjusts itself in such a way that the rate of emission or precipitation of vacancies is the same all over each boundary. As soon as this homogeneous precipitation rate is attained, the stresses no longer vary. The ultimate stress pattern is shown qualitatively in Fig. 5. The average stress across either boundary remains equal to the initial stress.

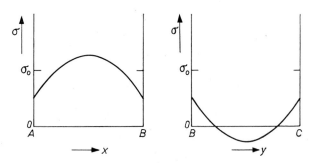

Fɪɢ. 5.—Stress distribution across the grain boundaries of Fig. 3 when the stationary state is reached.

The second step of the derivation is the diffusion of the vacancies. In Fig. 3ᴀ certain diffusion paths have been indicated. Because of the stress distribution mentioned above, the concentration difference along a diffusion path is more or less proportional to its length to warrant homogeneous precipitation along the boundary. The diffusion path corresponding to the stress difference σ_0 and a concentration difference ΔC, given by Equation (1), is approximately $L/2$ where L is the grain dimension. Hence the vacancy flux density is given by

$$ J = \frac{D_v \Delta C}{L/2} = \frac{2 D_v C_0 \Omega \sigma_0}{kTL} = \frac{2 D_s \Omega \sigma}{kTL} \qquad . \qquad . \qquad (2) $$

Here D_v is the diffusion constant of the vacancies and $D_s = D_v C_0$ is the self-diffusion constant if C_0 is the atom fraction of vacancies.

It is assumed here that only lattice diffusion of vacancies occurs; if self-diffusion occurs predominantly by grain boundary diffusion,

Equation (2) is not correct. Grain-boundary diffusion is negligible if the product of grain boundary width and grain boundary diffusion constant $\delta D_{g.b.} < L D_s$, i.e. if the grains are not too small.

Now we have to calculate the deformation rate from the vacancy flux density. The velocity v with which the two grains separated by AB approach each other is equal to the rate of vacancy precipitation per unit boundary area. Because vacancies flow in from both sides, $v = 2J$. The deformation rate $\dot{\epsilon}$ is equal to the velocity with which two grains at unit distance approach each other. This rate is obtained by multiplication of v by the number of grains per unit length, $1/L$. Hence

$$\dot{\epsilon} = \frac{v}{L} = \frac{2J}{L} = \frac{4 D_s \Omega \sigma_0}{kTL^2} \quad . \quad . \quad . \quad . \quad (3)$$

This expression is equal to Herring's result except for the numerical constant, which depends on the grain boundary configuration of the model.

Some successful experiments have been made to corroborate Equation (3). A recent paper on this subject is that of FOLWEILER,[8] who studied the creep behaviour of pore-free polycrystalline aluminium oxide. He found stress proportional to the deformation rate and to the square of the grain diameter. This is in agreement with the Nabarro-Herring mechanism. From his results he could calculate the self-diffusion constant because all other factors are known. In the case of a compound the self-diffusion constant must be taken as that of the most slowly diffusing species, in this case oxygen. Folweiler's result is much higher than the oxygen diffusion constant determined in single crystals.[9] However, in polycrystalline specimens oxygen diffuses faster, probably along grain boundaries. In this way a satisfactory interpretation of the experiments is possible.[10]

4. GRAIN BOUNDARY SLIDING

In the preceding section it was assumed that grain-boundary sliding in polycrystals is faster than grain-boundary squeezing. This assumption is based on the following argument. Sliding depends on the roughness of the boundary, and is easy along a smooth boundary and difficult along a wavy or zigzag boundary. On a zigzag boundary, sliding can only take place by way of diffusion of vacancies along the boundary—that is, by a kind of Nabarro-Herring creep. But this creep velocity can be calculated along similar lines as in the preceding section. The only difference is that the factor L^2 in the denominator is replaced by $L\lambda$, where λ is the

" wavelength " of the zigzagging. Because always $\lambda < L$, sliding in polycrystals must be faster than squeezing.

It is also interesting to calculate the creep behaviour of the grain configuration in Fig. 4. In the beginning, creep is very fast because it is assumed that sliding is much faster than squeezing. However, very soon boundaries are produced that have to be squeezed. This squeezing is initially rather rapid, because the stress is concentrated on the small area of these squeezing boundaries. So Equation (3) can be used if the right side is multiplied by the stress concentration factor. Estimating the area of the squeezing boundary at εL^2, proportional to the deformation ε, we find a stress concentration factor of $1/\varepsilon$. This leads to

$$\dot{\varepsilon} = \frac{4D_s\Omega\sigma_0}{kTL^2\varepsilon} \cdot \quad . \quad . \quad . \quad . \quad . \quad (4)$$

After multiplication of both sides by ε and integration, we find ε proportional to $t^{\frac{1}{2}}$ instead of proportional to t. This extreme case shows how the creep rate can decrease with time by the increase of the area of squeezing boundaries. Real polycrystalline specimens are expected to show a behaviour intermediate between 3 and 4.

Sliding of bicrystals is quite a different matter. Initially, when the boundary is smooth sliding will be rapid, but jogs are formed later on and the sliding becomes slower and eventually stops. Experiments on sliding of bicrystals of non-metals have been made by ADAMS and MURRAY.[11] They investigated bicrystals of NaCl and MgO and found that sliding occurred in jumps. The displacement was roughly proportional to $t^{\frac{1}{2}}$. Similar results have been obtained on bicrystals of copper by INTRATER and MACHLIN.[12] These authors presented a theory of grain-boundary sliding based on activated jumps. The boundary is assumed to contain jogs, which migrate along the boundary. Each jump is initiated by the annihilation of a jog and terminated by the formation of a new jog. Jogs can be annihilated at the surface and at voids produced during sliding. This theory could also explain the experiments of Adams and Murray, at least qualitatively. Their results showed considerable scattering because different samples had different grain boundary orientations.

5. GRAIN BOUNDARIES AND SINTERING

Nowadays the role of grain boundaries in sintering has been well established [5, 13] and the experimental evidence for it has been reviewed in several papers.[10, 14] Their main role is to act as a sink for the vacancies diffusing away from the pores. In the sintering process three stages are distinguished. In the early stage necks are formed between the particles; in the intermediate stage the pores are still connected by channels along edges where three grains meet; and in the final stage only isolated pores are present.

In all stages the driving force of the process is the surface energy of the pores. In the first stage, surface diffusion may be an important mechanism, but in later stages the most important mechanism is the diffusion of vacancies from the pore surface to the grain boundaries and other vacancy sinks.

By these mechanisms many sintering experiments can be explained at least qualitatively. However, several complications may prevent a quantitative agreement between experiment and theory. One of these complications is the fact that grain growth occurs during sintering [13] and lowers the sintering rate, because the diffusion path of the vacancies becomes longer. A second complication is presented by the role of vacancy sinks, other than grain boundaries.[14] A third problem is the diffusion mechanism; both lattice diffusion and grain-boundary diffusion may occur. In compounds it is even possible that one ion species diffuses through the lattice whereas the other one diffuses along grain boundaries.[10] Still another complication arises from the fact that not all pores have the same size, so that the number of pores decreases long before complete density is attained, and the overall sintering-rate depends on the pore size distribution.[5]

As has been explained in Section 3, the flow of vacancies towards the grain boundaries is controlled by elastic stresses, because the rate of precipitation must be constant over the entire boundary. The order of magnitude of these stresses is given by $\sigma = \gamma/r$, where γ is the pore surface energy and r is the pore radius. In the case of fine particles these stresses may be considerable and give rise to local deformation, e.g. by grain-boundary sliding. However, it is difficult to estimate the relative importance of this effect, because it depends on the irregularity of the configuration of pores and particles.

6. GRAIN-BOUNDARY MIGRATION

In the introduction the effect of elastic stresses on low-angle grain boundaries was mentioned. If the dislocation structure of these boundaries leads to a coupling of sliding and migration, elastic stresses may cause migration of the boundary. In general, this coupling will not occur, and elastic stresses cannot cause migration.

The driving force for grain-boundary migration occurring during recrystallization and grain growth will therefore be of another nature. In cold-worked metals primary recrystallization is caused by the stored deformation energy, i.e. the dislocation density. Grains of low dislocation-density grow at the expense of grains with a high dislocation-density. The driving force per unit boundary area is simply equal to the energy density

$$P_1 = AN_D Gb^2,$$

where N_D is the dislocation density of the strongly deformed material, G the shear modulus, b the Burgers vector of the dislocations and A a constant of order unity. If $N_D = 10^{10}$ cm^{-2}, $G = 10^{12}$ dyn/cm^2, and $b = 10^{-7}$ cm, the driving force is $P_1 \approx 10^8$ dyn/cm$^2 =$ 1,500 p.s.i.

In secondary recrystallization and grain growth this driving force is absent; now the grain-boundary energy is the only available one, which means that grain boundaries always move towards their centre of curvature. This driving force is given by

$$P_2 = \gamma_b \left(\frac{1}{R_1} + \frac{1}{R_2} \right),$$

where γ_b is the interfacial energy of the grain boundary and R_1 and R_2 are its principal radii of curvature.

If $\gamma_b = 500$ erg/cm^2 and $R_1 = R_2 = 10^{-4}$ cm, the driving force $P_2 = 5.10^6$ dyn/cm$^2 = 70$ p.s.i. This is an order of magnitude smaller than in the case of primary recrystallization.

Another possible driving force exists if the grain on one side of the boundary is supersaturated with vacancies or impurities, whereas the grain on the other side contains the equilibrium concentration. In the case of impurities, this type of migration requires unlimited precipitation of the impurities at the boundary, which can only take place if the boundary contains a second phase and is, therefore, strictly speaking, no longer a grain boundary. The driving force is again equal to the difference in free energy per unit volume. In the case of ideal mixtures,

$$P_3 = \Delta G = kT \left\{ n' \ln \frac{n'}{n} - (n' - n) \right\},$$

where n' is the actual concentration of impurities or vacancies (number per cm^3) and n the equilibrium concentration. With vacancies n' may be 10^{18} cm^{-3} and $n = 10^{15}$ cm^{-3}. If $kT = 10^{-13}$ erg, $P_3 = 10^6$ dyn/cm^2. With impurities, n' may be 10^{20} cm^{-3} and $n = 10^{19}$ cm^{-3}, which leads to $P_3 = 10^7$ dyn/cm^2. In both cases the driving force is of the same order of magnitude as in the case of secondary recrystallization. This driving force will be fully active only if the excess concentration n' remains constant up to the boundary, i.e. if diffusion of the impurities in the grains is very slow and boundary migration is very fast. This will probably not occur in metals, but perhaps in compounds with a high melting point.

Several theories exist on the relation between driving force and migration velocity.[1, 15, 16] However, it has been found by experiment that impurities have a great influence on the migration velocity. Even in very pure materials, impurities may have a not negligible concentration at the boundary because of segregation effects. These impurities have a retarding effect on boundary migration. This impurity drag effect was first calculated by LÜCKE and DETERT[17]; recently this theory has been refined by GORDON and VANDERMEER,[18] by CAHN,[19] and by MACHLIN.[20]

The situation is rather complicated. Not only impurities that are attracted by the boundary but also impurities that are repelled have a drag effect. This drag effect depends on the migration velocity compared to the diffusion constant of the impurity divided by the distance of interaction between grain boundary and impurity atoms. If migration is fast, the boundary will lose impurities by mechanical break-away and the drag will be small. If migration is slow, the impurities will try to keep up with the boundary by diffusion and so exert a considerable drag. The behaviour of boundaries with an intermediate velocity is rather complex. Another complication is whether the relevant diffusion constant of the impurities is the bulk diffusion constant, the grain-boundary diffusion constant, or something in between. Even this diffusion constant may depend on the migration velocity.

These theories do not discuss the case in which the impurity concentration is so high that a second phase is formed at the boundary. The presence of a liquid phase at the grain boundary is very important in sintering and hot-pressing. It will make sliding of the grains very easy because it acts as a lubricant. Moreover, material transport can proceed by diffusion through the liquid.[21, 22]

7. CONCLUSION

The theory of the dynamic properties of grain boundaries is in rapid evolution. Much progress has been made already, especially in the field of metals. In the next few years grain boundaries in compounds can be expected to be the subject of experiment. One way of investigating the dynamic properties of grain boundaries has not been mentioned—grain-boundary damping. This type of experiment relates to grain-boundary motion on a small scale, and may therefore be the link between the theory of atomic processes and the dynamic properties of grain boundaries.

REFERENCES

1. McLean, D., "Grain Boundaries in Metals" (Oxford University Press, 1957).
2. "Propriétés des Joints de Grains; 4e Colloque de Métallurgie Saclay 1960" (Presses Universitaires de France, 1961).
3. Washburn, J., and Parker, E. R., *J. Metals,* **4**, 1076, 1952.
4. Bainbridge, D. W., Li, C. H., and Edwards, E. H., *Acta Met.,* **2**, 322, 1954.
5. Hornstra, J., *Physica,* **27**, 342, 1961.
6. Nabarro, F. R. N., "Rept Bristol Conf. on Strength of Solids" (Phys Soc., London, 1948), p. 75.
7. Herring, C., *J. Appl. Phys.,* **21**, 437, 1950.
8. Folweiler, R. C., *J. Appl. Phys.,* **32**, 773, 1961.
9. Oishi, Y., and Kingery, W. D., *J. Chem. Phys.,* **33**, 480, 1960.
10. Paladino, A. E., and Coble, R. L., *J. Amer. Ceram. Soc.,* **46**, 133, 1963.
11. Adams, M. A., and Murray, G. T., *J. Appl. Phys.,* **33**, 2126, 1962.
12. Intrater, J., and Machlin, E. S., *J. Inst. Metals,* **88**, 305, 1960.
13. Coble, R. L., *J. Appl. Phys.,* **32**, 787, 793, 1961.
14. Seigle, L., "Kinetics of High-temperature Processes," W. D. Kingery, Ed. (J. Wiley & Sons: New York 1959), p. 172.
15. Mott, N. F., *Proc. Phys. Soc.* (London), **60**, 391, 1948.
16. Burke, J. E., and Turnbull, D., *Progress in Metal Phys.,* **3**, 220, 1952.
17. Lücke, K., and Detert, K., *Act Met.,* **5**, 628, 1957.
18. Gordon, P., and Vandermeer, R. A., *Trans. Met. Soc. AIME,* **224**, 917, 1962.
19. Cahn, J. W., *Acta Met.,* **10**, 789, 1962.
20. Machlin, E. S., *Trans. Met. Soc. AIME,* **224**, 1153, 1962.
21. Kingery, W. D., *J. Appl. Phys.,* **30**, 301, 307, 1959.
22. Kingery, W. D., Niki, E., and Narasimhan, M. D., *J. Amer. Ceram. Soc.,* **44**, 29, 1961.

13—The Use of Controlled Atmospheres

By P. W. BERG

*Department of Mortar, Glass and Ceramics,
The Royal Danish Technical University,
Copenhagen, Denmark.*

ABSTRACT   B35

Water vapour-gas atmospheres are convenient to produce in a furnace and the oxidizing and reducing power of the atmosphere can be easily regulated. These atmospheres have been used for the firing of iron-containing ceramics such as porcelain and blue bricks. In particular the results of laboratory and works experiments on the bluing of bricks are referred to. Blue bricks can be cooled after firing by introducing small proportions of reducing material into the furnace as a dilute aqueous solution or emulsion. The heat used in evaporating the water can be used for the controlled fast cooling of the fired bricks.

L'emploi des atmosphères contrôlées

Des atmosphères de gaz-vapeur d'eau sont aisément produites dans un four et le pouvoir d'oxydation et de réduction de l'atmosphère peut facilement être réglé. De telles atmosphères ont été utilisées pour la cuisson de céramiques contenant du fer telles que la porcelaine et les briques bleues. Les résultats d'expériences faites au laboratoire et en usine sur des briques bleues sont en particulier indiqués. Les briques bleues peuvent être refroidies après cuisson par introduction de petites proportions de substance réductrice dans le four sous la forme de solution ou d'émulsion aqueuse diluée. La chaleur utilisée dans l'évaporation de l'eau peut être employée pour le refroidissement rapide contrôlé des briques cuites.

Anwendung kontrollierter Atmosphären

Wasserdampfatmosphären lassen sich in einem Ofen leicht einstellen, ebenso die Oxydations- oder Reduktionswirkung dieser Atmosphäre. Diese Atmosphären wurden verwendet, um eisenhaltige Keramik wie Porzellan und Klinkersteine zu brennen. Im besonderen werden die Untersuchungsergebnisse von Laboratorien und Betrieben über Klinkersteine (durch Blaudämpfen hergestellt) besprochen. Klinkerstein können nach dem Brand gekühlt werden, indem man kleine Mengen von reduzierenden Stoffen in den Ofen gibt in Form einer verdünnten wässerigen Lösung oder Emulsion. Die Wärme, die zum Verdampfen des Wassers benötigt wird, kann benutzt werden, um die schnelle Kühlung der blaugedämpften Steine zu kontrollieren.

1. INTRODUCTION

An earlier publication [1] has explained the advantages of using water-vapour/gas atmospheres in the reduction of copper-containing lead glazes. These atmospheres were obtained by pouring into the furnace an aqueous solution of methanol at the temperature of reduction. At high temperatures the methanol is decomposed according to the equation:

$$CH_3OH = 2H_2 + CO$$

As the composition of this atmosphere is determined by the water-gas reaction,

$$CO + H_2O = H_2 + CO_2 \quad . \quad . \quad . \quad (1)$$

it is possible from the equilibrium constant of this reaction to calculate for various temperatures the concentration of methanol solution required in order to produce an atmosphere with a given p_{H_2}/p_{H_2O} ratio. This ratio determines whether an equilibrium of the type

$$M + H_2O = MO + H_2$$

is shifted to the right or to the left at high temperatures. The reaction of a water-vapour/gas atmosphere therefore depends largely on the value of the ratio just mentioned.

As atmospheres containing water vapour can be conveniently produced, and the oxidizing or reducing power can be regulated fairly easily by adjusting the value of the p_{H_2}/p_{H_2O} ratio, this method has been experimented with in the firing of iron-oxide-containing ceramics, such as porcelain [2] and bricks.

2. CALCULATIONS CONCERNING IRON-OXIDE-CONTAINING CERAMICS

Most deposits of clay and china-clay contain iron compounds in greater or smaller proportion, which may give the fired material a more or less distinct colouring. With porcelain artware and table-ware a good white colour is essential and as the china clay contains iron, special measures must be adopted in order to achieve the desired result. Firing is so controlled that the iron oxides in the body are reduced to ferrosilicates, the colour of which is near-white, with only a faint tinge of blue. In this way the iron compounds are reduced to the first stage of oxidation, FeO.

Blue bricks are produced from iron-containing clay through a reducing firing, which converts the red Fe_2O_3 into the dark Fe_3O_4 or FeO.

When blue bricks are fired, it is presumably unnecessary to reduce the iron oxides to the extent of converting them into FeO; a reaction corresponding to complete conversion of the red Fe_2O_3 into the almost black Fe_3O_4 seems sufficient. The following reactions are therefore of interest to the ceramist.

$$2Fe_3O_4 + H_2O = 3Fe_2O_3 + H_2 \qquad . \quad . \qquad (2)$$

$$3FeO + H_2O = Fe_3O_4 + H_2 \quad . \qquad . \qquad . \qquad (3).$$

The equilibrium constant $K = p_{H_2}/p_{H_2O}$ of these reactions can be calculated for various temperatures, for example from the standard free energy of formation of the substance of the reactions in question, thus:

$$- \triangle G° = 4.57 \times T \times \log_{10} K.$$

From these data the values of p_{H_2}/p_{H_2O} can be calculated which at a given temperature favour the formation of a given oxidation stage of the iron, with particular reference to the production of blue bricks.

The bluing of bricks is normally done by introducing excess fuel into the furnace at the firing-temperature (900° – 1,000°C.).[3] The furnace is then closed, and not re-opened until the temperature has fallen to about 300°C., for not until cooling has proceeded this far can the possibility of re-oxidation of the lower oxides of iron in the surface of the fired bricks be ruled out. Because of the specific conditions for cooling, blue bricks are usually fired in intermittent kilns.

Since the iron in the clay from which blue bricks are made is present mainly as Fe_2O_3, and since the firing temperature is fairly low—below 1,000°C.—one can safely assume that reaction (2) is concerned, and so the reduction of ferric oxide with CO need not be considered:

$$2Fe_3O_4 + CO_2 = 3Fe_2O_3 + CO \quad . \qquad . \qquad . \qquad (4)$$

The relationship between the equilibrium constants of the reactions (2) and (4) and the equilibrium constant of reaction (1) makes it necessary merely to control either the ratio p_{H_2}/p_{H_2O} or p_{CO}/p_{CO} in order to judge whether Fe_2O_3 will be reduced or not.

The equilibrium constant of reaction (2) is found by calculation from the equations

$$4Fe_3O_4 + O_2 = 6Fe_2O_3 \quad . \qquad . \qquad . \qquad (5) \text{ and}$$

$$2H_2 + O_2 = 2H_2O \quad . \qquad . \qquad . \qquad (6)$$

By subtracting Equation (6) from Equation (5), and by dividing the result by 2, one gets Equation (2). And from the alteration in the standard free energy in reactions (5) and (6), $\triangle G°$ for reaction (2) can be calculated by subtraction and division by 2.

One finds that within the temperature range of 400° to 1,000°C. $\triangle G°$ of reaction (2) increases from about 16.5 kcal to about 27.0 kcal. The equilibrium constant K_2 is calculated on the basis of these figures from

$$-\triangle G^{\circ} = 4 \cdot 57 \times T \times \log_{10} K_2.$$

Within this temperature range one gets

$$3 \times 10^{-6} < K_2 = p_{H_2}/p_{H_2O} < 3 \times 10^{-5},$$

which means that, with all values of p_{H_2}/p_{H_2O} above 3×10^{-5}, there is a tendency towards the complete conversion of Fe_2O_3 to Fe_3O_4.

It should be noted that the activity of the iron oxides has been estimated as unity, since one assumes them to be present in the solid state.

Consequently it seems possible to fire blue bricks even with a very small proportion of hydrogen in the kiln atmosphere.

If the atmosphere contains mainly water vapour, together with a comparatively small proportion of H_2, the partial pressure of hydrogen necessary for blue firing of bricks is obtained from $p_{H_2}/p_{H_2O} = K_2 \sim 3 \times 10^{-5}$, which corresponds to the equilibrium constant for the reaction

$$2Fe_3O_4 + H_2O = 3Fe_2O_3 + H_2 \quad . \quad . \quad . \quad (2).$$

The magnitude of the partial pressure of hydrogen will be in the range $3 \times 10^{-5} \times 760 \sim 3 \times 10^{-2}$ mm Hg, equivalent to 0·003 vol. % H_2.

So only a very slight excess of fuel is necessary for the bluing of bricks. For reasons of economy, amongst other things, this slight excess of fuel can be suitably obtained by introducing into the furnace a very dilute solution of alcohol or some other soluble organic substance, or a weak emulsion of oil, just before bluing begins, for the products of cracking will contain the necessary hydrogen. Whatever is used, the amount of solution or emulsion must contain enough organic substance for the desired degree of reduction to be attained.

3. LABORATORY EXPERIMENTS

Firing-experiments have been performed to illustrate how clay products can be reduced in this way. The kiln concerned was electric, the heating-elements being Kanthal wire situated at the sides, bottom and roof (Fig. 1). The furnace was also gas-tight, and had a useful capacity of about 15 litres.

The kiln door had three openings: through the top opening the thermocouple was inserted; the bottom opening was kept open, to act as an outlet from the interior of the furnace; through the middle opening was inserted a copper tube with an outside diameter of 8 mm. A length of about 500 mm remained outside the furnace.

The external end of the tube was bent upwards, and to it a funnel was fitted, above which was a funnel acting as a reservoir for the solution or emulsion that was to be introduced into the kiln. The entire length of the copper tube outside the furnace could be heated by means of a special Bunsen burner (see Fig. 1).

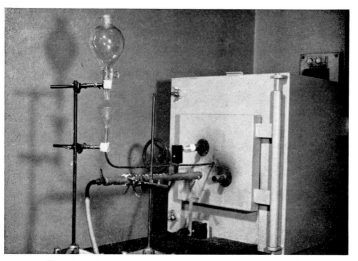

FIG. 1.—Furnace with funnel reservoir and copper tube

When the solution or emulsion was passing through the copper tube it was almost completely vaporized before reaching the interior of the kiln. Before each experiment, the copper tube had been blown through with vapour when red-hot.

The test pieces were cylinders of red-firing clay (50 mm long × 30 mm diam). Twelve were placed for each firing experiment in various positions in the kiln room, and fitted in open chamotte capsules.

During the experiments the kiln, containing the test-pieces, was heated to a temperature of 980°C.; when this temperature had been reached, solution from the separate funnel was added at the rate of 2 l/h. The temperature had to be maintained for the first half-hour during which the solution was being added; after that, the electricity to the furnace was turned off, but solution from the separate funnel continued to be introduced into the furnace through the red-hot copper tube. When the temperature in the kiln had fallen to 300°C.—about 2 h after the current had been switched off—the kiln door was opened, and the test specimens were taken out for examination.

3.1 Reduction with Methanol or Oil

According to calculations, blue specimens should be obtained when solutions with a methanol content as low as 0·1% are used, but owing to the fairly high proportion of iron oxide in the clay a solution containing less than 1% methanol was not used. In fact aqueous solutions of 1, 2·5, and 5% methanol, respectively, were tested, and also an emulsion of 1% gas oil in water (weight %) (Fig. 2). It is obvious that, during cooling, p_{H_2}/p_{H_2O} is constantly above 3×10^{-5}, and so the value necessary for the bluing of the specimens is obtained.

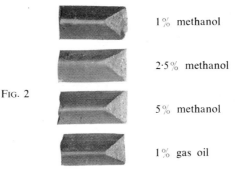

FIG. 2

1% methanol

2·5% methanol

5% methanol

1% gas oil

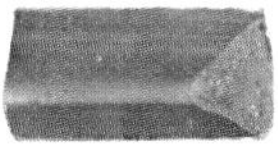

FIG 3

5% methanol
0·1% methanol during cooling

During the experiment in which gas-oil emulsion was introduced into the furnace, samples were taken from the vapour-gas mixtures at 980°, 800° and 500° C. respectively, and analysed.[4]

Table 1 shows the results and the content of the products resulting from cracking. Apart from them, the atmosphere essentially contains water vapour only.

After firing, test-pieces were bluish grey. When sawed through, those pieces fired with a 5% solution of methanol were bluish grey all through, whereas those fired with a more dilute solution of methanol or a 1% oil emulsion had a greyish brown core, obviously less reduced than the surface (Fig. 2). This is probably because the amount of reducing agent in the kiln atmosphere had not been enough to completely convert the ferric oxide in the specimens.

Table 1

Water-vapour/Gas Atmosphere (Composition, vol. %)

	Temperature		
	980°C.	890°C.	500°C.
Carbon dioxide	0·6	0·3	0.3
Heavy hydrocarbons	0·0	0·1	0.02
Oxygen	0·0	0·0	0·0
Carbon monoxide	0·3	0·3	0·1
Hydrogen	0·5	0·4	0·03
Methane	0·3	0·2	0·06

Another experiment was then carried out with a 5% solution of methanol during the ½ h when the temperature was kept at 980°, but with only a solution of 0·1% methanol during the entire cooling-period—a solution which, during cracking, could generally be expected to provide an atmosphere the composition of which is close to the equilibrium composition of reaction (2).

The core and the surface of the fired pieces were found to be an even, bluish grey (see Fig. 3).

3.2 Results

The results suggest that bricks can be blued as follows: when the maximum temperature is reached (about 1,000°C.) and the openings in the kiln have been closed, the fires are extinguished by being slowly sprinkled with water. The damper between the kiln to the chimney must be kept open. The water gas formed from the excess fuel $(C + H_2O \longrightarrow CO + H_2)$ acts as reducing agent on the setting. When, owing to cooling, water gas has ceased to form, the setting is sprinkled with water to which has been added a small amount of reducing agent $(0·1 - 5\%$ of the water) and the resulting atmosphere protects the blue bricks.

This procedure is not only economical in fuel, but also so shortens the time taken for the kiln to cool that the risk of the bricks re-oxidizing is eliminated, for the water vapour formed will provide positive pressure in the furnace and so keep the oxygen out of the furnace. Instead of the not unusual cooling-period of approximately 3 weeks, the rate of cooling may be expected to be as fast as the rate of heating, which means that the cooling-period is presumably reduced to 1/10 of the normal time.

3.3 Strength of Blue Bricks

The strength of the blue bricks was tested, to see whether the method of cooling had impaired this property. From a red brick

20 test-pieces ($10 \times 20 \times 70$ mm) bars were cut; 10 were fired blue, in the way described, with the furnace atmosphere formed from a 2% solution of methanol. The other 10 pieces were fired according to the same schedule, but with an air atmosphere. The average bending strength of the blued test pieces was $\bar{\rho} = 115$ kg/cm², while that of the other test bars was $\rho = 82$ kg/cm² (Table 2).

Table 2

	Test bar No.	Bending-strength (kg/cm²)	
		ρ	$\bar{\rho}$
OXIDIZED BARS	1	84	
	2	85	
	3	86	
	4	—	
	5	74	82
	6	86	
	7	97	
	8	86	
	9	70	
	10	71	
BLUE FIRED BARS	1	113	
	2	104	
	3	110	
	4	106	
	5	103	
	6	112	115
	7	136	
	8	132	
	9	—	
	10	—	

4. WORKS EXPERIMENTS

In a further experiment, tiles were fired blue in an industrial kiln—a coal-fired down-draught having a capacity of about 35 m³ (kindly supplied by Frederiksholms Kalk- og Teglvaerker, Holte). The furnace held about 6,000 tiles of ordinary red-firing clay, and was heated to about 980°C. in about 36 h.

When the kiln temperature had been kept at 980°C. for about $\frac{1}{2}$ h, the flue and the firemouths were closed with sand seals. The damper between the flue and the chimney was closed, but an outlet to atmosphere below the furnace was kept open.

About 25 litres of water was then poured into each combustion chamber, and a vigorous steaming was observed at the outlet from the furnace. After a few minutes, a 5% solution of methanol was introduced at three places in the top of the kiln at about 5 l/min.

When the temperature had fallen to about 650°C., the rate was lowered to 1 1/min; when the temperature had dropped to 500°C., the rate was restored to 5 1/min. Altogether about 5 m³ of solution was added.

After about 36 h the kiln was opened, and the colour of the bricks was bluish grey. Moreover, both the bricks and the inside of the furnace were free from soot and graphite but the bricks that had been immediately under the point at which solution was injected were cracked, obviously due to uneven distribution of the solution within the furnace. This feature can no doubt be remedied.

5. CONCLUSIONS

As with the reduction of Cu-containing glazes, it is economical to be able to reduce with very dilute solutions of alcohol or with oil emulsion, which not only conserves that part of the reducing agent uniting by combustion with the oxygen in the setting just before the beginning of reduction, but also that part used owing to the entrance of air through leaks is saved.

This method also enables the reducing atmosphere to be easily controlled and a given ratio of the partial pressure of hydrogen to that of water vapour can be maintained during firing.

Finally the heat used to evaporate the aqueous phase can also be used to accelerate the cooling of the fired product.

REFERENCES

1. Berg, P. W., " Reduction of Glazes containing Copper and Provision of the Reducing Atmosphere," " Science of Ceramics," Vol. 1, p. 51. (Academic Press, London, 1962.)
2. Berg, P. W., " Wie Einwirkung der Ofenatmosphäre während des Porzellanbrandes," Ber. Deutsch. Keram. Ges., **40**, 417, 1963.
3. Zimmerman, K., " Untersuchungen uber das Blaudämpfen von Dachziegeln ", Ber. Deutsch. Keram Ges., **18**, 110, 1937.
4. Berg, P. W., " Kontrollerede atmosfaerers anvendelse i nogle keramiske industrier. 34-36. Teknisk Forlag, Kobenhavn, 1963.

14—Quelques Aspects du Frittage d'Oxydes Purs

Par S. J. Teichner, R. Caillat, J. Elston, F. Juillet,
A. Bourrasse, B. François, et P. Vergnon

*Université de Lyon, Institut de Recherches sur la Catalyse et
Commissariat à l'Energie Atomique, Centre de Saclay, France*

RÉSUMÉ
A432

Le frittage d'une poudre d'un oxyde pur, tel que UO_2, BeO ou Al_2O_3, pressée
sans liant, est plus efficace si la vitesse de montée en température est élevée.
Dans le cas d'une montée de 100°C. par minute, la poudre UO_2 fournit un
corps de densité égale à 10,40 grammes par centimètre cube, après un palier
de 10 minutes à 1700°C. Cette influence de la vitesse de la montée en température a également été observée dans le cas du frittage de la poudre
d'oxyde de béryllium. La poudre d'alumine peut être obtenue sous deux
formes cristallines, δ et α. La dernière, considérée comme la moins réactive
se fritte beaucoup mieux que la première lorsque l'on élève rapidement la
température. La différence de comportement des deux types d'alumine doit
être attribuée à la vitesse de migration des limites de grain. Si cette migration
est trop rapide, la porosité initialement intergranulaire peut devenir isolée
à l'intérieur des grains.

Some Aspects of the Sintering of Pure Oxides

The sintering of a pure oxide powder, such as UO_2, BeO, or Al_2O_3, pressed
without a binding-agent is more effective if the rate of rise of temperature is
high. With a heating-rate of 100°C. min^{-1}, UO_2 powder yields a body of
10·40 g.cm^{-3} density after only 10 min at 1700°C. This influence of heating-
rate has also been observed with the sintering of a beryllia powder. Alumina
powder can be obtained in two crystalline forms, δ and α. The latter,
reputedly the less reactive, nevertheless sinters very much better with rapidly
rising temperature than does the former. The difference in behaviour of the
two types of alumina is to be sought in the rate of grain-boundary migration.
If this migration is too rapid, the originally intergranular porosity may become
isolated within grains.

Einige Gesichtspunkte zum Sintern reiner Oxide

Das Sintern von reinen Oxidpulvern wie UO_2, BeO oder Al_2O_3, die ohne
Binder verpresst wurden, ist wirksamer, wenn der Temperaturanstieg
schneller vonstatten geht. Bei einer Aufheizgeschwindigkeit von 100°C./min.
erhält man aus UO_2 einen Körper mit einem Raumgewicht von 10,40 g/cm^3,
wobei die Temperatur nur 10 Min. bei 1700°C. belassen wurde. Dieser
Einfluss der Aufheiztemperatur wurde ebenfalls beim Sintern von Beryllium-
oxidpulver beobachtet. Al_2O_3-Pulver kann in den beiden kristallinen Formen
δ und α erhalten werden. Letztere, bekanntermassen die weniger aktive,
sintert viel besser als erstere, wenn die Temperatur rasch erhöht wird. Der
Unterschied im Verhalten dieser beiden Al_2O_3-Arten wird in der Kornwachs-
tumsgeschwindigkeit gesehen. Wenn diese Geschwindigkeit zu gross ist,
kann die anfänglich zwischen den Körnern vorliegende Porosität innerhalb
der Körner eingeschlossen werden.

1. INTRODUCTION

Les méthodes habituelles du frittage des oxydes font généralement appel à des cycles longs de traitement thermique, comportant une montée en température lente (de l'ordre de 100° à 300°C./h) et une durée de maintien à la température maximale assez longue (de l'ordre de plusieurs heures). Il est cependant bien établi que la densification de la matière à fritter se produit déjà lors de l'échauffement conduisant à la température maximale. Il est donc évident que la manière dont cet échauffement est conduit, lentement ou rapidement, peut influer sur le résultat final du frittage.

Les différents mécanismes physico-chimiques qui interviennent dans la densification de l'échantillon peuvent prendre au cours de cette première étape une part plus ou moins importante, suivant la vitesse de la montée en température.

Il a été ainsi observé que les échantillons d'oxyde d'uranium de grande surface spécifique se frittaient mieux dans certaines conditions que des échantillons dotés d'une surface spécifique plus faible.[1] Cependant, il est fréquent qu'une poudre présentant initialement une grande surface spécifique devienne moins apte à la densification à la température du frittage qu'une autre poudre de surface spécifique initiale plus faible. Ce comportement s'explique par le fait que l'état de division, se traduisant par une surface importante, ne se conserve pas pendant la montée en température de l'échantillon.

Afin de conserver une réactivité élevée aux poudres à fritter, il a été imaginé qu'une solution, applicable en principe à tous les oxydes, consistait à porter l'échantillon à la température de densification aussi rapidement que possible. Cette hypothèse nous a amenés à étudier la cinétique du frittage des oxydes d'uranium, de béryllium et d'aluminium en portant l'échantillon à la température finale du frittage d'une manière très rapide, et pour comparaison, de manière modérée comme dans les études antérieures.

2. MATIÈRES PREMIÈRES ET TECHNIQUES EXPÉRIMENTALES

Les échantillons d'oxyde d'uranium UO_2 cubique proviennent de la réduction à 400°C. de l'oxyde UO_3, issu d'uranate d'ammonium. La poudre d'oxyde UO_2 stoechiométrique sortant du four de réduction est pyrophorique. Afin de lui faire perdre cette propriété gênante, elle est soumise à une réoxydation modérée, au voisinage de la température ambiante, au moyen d'un courant d'azote à 2%

d'oxygène. Les caractéristiques de trois échantillons étudiés sont résumées dans le tableau 1.

Tableau 1

Caractéristiques des Echantillons

	Echantillon		
	GJ	GW	GY
Surface spécifique B.E.T. (m²/g)	14,8	17	9,3
Rapport O/U	2.13	2,14	2 14
Densité apparente des comprimés	5.50	5.30	5,4

La mise en forme des échantillons d'oxyde d'uranium se fait par compression à froid, sous $4t/cm^2$, sans adjonction de liant dans une matrice cylindrique d'un diamètre de 10 mm. La hauteur des comprimés cylindriques est de 10 mm et leurs densités apparentes, calculées à partir des dimensions géométriques, figurent dans le tableau 1.

Le traitement thermique des comprimés s'éffectue sous atmosphère d'hydrogène dans un four à passage continu, où les comprimés atteignent la température de 1000°C. en une heure. A cette étape de chauffage, l'oxyde d'uranium, contenant primitivement un excès d'oxygène, est rendu stoechiométrique $(O/U=2)$. La température de 1000°C. représente, par ailleurs, approximativement le seuil au-delà duquel commence la densification de UO_2 sous atmosphère d'hydrogène.[1]

Au-delà de 1000°C., la vitesse de montée en température jusqu'à la température maximale est portée à 100°C./min. La durée du maintien du comprimé à la température maximale varie entre 2 min et 15 h pour les températures de 1400°, 1500°, 1600° et 1700°C. Le comprimé est ensuite refroidi, en quinze minutes, jusqu'à la température ambiante, où sa densité au toluène est mesurée.

L'oxyde de béryllium hexagonal pulvérulent a été préparé par calcination du sulfate de béryllium à 1000°C. pendant 10 h. La densité apparente de BeO est d'environ 0,4 alors que sa surface spécifique est de 11 m²/g, ce qui correspond à un diamètre moyen d'environ 2000 Å des particules supposées sphériques. Mesurée par la méthode de l'élargissement des raies de diffraction X, la dimension moyenne des particules est d'environ 1000 Å. L'oxyde de béryllium est très pur. Il ne contient que 20 p.p.m. de Fe, 40 p.p.m. d'Al, 20 p.p.m. de Ca, 20 p.p.m. de Si, 2 p.p.m. de Mg et 700 p.p.m. de S provenant du sulfate initial.

La poudre sans liant est tassée dans un récipient cylindrique en caoutchouc, désorbée sous vide, puis comprimée hydrostatiquement sous 5 t/cm². Dans les cylindres plus ou moins réguliers, ainsi obtenus, sont taillées des éprouvettes parallélépipédiques de dimensions $25 \times 20 \times 9$ mm.

Le frittage s'effectue en atmosphère d'hydrogène dans un rétractomètre à poussoir d'alumine solidaire d'une jauge de contrainte par l'intermédiaire d'une lame de ressort. Les courbes rétractométriques, traduisant le frittage, sont ainsi enregistrées de façon continue.

L'alumine est constituée par des particules sphériques non poreuses, sensiblement homodispersées. Elle a été préparée à partir du chlorure d'aluminium anhydre, dirigé à l'état de vapeur, dans la flamme d'un chalumeau oxhydrique.[2] Ce procédé permet de produire des particules dont le diamètre varie à volonté entre 100 Å et plusieurs microns. L'alumine obtenue présente la structure cristalline delta.[3] Le traitement thermique de la poudre, à 1200°C. pendant 24 h, transforme quantitativement la forme delta en alpha, sans grossissement exagéré de grains. C'est ainsi, par exemple, que les grains de l'alumine delta, d'un diamètre moyen de 160 Å (surface spécifique 110 m²/g), se transforment en alumine alpha dont les particules gardent la forme sphérique et présentent un diamètre moyen de 390 Å (surface spécifique 39 m²/g). Une autre classe des particules de l'alumine delta, de diamètre moyen de 700 Å (surface spécifique 23 m²/g) fournit des particules de l'alumine alpha de diamètre moyen de 1500 Å (surface spécifique 10 m²/g).

La poudre d'alumine a été comprimée dans une matrice de section rectangulaire, à double effet. Le comprimé a la forme d'un parallélépipède rectangle, de dimensions $20 \times 3,5$ mm, avec une hauteur de 2 mm environ pour un remplissage de la matrice avec 230 mg d'alumine, lorsque la pression appliquée est de 4 t/cm².

Pour tous les échantillons, cette pression a été atteinte en 2 min 30 sec et elle a été maintenue pendant 1 min 30 sec. Des variations notables de ces durées ne modifient pratiquement pas les propriétés des comprimés.[4]

Les comprimés ont été chauffés, à différentes températures, dans un four à résistance de platine et leur longueur a été mesurée après refroidissement à l'aide d'un cathétomètre au 1/100 mm.

La technique de prise de vues photographiques du comprimé placé dans le four[5] a été utilisée pour suivre la cinétique du retrait isotherme, après l'introduction rapide du comprimé dans le four, dans la zone de haute température.

Pour les expériences à température linéairement croissante, il a été fait appel au dilatomètre Chevenard, type DHT 60, qui a été modifié pour pouvoir fonctionner en rétractomètre.

3. RÉSULTATS ET DISCUSSIONS

3.1 Oxyde d'Uranium

Les comprimés d'oxyde d'uranium, portés préalablement à 1000°C. en 1 h sous atmosphère d'hydrogène, ont été ensuite chauffes jusqu'à 1400°C. avec une vitesse de montée en température de 100°C./min. Un autre lot a été de même porté à 1500°C., etc. . . jusqu'à 1700°C. Les densités mesurées au toluène après le maintien pendant des temps variables aux paliers des températures précédentes, sont données dans le tableau 2. La figure 1 représente les densités en fonction de la durée du maintien du comprimé aux différentes températures maximales.

Tableau 2

Densités des Comprimés d'Oxyde d'Uranium UO$_2$

Echantillon	Durée du maintien de la température maximale	Température maximale (°C.)			
		1400°	*1500°*	*1600°*	*1700°*
GJ 14,8 m²/g	1 h	10,12	10,22	10,32	
	2 h	10,26	10,30	10,39	
	5 h	10,33	10,46	10,50	
	15 h	10,44	10,54	10,64	
GW 17 m²/g	2 min			10,03	10,32
	3 min		9,65		
	10 min		9,69	10,20	10,40
	20 min			10,37	
	30 min		10,08		
	50 min				10,50
	1 h		10,21	10,43	
GY 9,3 m²/g	10 min				10,18
	20 min		9,74		
	30 min		9,88	10,29	
	1 h	9,79	10,04	10,38	
	2 h	9,99	10,17	10,42	

Ces résultats permettent de tirer les conclusions suivantes. Il est possible d'obtenir par ce procédé de frittage rapide des cylindres dont la densité est voisine de 95% de la densité théorique, valeur exigée pour les applications de UO$_2$. Mais si à 1600°C. la durée de ce traitement doit être de 1 h, 10 min suffisent si le traitement est effectué à 1700°C. (éch. GW).

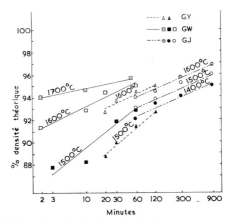

Fig. 1.—Densité des comprimés d'oxyde d'uranium UO₂ en fonction de la durée du maintien de la température maximale

L'échantillon GY, de surface spécifique nettement plus faible que celle des deux autres, se fritte moins bien à 1400°C., et encore à 1500°C., que les échantillons GJ et GW pour des durées comparables du maintien à la température maximale. Mais après le chauffage à 1600°C., les densités de l'échantillon GY sont sensiblement identiques à celles que présente l'échantillon GW de surface spécifique la plus élevée.

Il a été montré, dans un travail antérieur, [6] que lors de la mise en température des fours de frittage la surface spécifique des poudres d'oxyde d'uranium diminue d'autant plus fortement que la surface initiale est plus grande. Dans ces conditions, la densification finale était d'autant moins bonne que la surface initiale était plus forte. Ces considérations ont été étendues aux comprimés dans le présent travail. La présence d'hydrogène a pour effet, entre autres, de préserver la diminution excessive de la surface spécifique du comprimé à haute température [6, 7] alors que la mise rapide à la température maximale permet d'atténuer les différences dans la densification des comprimés des surfaces spécifiques variées.

Enfin, il semble que l'intérêt économique du frittage rapide d'oxyde d'uranium doit également être pris en considération.

3.2 Oxyde de Béryllium

Lorsque le parallélépipède d'oxyde de béryllium, placé dans le rétractomètre, est porté à 1600°C. avec une vitesse de mise en température de 100°C./h, le retrait enregistré est de 10% lorsque la température maximale est atteinte. Ce n'est qu'après 4 h de main-ien à cette température qu'un retrait limite de 13,7% est observé. La densité du comprimé refroidi est 2,58, alors que la densité théorique de BeO est 3,01.

Ce frittage que l'on peut qualifier de lent a été comparé au frittage rapide où la vitesse de mise en température est portée à 50°C./min. Lorsque la température du four atteint 1600°C., le retrait enregistré est déjà de 12% et il est probablement de 14% environ lorsque l'échantillon atteint son équilibre thermique. Quinze minutes suffisent pour que la valeur finale du retrait de 15,6% soit observée. La densité finale, 2,90, est de même plus élevée que dans le cas précédent du frittage lent.

Ces résultats,[8] ainsi que ceux obtenus en limitant la température du frittage à 1500°, 1400°, 1300° et 1200°C., sont rassemblés dans le tableau 3.

Tableau 3

Résultats obtenus d'Oxyde de Béryllium (BeO)

Vitesse de mise en température	Température du frittage (°C.)	Durée du maintien	Retrait (%) Initial	Retrait (%) Final	Densité finale
100°C./h	1600°	4 h	10	13,7	2,58
50°C./min	1600°	15 min	12	15,6	2,90
50°C./min	1500°	3 h	10,5	14,9	2,79
50°C./min	1400°	4 h	9	14,9	2,73
50°C./min	1300°	4 h	8	14.8	2,70
25°C./min	1200°	5 h	4,3	10	2,36

Il apparaît de ces résultats que, même dans le cas du traitement rapide jusqu'à 1300°C. seulement, le retrait global et la densité finale sont encore plus importants que dans le cas du frittage lent jusqu'à 1600°C.

La Fig. 2 reproduit schématiquement les courbes rétractométriques enregistrées au cours de ces essais. Il importe de remarquer que pendant la période non isotherme du frittage la vitesse du retrait reste apparemment constante. Pendant la période isotherme la vitesse croît avec la température, la variation la plus considérable se produisant dans l'intervalle 1200°–1300°C.

Le frittage rapide permet donc d'obtenir, à une température donnée, des frittés d'oxyde de béryllium de densité nettement supérieure à celle des échantillons portés lentement à la température finale. A densité égale, les échantillons frittés rapidement présentent des grains beaucoup plus fins que ceux des échantillons frittés lentement.

Enfin la porosité dans les comprimés de BeO frittés rapidement

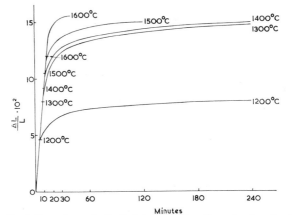

FIG. 2.—Evolution du retrait linéaire en fonction du temps pour les comprimés d'oxyde de béryllium

est rassemblée dans les joints de grains (Figs. 3 et 4). Elle ne devient intragranulaire que dans le cas où le frittage rapide est effectué à une température supérieure à 1600°C. (Fig. 5, frittage à 1700°C.).

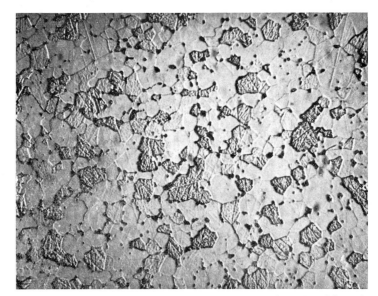

FIG. 3.—Frittage rapide de BeO, 4 h à 1600°C. ($d = 2,91$). Dimension moyenne des grains: 10 microns. Présence de porosité intergranulaire ($\times 580$)

FIG. 4.—Frittage rapide de BeO, 50 h à 1600°C. ($d=2{,}90$). Dimension moyenne des grains: 85 μ. Présence de porisité intergranulaire ($\times 160$)

FIG. 5.—Frittage rapide de BeO, 2 h à 1700°C. ($d=2{,}97$). Dimension moyenne des grains: 14 μ. Présence de porisité intragranulaire ($\times 580$)

Ces résultats tendent à montrer qu'une mise rapide en température des comprimés de BeO favorise la densification et que celle-ci atteint une limite pour une durée moindre de traitement isotherme que dans le cas d'une montée lente à la température finale.

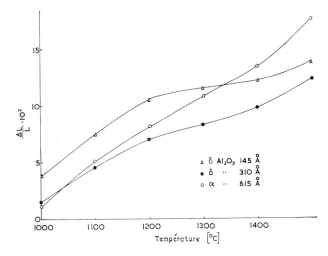

FIG. 6.—Retrait linéaire final dans le frittage rapide des comprimés d'alumine delta et alpha dans le domaine de températures 1000°–1500°C.

3.3 Alumine

3.31 Influence de la Vitesse de Montée en Température

Il a été déjà montré [4] qu'une rapide mise en température des comprimés d'alumine delta entraîne une diminution plus importante de la surface spécifique de ceux-ci que lorsque l'élévation de la température est lente. Il a été de même observé que la durée de la mise en température du comprimé influence le retrait final observé dans un traitement isotherme. Dans le cas d'une montée lente en température (300°C./h), le retrait final à 1300°C. est bien plus faible (6,5%) que dans le cas d'une montée rapide (100°C./min) (11,4%).

Sur la Fig. 6 sont représentés les retraits linéaires des comprimés confectionnés avec les particules de l'alumine delta de deux diamètres différents (145 et 310 Å) et de l'alumine alpha (615 Å). Ces comprimés, appartenant aux trois types d'échantillons, ont été portés rapidement (100°C./min) à 1000°C. et maintenus à cette température pendant 22 h. De la même façon, des comprimés frais ont été chauffés à 1100°, à 1200°, à 1300°, à 1400° et à 1500°C. Le retrait total, mesuré après refroidissement de chaque comprimé à la température ambiante, est représenté par les points de la Fig. 6 qui donnent les courbes représentatives des trois types d'échantillons. L'alumine alpha accuse un comportement différent de celui des deux autres échantillons delta. Elle accuse des retraits limites qui paraissent augmenter rapidement avec la température.

Lorsque les *mêmes comprimés* sont portés successivement aux températures croissantes selon le même protocole que précédemment, les courbes représentées sur la Fig. 7 traduisent alors une vitesse infiniment lente de la mise en température, au-delà de 1000°C. En effet, un comprimé chauffé à 1500°C., par exemple, a d'abord été maintenu 22 h à 1400°C., à 1300°C., etc. . . . , contrairement aux essais de la Fig. 6, où un comprimé a été introduit directement et très rapidement à 1500°C. sans avoir été chauffé

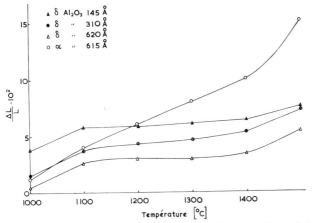

Fig. 7.—Retrait linéaire final dans le frittage lent des comprimés d'alumine delta et alpha dans le domaine de températures 1000°–1500°C.

au préalable. Pour le traitement thermique progressif de la Fig. 7 les valeurs finales de retrait, à chaque température, sont bien plus faibles que pour les expériences de la Fig. 6 correspondant à la mise rapide à la température finale. Pour l'alumine delta à 1500°C., par exemple, le retrait final est d'environ 13% dans le cas du frittage rapide (Fig. 6) contre environ 5% pour le frittage lent.

Il est donc montré que le traitement isotherme progressif a pour effet de figer certaines propriétés des comprimés d'alumine, empêchant leur évolution ultérieure. Cette action inhibitrice est cependant moins sensible pour l'alumine alpha qui continue à évoluer avec la température, malgré les traitements thermiques antérieurs.

L'enregistrement photographique du comprimé à des intervalles rapprochés a permis de suivre la vitesse du retrait lors de l'introduction rapide du comprimé dans la zone de température du frittage. La Fig. 8 représente la cinétique du retrait linéaire lorsque la température finale (1300°C.) du comprimé d'alumine delta est atteinte en 40 sec (courbe 1) et en 6 min (courbe 2). Le retrait total aprés 24 h est de 12,3% pour le comprimé chauffé en 40 sec et de 11,7%

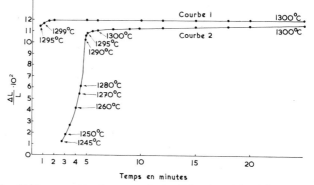

FIG. 8.—Frittage rapide des comprimés d'alumine delta (diamètre 160 Å). Cinétique de retrait linéaire à 1300°C.

seulement pour le comprimé chauffé en 6 min. Il importe ici de souligner qu'à 1300°C. le frittage de l'alumine delta est extrêmement rapide, car environ 98% du retrait limite sont atteints en deux minutes lors du chauffage rapide du comprimé. A la même température le temps nécessaire pour que le comprimé de l'alumine alpha subisse 98% du retrait limite est de 10 h, comme le montre la Fig. 12, examinée plus loin.

Le retrait linéaire du comprimé est bien accompagné du grossissement des grains comme le montrent les microphotographies électroniques. Les surfaces spécifiques des comprimés de l'alumine delta introduits rapidement dans le four à 1320°C. et maintenus à cette température respectivement 10, 20 et 90 sec, diminuent selon les données du tableau 4.

Tableau 4

Surfaces Spécifiques des Comprimés de Al_2O_3-δ

Durée du maintien du comprimé à 1320° C. (sec)	Surface spécifique (m^2/g)	Densité apparente
0	109	1,32
10	73	1,47
20	59	1,60
90	9	1,97

Le dosage de la phase alpha par diffraction X dans le comprimé confectionné initialement avec les particules de l'alumine delta et porté instantanément à 1300°C. (Fig. 8) indique un taux de transformation en alpha de 45% après un séjour d'une minute et de 60% après un séjour de 2 min à cette température. La transformation totale en alpha est atteinte en 4 min environ.[9]

Les valeurs du tableau 4 de la densité apparente des comprimés, déterminée d'après les dimensions géométriques de ceux-ci, indiquent la présence des vides entre les particules. La Fig. 9 représente la densité apparente des comprimés non chauffés, confectionnés sous la pression de 4 t/cm² à partir des particules de surfaces spécifiques croissantes. Il apparaît de ce graphique que la densité apparente décroît lorsque la surface spécifique de la poudre initiale croît. Ainsi l'empilement des particules dans le comprimé, qui théoriquement devrait être indépendant de leur taille, s'améliore lorsque leur diamètre s'accroît.

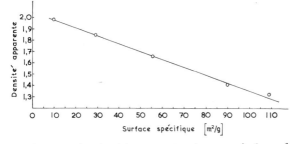

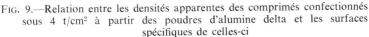

FIG. 9.—Relation entre les densités apparentes des comprimés confectionnés sous 4 t/cm² à partir des poudres d'alumine delta et les surfaces spécifiques de celles-ci

Il est de nouveau montré, en résumé, que le frittage des comprimés se traduisant par leur retrait est d'autant plus efficace que la température finale est atteinte plus rapidement. Le comportement particulier de l'alumine alpha est examiné dans la partie suivante.

3.32 Différence de Comportement des Alumines Delta et Alpha

Il a été indiqué précédemment que les comprimés de l'alumine alpha portés rapidement à des températures croissantes présentent une vitesse de retrait plus faible mais leurs retraits limites paraissent augmenter davantage avec la température que pour les comprimés de l'alumine delta.

Ce même comportement est observé pour des comprimés de l'alumine alpha chauffés à température linéairement croissante

(300°C./h) dans le dilatomètre Chevenard transformé en rétracto-mètre. La Fig. 10 représente les courbes rétractométriques des comprimés confectionnés avec des particules de l'alumine alpha de diamètre de 390 Å (courbe 3) et des comprimés confectionnés avec des particules de l'alumine delta de deux diamètres différents: 165 Å (courbe 1) et 300 Å (courbe 2). Au-delà de 1250°C. le retrait observé est plus important pour les particules alpha que pour les particules delta, bien que la transformation delta-alpha soit com-plète à cette température.[9] L'allure de la courbe relative à l'alumine alpha n'accuse même pas de tendance à s'infléchir pour la tem-pérature la plus élevée atteinte (1500°C.), laissant supposer un retrait encore plus important aux températures plus élevées.

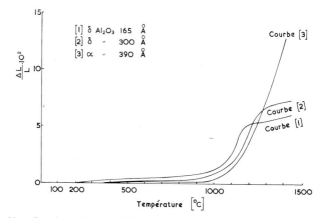

FIG. 10.—Courbes rétractométriques à température linéairement croissante (300°/h) des comprimés d'alumine delta (courbe 1, diamètre 165 Å, courbe 2, diamètre 300 Å) et alpha (courbe 3, diamètre 390 Å)

Ce comportement très particulier de l'alumine alpha par rapport à l'alumine initialement à l'état delta a fait également l'objet d'une étude par rétractométrie isotherme avec prises de vues photo-graphiques du comprimé porté rapidement à la température de l'expérience.

Les comprimés des particules delta, quel que soit le diamètre de celles-ci, donnent des courbes de retrait en fonction du temps représentées sur la Fig. 11 relative à des particules de 300 Å de diamètre.

Aprés une durée initiale nécessaire pour la mise en température du comprimé, le retraite augmente sensiblement linéairement avec le temps pour s'atténuer assez brutalement au bout de 11 min par ex-emple à 1197°C. L'énergie d'activation correspondant à la partie

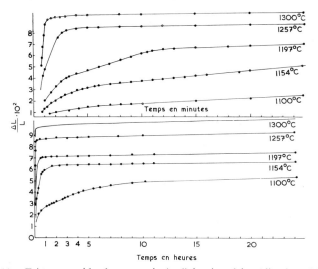

FIG. 11.—Frittage rapide des comprimés d'alumine delta (diamètre 300 Å). Cinétique de retrait linéaire dans le domaine de températures 1100°–1300°C.

rectiligne est de 145 kcal/mole, quelle que soit la taille des particules de l'alumine delta (Fig. 12).

La Fig. 13 présente la cinétique du retrait des comprimés d'alumine alpha (diamètre de particules 390 Å). Le phénomène est suffisament lent pour que l'échelle des temps puisse être exprimée en heures, malgré le fait que, comme pour l'alumine delta, le comprimé soit porté très rapidement à la température désirée. Ainsi pour les comprimés de l'alumine alpha la vitesse du retrait à tout instant est plus faible que pour l'alumine delta et elle décroît avec le temps de façon plus progressive.

L'alumine alpha, terme ultime de l'évolution cristalline de l'oxyde d'aluminium, est en général dotée d'une faible réactivité physico-chimique. La vitesse de cette transformation implique une énergie d'activation de 130 kcal/mole,[9] donc du même ordre de grandeur que celle relative à la vitesse de retrait de l'alumine delta. Le grossissement des grains que traduisent la diminution de la surface spécifique et le retrait linéaire doit être favorisé par la transformation cristalline en alpha de l'alumine delta qui, entraîne le relâchement des forces de cohésion du réseau. Mais une migration accélérée des joints de grains risque de ne pas laisser éliminer la porosité inter-granulaire qui se trouverait ainsi figée à l'intérieur des grains. Il en résulte par conséquent un retrait limite plus faible.

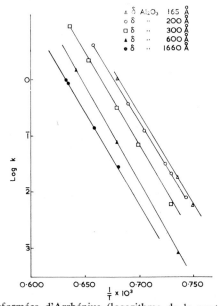

Fɪɢ. 12—Transformées d'Arrhénius (logarithme de la pente de la portion linéaire des courbes de la Fig. 11 en fonction de l'inverse de la température) pour les comprimés des particules d'alumine delta de diamètres 165, 200, 300, 600 et 1660 Å.

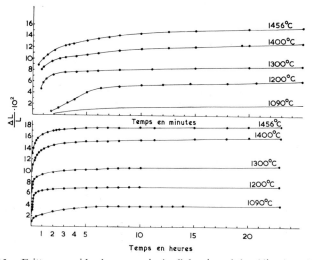

Fɪɢ. 13.—Frittage rapide des comprimés d'alumine alpha (diamètre 390 Å). Cinétique de retrait linéaire dans le domaine de températures 1090°–1456°C.

L'alumine alpha en comprimés ne subit aucune transformation cristalline au cours de son traitement thermique. La migration des joints de grains doit se produire plus lentement, ce qui permettrait une meilleure élimination de la porosité intergranulaire. Il en résulte un retrait limite plus fort ainsi qu'une vitesse de retrait plus faible et plus progressivement décroissante.

L'examen au microscope électronique des répliques des comprimés semble confirmer cette hypothèse.

BIBLIOGRAPHIE

1. Carteret, Y., Portnoff, M., Elston, J., et Caillat, R., *Proc. 4th Internat. Symp. React. Solids* (Amsterdam 1960), p. 540.
2. Caillat, R., Cuer, J. P., Elston, J., Juillet, F., Pointud, R., Prettre, M., et Teichner, S. J., *Bull. Soc. Chim.*, p. 152, 1959.
   Cuer, J. P., Elston, J., et Teichner, S. J., *Bull. Soc. Chim.*, 81, 89 et 94, 1961.
3. " Alumina Properties," *Alcoa Technical Paper No.* 10, 1956.
4. Juillet, F. Thèse, Lyon, 1961.
5. Makipirtti, S., *Powder Metallurgy* (Interscience Ed., N.Y., 1961), p. 97.
6. Carteret, Y., Portnoff, M., Elston, J., et Caillat, R., *Rapport CEA No.* 1661, 1960.
7. Belle, J., et Lustman, B., *Rapport W.A.P.D. No.* 184, 1957.
8. Bernier, M., Boivineau, J. C., Bourrasse, A., Maillard, A., et Morize, P., *Rapport C.E.A. No.* DM 1236.
9. Juillet, F., sous presse.
10. Arghiropoulos, B., Elston, J., Hilaire, P., Juillet, F., et Teichner, S. J., *4th Internat. Symp. React. Solids* (Amsterdam 1960), p. 524.

15—Influence of Technological Factors on the Sintering Behaviour of a Ferrite

By A. L. Stuijts and C. Kooy

Philips Research Laboratories
N.V. Philips' Gloeilampenfabrieken,
Eindhoven, Netherlands

ABSTRACT   E74

The sintering of prefired nickel–zinc ferrite powders, prepared from pure and impure iron oxides, has been studied. The density of powder compacts prepared in the normal ceramic way is not uniform and the density fluctuations give rise to inhomogeneous shrinkage within the compact. It has been found that the sintering behaviour is strongly determined by these fluctuations. The formation of a rigid network or a rigid shell during the sintering of a powder compact causes densification to theoretical density to take a very long time.

Influences des facteurs technologiques sur le comportement au frittage d'un ferrite

On étudie le frittage de poudres de ferrites de zinc-nickel préalablement cuites et préparées à partir d'oxydes de fer purs et impurs. La densité de produits pulvérulents compactés, préparés par voie céramique normale n'est pas uniforme et les variations de densité provoquant un retrait inégal dans le produit compacté. Il est démontré que ces variations exercent une influence déterminante sur l'aptitude au frittage. La formation d'un réseau rigide ou d'une écorce rigide au cours du frittage d'un produit pulvérulent compacté est la raison pour laquelle il faut un temps très long pour que la densification atteigne la densité théorique.

Einfluss der technischen Faktoren auf das Sinterhalten von Ferriten

Es wurde das Sintern von vorgebrannten Nickel-Zink-Ferritpulvern untersucht, die aus reinen und verunreinigten Eisenoxiden hergestellt wurden. Die Dichte der nach normalen keramischen Verfahren hergestellten Pulverpresslinge ist nicht einheitlich und die Dichteschwankungen verursachen inhomogenes Schrumpfen innerhalb der Probe. Es wurde gefunden, dass das Sinterverhalten sehr stark von diesen Schwankungen abhängt. Die Bildung eines starren Netzwerks oder einer starren Schale während des Sinterns eines Pulverpresslings ist der Grund dafür, dass das Erreichen der theoretischen Dichte sehr lange dauert.

1. INTRODUCTION

Both from quantitative model experiments and from qualitative observations of phenomena which occur in the later stages of sintering, it has become evident that diffusion is the predominant mechanism of material transport during the sintering of a crystalline solid.[1-4] In the densification of a compact the grain boundaries have an essential role, as they are only effective means of absorbing the extra vacancies generated by the surfaces of the pores. During sintering, grain growth occurs and decreases the sintering rate. It has become clear, especially from the work of COBLE [5, 6] on alumina, that a study of density/time and grain-size/time relationships is necessary to evaluate the diffusion-sintering models for a powder compact.

The decrease in densification rate, as caused by an increase in grain size with time, can actually be observed. No satisfactory results are obtained by introducing the time dependency of grain size into the equation of the densification rate. From diffusion-sintering models, Coble has predicted linear densification rates when plotted on a density/log time curve. In his equation a grain size dependence on time, $G^3 = At$, is inserted, but although COBLE found agreement in one of his sintering curves of alumina,[6] BRUCH found a different time dependence.[7] The reason for this discrepancy is that measurements of the time dependence of the densification of a powder compact are affected by a large number of technological parameters, one of which is the variation of the bulk density within the powder compact. Another factor is the green density, BRUCH [7] having shown that alumina compacts with a green density below a certain limit cannot readily be sintered to a high density and densify at a different rate from specimens with a green density above that limit.

In this paper a study of the sintering behaviour and the grain-growth pattern of nickel–zinc ferrite powders of different impurity content is reported. This work is part of our investigations directed to the development of magnetic ferrites with very low porosities.[8, 9] Another purpose of these investigations is the control of the microstructure of these ferrites. Some of their physical properties depend on grain size, pore size, pore distribution, etc., and a study of the kinetics of the sintering behaviour is essential to obtain specimens with a given microstructure.

2. MECHANICAL EFFECTS DURING SINTERING

Sintering between two particles results in a shrinkage which is perpendicular to the grain boundary. This anisotropic effect will in general create stresses in an assemblage of particles (Fig. 1). Along the path indicated (dotted line) the vector sum of all the shrinkage vectors will in general not be zero. The result is that tensile or compressive stresses are created which locally inhibit or enhance sintering. Whether such an assemblage can regulate local

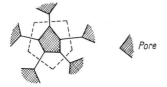

Fɪɢ. 1.—Assemblage of particles around a void. Shrinkage occurs perpendicular to the grain boundaries, requiring the vector sum of the shrinkage vectors along the path indicated (dotted line) to be zero

shrinkage or not remains an open question. It is known that deformation of a compact occurs while it is sintered under a tensile stress.[10] At the beginning of sintering, when the grain size is still small, a Nabarro-Herring creep-like process can occur, and even grain-boundary sliding is possible, but these deformation processes become less effective during sintering, as either the grain size has increased too much or the density is too high.

Thus mechanical effects during sintering have to be taken into account if creep is not fast enough to accommodate inhomogeneous shrinkage. We shall discuss a number of inhomogeneities originating from the technology of ceramic powders.

The very small particles necessary to obtain high sintered densities are difficult to press into a particular shape and in consequence the green density is low. Owing to the non-ideal packing of the particles at the microscopic level, spread in the particle sizes, etc., local stresses will be set up. At low green density an accumulation of these stresses in an array of particles, as shown in Fig. 1, can cause the weakest bond between two particles to break, resulting in the formation of a very large pore. The decreased densification rate in a compact of alumina powder with low green density accompanied by the formation of large voids, as observed by Bʀᴜᴄʜ,[7] might also be caused by these local stresses.

The use of granules to facilitate pressing causes density fluctuations in a compact. Granules are made by mixing the powder with a suitable binder and/or lubricant and then subjecting the mixture to some process such as spray drying or sieving which produces rounded particles of suitable size. There are good reasons to suppose that, after pressing, granules are not completely destroyed. Particularly with very fine powders of $0.1–0.5\ \mu$, the capillary forces which operate during the drying of the wet granules can become strong and in some cases very hard agglomerates are formed. During sintering, the regions with the highest density give rise to the formation of a rigid skeleton, and lower the end-point density.

A typical effect caused by the presence of hard isolated agglomerates in a powder compact is the formation of "blots", as shown in Fig. 2 for a sintered nickel–zinc ferrite compact. These blots can be induced, for example, in the following way. Granules are made from the fine powder by briquetting at high pressure, breaking, and sieving. Some of these granules are mixed with the dry powder and pressed at a lower pressure. After sintering, the blots are formed, clearly showing their origin. They have a typical structure: a central hole from which large grains with trapped pores radiate. In translucent alumina these regions appear as white blots. It is clear that, in the case described here, the difference in density results both in the formation of a large pore and in inhomogeneous grain-growth phenomena.

FIG. 2.—Dark-field photomicrograph of a polished and etched nickel–zinc ferrite sample, showing "blots" caused by the presence of hard agglomerates in the powder compact (× 100)

Mechanical effects from density differences in a powder compact on a scale larger than the size of the granules used can also influence sintering. Although no work has been done on measurements of the density distribution within a compact of a fine ceramic powder consisting of particles of $0.1–1\ \mu$, reference can be made to the results obtained with other coarser powders.[11] Wall friction in a die gives rise to complicated density gradients in a compact. Hydrostatic pressing gives a more homogeneous compact, although there can still be a region of lower density in the centre. These inhomogeneities and the effect of a temperature gradient within the compact during sintering cause the formation of a rigid outer shell, hindering full densification.

3. EXPERIMENTAL

The ferrite investigated was a spinel with the chemical composition $Ni_{0.36}Zn_{0.64}Fe_2O_4$. Two different types of material were prepared:

(1) A powder was made from technically pure raw materials, nickel oxide, zinc oxide and iron oxide, with a total impurity content (cations and anions such as SO_4^{2-}) of about 0·5%. After the oxides had been mixed, the powder was preheated at about 1,050°C., to obtain complete reaction. The presintered powder was very intensively wet-milled in a laboratory vibratory mill, with ⅛-in. steel balls. After milling, a chemical analysis was carried out and the requisite extra amounts of nickel oxide and zinc oxide to obtain the correct stoicheiometric composition were added as solid and the whole charge was subjected to mixing. This powder will be referred to as TP 1050.

A part of the mixed raw material was preheated for 1 h at 900°C. and then mildly milled in a ball mill with ethyl alcohol. This powder, referred to as TP 900, was somewhat less reactive than the previous one. Both powders consisted of particles of about 0·3–0·5 μ, as measured by electron microscopy.

(2) A powder made from chemically pure basic nickel carbonate, zinc oxide, and a very pure iron oxide (total impurity content <100 p.p.m.). The mixture was preheated at 900°C. for 1 h and then mildly milled in a ball mill with ethyl alcohol. This powder, consisting of particles of about 0·3 μ, will be referred to as CP 900.

Samples were pressed hydrostatically at a pressure of 1,000 atm. In order to study the effect of granules, two powder preparations were employed. Granules were made by mixing the powder with 12^w/$_0$ distilled water and pressing the mixture through a 40-mesh screen. These samples are denoted NG, in contrast to the samples that were pressed directly from the milled and dried powder, denoted HG. In the HG samples any agglomeration of the powder was disposed of by suitable treatment in a turbine mixer.

Sintering was carried out in a resistance-heated tube furnace in flowing oxygen. Two types of experiment were made:

(1) The samples were placed in the cold furnace and then heated at constant rate to the top temperature. After every 10° or 20°

increase in temperature a sample was drawn from the hot zone into a zone of the furnace at a temperature of about 900°C. When all the samples had been quenched in this way, they were furnace-cooled to room temperature.

(2) The samples were placed in that part of the hot furnace where the temperature was about 900°C. After thermal equilibrium had been reached, the samples were rapidly pushed into the hot zone. In this way the samples were quickly raised to the desired sintering temperature. After a fixed time a sample was withdrawn from the hot zone, in the same way as described in the previous case.

The relative density ρ of the samples was determined from measurements of weight and volume. The volume of the sample was determined from change in weight, either by water or by mercury displacement. The X-ray density for the composition used is 5·336 g/cm³. The percentage porosity is then:

$$P = 100 \left(1 - \frac{\rho}{5 \cdot 336}\right)$$

The samples were polished with various grades of diamond paste on grooved tin plates. Investigations were carried out on a metallographic microscope using both bright- and dark-field illumination. Dark-field illumination is especially useful in the microscope investigation of ferrites. The effects of porosity are somewhat exaggerated, the only drawback being the difficulty in obtaining sharp photomicrographs of the pores.

4. RESULTS AND DISCUSSION

4.1 Technical Grade Raw Materials

The technical grade powders show discontinuous grain-growth during sintering.

In Fig. 3 a density/temperature plot for different heating rates is presented for samples made from powder TP 1050; the effect of discontinuous grain-growth on the density/temperature curves is clearly demonstrated. Figure 4 shows photomicrographs of three samples (HG), heated at 250°C./h. At a temperature just below the bend in the curve (1,200°C.), grain growth is negligible. At a temperature 10° higher, corresponding to a time interval of only 2·5 min, discontinuous grain-growth has started, with grains up to 25 μ already present. This end-point density can therefore be well explained by the drastic decrease in grain-boundary area.

The samples made from granulated powder (NG) reach a lower end-point density. When the granules are connected and have

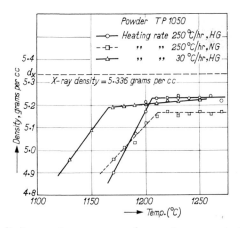

FIG. 3.—Density/temperature curves of samples pressed from powder
TP 1050: NG=pressed from granulated powder; HG=pressed from a
homogeneous powder

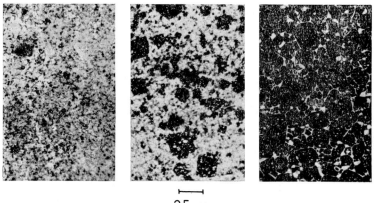

25 μ

T=1200°C   T=1210°C   T=1270°C

FIG. 4.—Photomicrographs of three samples of powder TP 1050 (Fig. 3,
heating-rate 250°C./h, HG). Dark-field illumination

reached their end-point density, a rigid skeleton is formed which
hinders further shrinkage.

However, the *isothermal* densification curves (Fig. 5) do not show,
except at 1,250°C., a break in the rate of densification corresponding with the appearance of discontinuous grain-growth. For example, in Fig. 6, the grain-growth behaviour of the powder TP 900

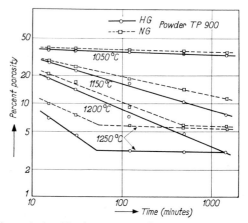

FIG. 5.—Isothermal densification curves of samples pressed from powder TP 900: NG=pressed from granulated powder; HG=pressed from a homogeneous powder

is shown at a sintering temperature of 1,200°C. There is a good linear relationship between the logarithm of porosity and the logarithm of sintering time, with no break in the curve for 1,200°C. On the other hand, in the samples heated at 1,250°C., where the sintering curve does show a break, discontinuous grain-growth has already started near zero time.

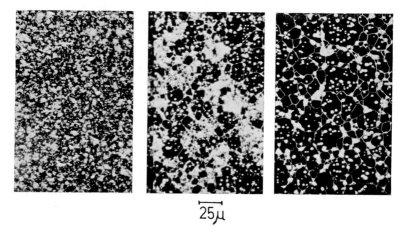

$$\overline{25\mu}$$

120   480   1440
Duration of sintering (min.)

FIG. 6.—Photomicrographs of three samples of powder TP 900 (Fig. 5, sintering-temperature 1,200°C., HG). Dark-field illumination

We have good reason to suppose that this inconsistent behaviour can be explained by a combination of two effects. Firstly there is the effect of discontinuous grain-growth. Apparently shrinkage can still proceed as long as a duplex structure is present in which the discontinuously grown crystals are embedded in a continuous matrix of grains of the original size, as shown by specimen TP 900 sintered for 480 min at 1,200°C. (Fig. 6). Shrinkage stops when the large grains form the continuous matrix. Because of their size, any grain-boundary sliding becomes impossible and the rigid network of the large grains that has formed causes sintering to stop.

Secondly there is the effect of a temperature gradient within a specimen. The velocity with which the large grains grow in the matrix must be related to this gradient. With the appearance of discontinuous grain-growth at the periphery of the specimen, a rigid shell is formed, hindering further densification. The break in the heating curves in Fig. 3 is caused by this effect, and is demonstrated by the photomicrographs in Fig. 7.

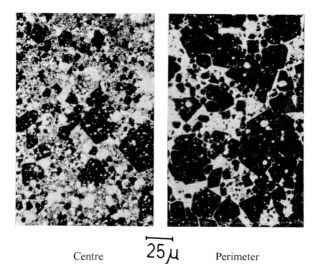

Centre $\overline{25\,\mu}$ Perimeter

Fig. 7.—Photomicrographs of one sample of powder TP 1050 taken at the perimeter and in the centre. Dark-field illumination

The shape of the crystals is typical, especially in the interior of the specimen. The formation of grains with sharp edges shows that they have grown in a matrix in which grain growth is impeded by the presence of a liquid phase,[12]

4.2 Pure Raw Materials

The powders prepared from the very pure raw materials do not show discontinuous grain-growth. It was therefore interesting to make the same measurements as in the preceding paragraph with these powders, and check their behaviour during sintering.

Figure 8 shows the density/temperature curves of powder CP 900 for a heating-rate of 200°C./h. For other heating-rates analogous behaviour has been found. The break in the curves cannot be related to discontinuous grain growth, as can be concluded from the photomicrographs shown in Fig. 9.

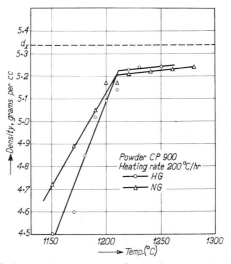

FIG. 8.—Density/temperature curves of samples pressed from the pure powder CP 900; NG=pressed from granulated powder; HG=pressed from a homogeneous powder; $d_x=5\cdot336$ g/cm³

The isothermal densification curves also show essentially the same pattern (Fig. 10). No discontinuous grain-growth occurs in these samples and at higher temperatures no essential difference is noted.

To explain this behaviour we suppose that there is still another reason for a break in the sintering velocity. It is clear that every compact shows a range of pore sizes. HORNSTRA [13] calculated a gradual change in sintering velocity from the pore-size distribution function. We think that a sudden change in sintering velocity occurs when most of the grains have no pores left at their boundaries. If the remaining pores, i.e. those left after elimination of

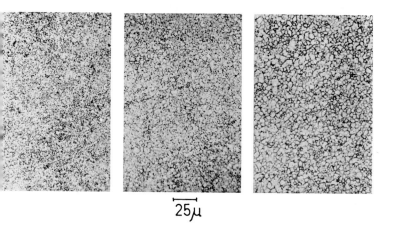

| T = 1200°C | T = 1220°C | T = 1250°C |

FIG. 9.—Photomicrographs of three samples of powder CP 900 (Fig. 8, HG).
Bright-field illumination

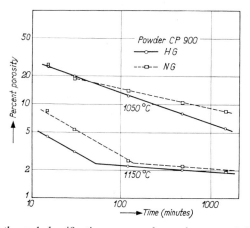

FIG. 10.—Isothermal densification curves of samples pressed from powder
CP 900

he smallest ones, are separated by distance which is of the order of
two grain diameters or more, further shrinkage will be controlled
either by very large diffusion distances or by creep-like processes
as the rate-determining mechanism.

5. CONCLUSION

Some effects of technological factors on the densification rate during sintering of an assemblage of powder particles have been described. The deduction that mechanical effects play an important role, especially in the last phase of densification, follows from the present work on a number of phenomena relating to the formation of a rigid network in the compact or a rigid shell around the compact. In the last phase of sintering, a creep-like process, necessary to eliminate inhomogeneities, is inactive, because generally the grain size has already increased considerably. Even a material showing controlled grain-growth needs very long sintering-times to attain full density. The factors discussed stress the point that, in order to obtain the highest densities in reasonable sintering-times, the method used for preparing the powder compact must be one which results in the highest possible homogeneity, even at the microscopic level.

ACKNOWLEDGMENT

The authors wish to thank Mr. D. Veeneman and Mr. H. C. Hoefnagels for their assistance with the experiments.

REFERENCES

1. Kuczynski, G. C., *Trans. AIME,* **185,** 169, 1949.
2. Kingery, W. D., and Berg, M., *J. Appl. Phys.,* **26,** 1205, 1955
3. Burke, J. E., *J. Amer. Ceram. Soc.,* **40,** 80, 1957.
4. Coble, R. L., *J. Amer. Ceram. Soc.,* **41,** 55, 1958.
5. Coble, R. L., *J. Appl. Phys.,* **32,** 787, 1961.
6. Coble, R. L., *J. Appl. Phys.,* **32,** 793, 1961.
7. Bruch, C. A., *Bull. Amer. Ceram. Soc.,* **41,** 799, 1962.
8. Stuijts, A. L., Verweel, J., and Peloschek, H. P., *Proc. Int. Conf. on Nonlinear Magnetics, A.I.E.E.E.,* April 17–19, 1963.
9. Stuijts, A. L., *Philips Techn. Rev.* To be published.
10. Dawihl, W., and Rix, W., *Z. Metallkunde,* **40,** 115, 1949.
11. Train, D., and Lewis, C. J., 3rd Congress of the European Federation of Chemical Engineering, Olympia, London, 20–29 June 1962; Proceedings of the Symposium on the Handling of Solids, The Institution of Chemical Engineers, London.
12. Kooy, C., " Science of Ceramics " (Academic Press, London), Vol. 1, p. 21, 1962.
13. Hornstra, J., *Physica,* **27,** 342, 1961.

16—Reactions at the Point of Contact Between SiO₂ and Al₂O₃

By W. L. DE KEYSER

Laboratory of the Chemistry of Solids
University of Brussels, Belgium

ABSTRACT   A422 (Al₂O₃/SiO₂)

Reactions between SiO₂ and Al₂O₃ have been studied at high temperatures by examining the surfaces of contact between pellets of SiO₂ and Al₂O₃ or between pellets of Al₂O₃ and kaolinite. Several techniques have been employed to maintain contact between the pellets while they are being heated at a temperature of 1600°C. By the combined use of X-ray fluorescence, optical and X-ray crystallographic analyses it has been possible to show that, as a result of the diffusion of Al₂O₃ into the silica zone, a glass phase is formed, surrounding cristobalite. Moreover, during the diffusion of SiO₂ into Al₂O₃ the mullite crystals tend to grow along the c axis parallel to the direction of the diffusion of silica into Al₂O₃.

Les réactions au contact de SiO₂ et Al₂O₃

Les réactions entre SiO₂ et Al₂O₃ ont été étudiées à haute température en examinant les surfaces de contact entre des pastilles de SiO₂ et de Al₂O₃ ou entre des pastilles de Al₂O₃ et de kaolinite. Plusieurs techniques ont été employées pour maintenir le contact entre les pastilles pendant leur chauffage à 1600°C. En combinant les analyses par fluorescence des rayons X, optiques et radiocristallographiques, il a été possible de montrer qu'une phase vitreuse, entourant la cristobalite, se forme par diffusion de Al₂O₃ dans la zone de la silice. En outre, au cours de la diffusion de SiO₂ dans Al₂O₃, les cristaux de mullite tendent à croître le long de l'axe-c parallèlement à la direction de la diffusion de la silice dans Al₂O₃.

Die Reaktionen an der Berührungsstelle zwischen SiO₂ und Al₂O₃

Reaktionen zwischen SiO₂ und Al₂O₃ bei hohen Temperaturen wurden bestimmt, indem die Kontaktflächen zwischen SiO₂- und Al₂O₃-Tabletten oder zwischen Tabletten aus Al₂O₃ und Kaolinit untersucht wurden. Verschiedene Untersuchungsmethoden wurden angewandt, um sicherzustellen, dass der Kontakt zwischen den Tableten erhalten bleibt, während sie auf 1600°C. aufgeheizt werden. Durch eine Kombination von Röntgenfluoreszenz-, optischen und radiokristallographischen Analysenmethoden war es möglich, zu zeigen, dass infolge der Diffusion des Al₂O₃ in der Quarzzone eine Glasphase entsteht, die Cristobalit umgibt. Des weiteren neigen Mullitristalle bei der Diffusion von SiO₂ in Al₂O₃ dazu, entlang der c-Achse parallel der Diffusionsrichtung des Quarzes in das Al₂O₃ zu wachsen.

1. INTRODUCTION

The synthesis of mullite has been the subject of much research and many publications. Most workers have studied the results

243

obtained by mixing more or less finely ground powders. In the present case SiO_2 and Al_2O_3 or kaolin and Al_2O_3 were placed in contact over a plane surface and the reaction interfaces were studied after heating at high temperature. This method has already been used to study reactions at the CaO/Al_2O_3 and SiO_2/CaO inter faces.[1,2] The most difficult problem is to keep the two com ponents in contact during heating, for their respective shrinkages or expansions differ considerably.

2. PREPARATION OF SAMPLES

Several methods of preparation have been used in order to main tain the two reacting phases in close contact during heating:

(1) A relatively simple method consists in preparing concentric specimens as shown in Fig. 1. In the centre is placed the com ponent that expands more (or shrinks less) during heating and owing to the differential contraction and expansion, good contact is obtained at the interface. The coefficients of expansion or con traction must not, however, differ too much, otherwise the external ring becomes excessively cracked.

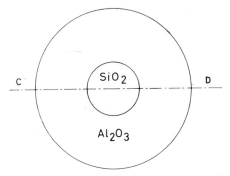

FIG. 1.—Contact maintained during heating between Al_2O_3 and SiO_2 by shrinkage of Al_2O_3 and expansion of SiO_2

(2) Other experiments were conducted with specimens prepared as shown in Fig. 2. A small pellet of alumina agglomerated with dextrin (A) is placed between two small pellets consisting of quartz grains of approximately 25μ diam., also agglomerated with dextrin (S_3, S_4). This assembly is placed in an alumina tube of 40 mm internal diameter, between two relatively thick plates of silica (S_1, S_2). The diameter of the first three pellets is less than 40 mm whereas that of S_1 and S_2 is close to that of the alumina tube.

As a result of the conversion of quartz to cristobalite, the silica expands. Plates S_1 and S_2 adjust themselves in the cylinder and by expanding exert a strong pressure on the system S_3AS_4, the constituent parts of which are thereby maintained in close contact during the reaction at 1,600°C. A platinum reference wire is placed between plates A and S_3 and between A and S_4, in order to determine the direction of diffusion.

This method was used in the preparation of specimens for experiments 1 and 2.

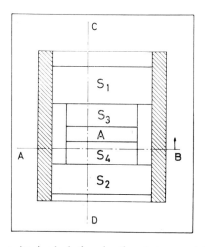

Fig. 2.—Contact maintained during heating between slabs of SiO₂ and Al₂O₃ by expansion of SiO₂

(3) In the reactions between kaolin and alumina, advantage could not be taken of the compression caused by the expansion of the silica; a pellet of kaolin (K) previously dehydrated at 700°, was therefore placed between two pellets of alumina (bayerite heated at 1,300° and agglomerated with dextrin)—(A,A). The whole assembly was placed in the oven and held in position by means of an alumina rod (DA), under a load of 2 kg. Platinum wires were placed between the pellets K and A.

3. METHODS OF INVESTIGATING THE REACTION ZONE

After heating, the specimens, prepared by one of the three methods, are impregnated under reduced pressure with an ethoxylic resin (Araldite) and polymerized at 140° for 20 h, when they are sufficiently hard to be cut.

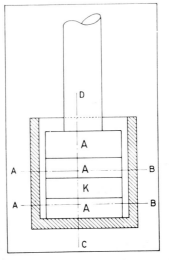

F<small>IG</small>. 3.—Contact maintained during heating between slabs of kaolin and Al_2O_3 by means of a loaded rod

For the optical investigation, the samples are cut along the plane CD (Figs. 1, 2 and 3), thereby providing thin sections in which the reaction zone can be observed (Figs. 4, 5 and 9).

For the X-ray crystallographic investigation and for the fluorescence analysis, the specimen is cut along plane AB (Figs. 2 and 3). The thickness of the sections is measured and their surface is exposed to X-rays. In this way the amount of Si and of Al in the irradiated face (fluorescence analysis) and its crystallographic composition (X-ray crystallographic analysis) can be determined.

The section is then ground with silicon carbide paper along a plane parallel to AB; parallelism of the planes that are obtained by successive grindings is maintained by fixing the plate firmly in a plastic support. The analyses are performed after successive thicknesses of about 0·02 mm have been removed. This method has been applied by the author in certain previous work.[2]

Figures 6, 7 and 8 show the results. The specimens prepared by method 1, the simplest, can only be used to provide thin sections; since the SiO_2/AL_2O_3 contact surface is cylindrical, the method of successive grinding is not applicable.

3.1 X-ray Crystallographic Analysis

The apparatus used was the well-known spectrometer with Geiger counter of the North American Philips Co., with a copper anti-cathode (Cu $K\alpha = 1.542$ Å).

3.2 X-ray Fluorescence Analysis

The apparatus was a Philips PW 1050 equipped with a gold anti-cathode, using a current of 24 mA at 38 kV.

For both SiO$_2$ and Al$_2$O$_3$ the analyser crystal is ADP ($2d = 10.648$) and the detection system is a gas-flow counter supplied with a voltage of 1,600. The whole is under a vacuum of less than 0·1 mm Hg.

For the analyses the lines Kα_1, Kα_2 are recorded, as follows:

$2\theta = 103.08°$ and $103.13°$ for Al
$2\theta = 84.00°$ and $84.03°$ for Si

4. EXPERIMENTAL RESULTS

4.1 Experiment 1. SiO$_2$/Al$_2$O$_3$ Interface. Heating at 1,600° for 2 h

The sample was prepared by method 2 (Fig. 2). The pellet of Al$_2$O$_3$ (A) was prepared from hydrated aluminium oxide (Merck 1093) heated at 1,300° (but not maintained at this temperature), and thin sections were cut perpendicular to the reaction face (Figs. 4 and 5).

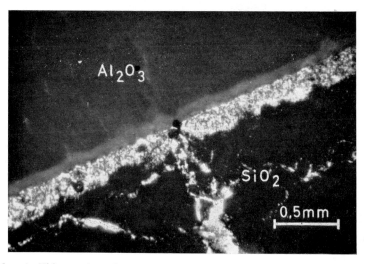

FIG. 4—Thin section along a plane perpendicular to the reaction face (polarized light)

The planes parallel to the reaction zone, obtained by successive grindings, were irradiated and each time the thickness of the section was measured in order to locate the results.

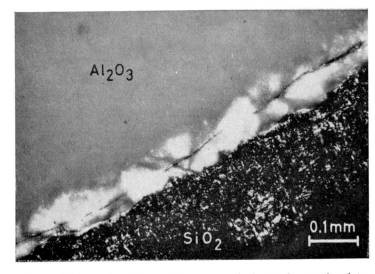

F IG. 5.—Thin section along a plane perpendicular to the reaction face
(polarized light)

The apparent specific gravity of α-Al_2O_3 and of cristobalite out side the reaction zone was determined, and the concentrations o Al_2O_3 and of cristobalite outside the reaction zone could be calcu lated:

On the Al_2O_3 side, 19.6×10^{-3} mole/cm^3 of Al_2O_3
On the SiO_2 side, 25×10^{-3} mole/cm^3 of cristobalite.

As the intensity of fluorescence of Al_2O_3 and SiO_2 varies as a approximately linear function of the amount irradiated per cm^3 the number of moles per cm^3 of Al_2O_3 and SiO_2 could be deter mined approximately at each successive new surface.

The same method enabled the amounts of α-Al_2O_3 and of cristo balite to be evaluated, it being assumed that the height of the charac teristic reflections obtained by X-ray crystallographic analysis in creases proportionally to the amount of cristobalite and of α-Al_2O (Fig. 6).

The same procedure could not be used for mullite, becaus mullite forming at the interface becomes oriented, and the charac teristic reflections no longer bear any relation to the amount o mullite. An attempt was therefore made to compute the proportio of mullite from the proportions of total Al_2O_3, total SiO_2, cristo balite and α-Al_2O_3.

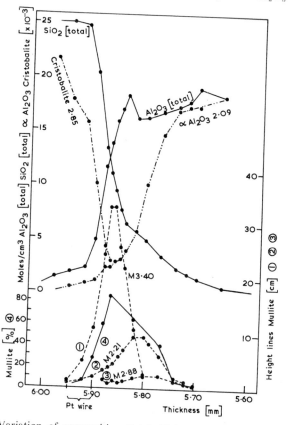

Fig. 6.—Variation of composition (total Al$_2$O$_3$, total SiO$_2$, α-Al$_2$O$_3$, cristobalite, mullite) at the interface after heating slabs of Al$_2$O$_3$ and SiO$_2$ (2 hours 1,600°)

mm)
5.98 Cristobalite, uncrystallized Al$_2$O$_3$ and SiO$_2$; no mullite or α-Al$_2$O$_3$. From the total SiO$_2$ and Al$_2$O$_3$ it is calculated that at 1,600°C. there is 8·2% Al$_2$O$_3$. It is assumed that, during cooling, much of the cristobalite is re-crystallized, leaving alumino-silicate glass which, by difference, represents 20% of the initial liquidus.

Figures 4 and 5 show, near the reference wire and in the direction of the silica, a zone edge the thickness of which can be estimated as 0·2 mm. In polarized light this zone appears partly black and consisting of cristobalite separated by white points which seem to be crystals but are, however, glass; between crossed nicols they appear white as a result of the strains due to relatively fast cooling. Strain patterns have in fact been observed in these white zones.

The same phenomenon is observed with the Araldite with which the specimens were impregnated: between crossed nicols, fissures filled with Araldite appear white.

In a few experiments several unconverted quartz grains in contact with Al_2O_3 were observed, no doubt due to the inhibiting by Al_2O_3 of the quartz-cristobalite conversion.

5.95 (Extreme edge of reference wire.) α-Al_2O_3; mullite negligible. By subtracting α-Al_2O_3 from total Al_2O_3, the liquidus was estimated to contain 8·4% Al_2O_3; during cooling a glass is formed, representing 34·7% of the total weight.

5.92. α-Al_2O_3, cristobalite and some mullite. At 1,600°C. the interface was assumed to consist of Al_2O_3, mullite, and liquid of the same composition as at 5·95 mm (8·4% Al_2O_3). Mullite was computed as 1·16%; liquidus at 1,600° was 94·2% which, on cooling, left 38·8% glass.

5.90 At 1,600°C., 70·2% liquid; 23·3% mullite. On cooling, 35% glass was left.

5.87 α-Al_2O_3 and mullite; no cristobalite (X-ray crystallography). All the SiO_2 was assumed to be combined as mullite; difference between total Al_2O_3 and α-Al_2O_3 to be combined with SiO_2. The product would contain 70% Al_2O_3, which is close to the proportion assumed for synthetic mullite; the calculation is therefore assumed to be valid. Mullite, 80·5% The 3·4Å peak is abnormally high, indicating orientation perpendicular to the corresponding planes (1 2 0), which are therefore parallel to the interface.

5.81 58·2% mullite, containing 72·8% Al_2O_3. The 2·21Å peak showed a maximum. This peak corresponds to planes (1 2 1), which are about 50° to the c axis, and therefore at about 40° to the direction of the $SiO_2 \longrightarrow Al_2O_3$ diffusion.

5.77 37·7% mullite, containing 72·1% Al_2O_3. The 2·88Å mullite reflection is abnormally strong. Since the corresponding planes (0 0 1) are perpendicular to the c axis, the mullite crystals grow in the direction of the c axis, which is therefore the direction of $SiO_2 \longrightarrow Al_2O_3$ diffusion.

5.74 Little mullite (2·6%); considerable proportion of α-Al_2O_3, and some SiO_2. The difference between total Al_2O_3 and α-Al_2O_3 is insufficient for all the SiO_2 to be combined with Al_2O_3. Therefore there is probably an amorphous phase containing SiO_2 which forms with Al_2O_3 an amorphous or very poorly crystallized compound.

5.70 No mullite. α-Al_2O_3, a little Al_2O_3 and SiO_2, probably forming an amorphous or poorly crystallized compound.

5.54 Only α-Al_2O_3.

4.2 Experiment 2

The preparation of the samples, as performed in Experiment 1, turned out to be very delicate and involved important precautions in order to reduce the fissures to a minimum. It was therefore attempted to modify the preparation of the pellets of Al_2O_3.

The precalcined alumina was agglomerated under high pressure (50 kg/cm²). The pellet was then slowly heated to 1,300°C., and aligned on both faces before being sandwiched between two SiO_2

pellets as in Experiment 1. The results were rather disappointing, because the penetration of SiO_2 into the Al_2O_3 zone is reduced by more than a half (Fig. 7).

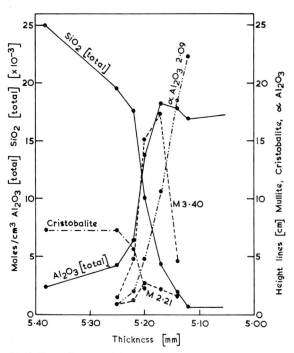

FIG. 7.—Variation of composition (total Al_2O_3, total SiO_2, α-Al_2O_3, cristobalite, mullite) at the interface after heating slabs of sintered Al_2O_3 and SiO_2 (2 hours 1,600°)

A single maximum is now observed in the 3·4Å mullite peak. As in Experiment 1, it lies in the alumina zone, near the reference wire.

The maximum amount of mullite (at 5·185 mm) is 62·4%, with 33·2% α-Al_2O_3 and 4·3% glass. The growth of mullite stops rapidly in the Al_2O_3 zone and no important orientation is indicated by the lines 2·21Å and 2·88Å.

These observations were confirmed by an examination of the thin sections. From a comparison of Experiments 1 and 2 it is concluded that degree of penetration of SiO_2 into the alumina zone and the simultaneous formation of mullite varies considerably, depending on the method of preparation of the alumina and especially its degree of sintering.

4.3 Experiment 3.   Kaolin/Al_2O_3 Interface.   Heating at 1,600°C. for 2 h

The amounts (in moles) of Al_2O_3 and of kaolin at the faces of the respective pellets were calculated from apparent specific gravity of these materials as used in the experiment.

Before grinding there was $18 \cdot 6 \times 10^{-3}$ mole/cm³ Al_2O_3 at the alumina face and $10 \cdot 6 \times 10^{-3}$ mole/cm³ Al_2O_3 and $21 \cdot 2 \times 10^{-3}$ mole/cm³ SiO_2 at the kaolin face. The amount of α-Al_2O_3 on the face of the alumina pellets equals the total alumina concentration.

As in Experiment 1, total SiO_2, total Al_2O_3, and the amount of α-Al_2O_3 were determined after each grinding, on the assumption that the intensity of fluorescence is proportional to the amounts of SiO_2 and of Al_2O_3 (within the limits of the experiment) and that the height of the 2·09Å peak of α-Al_2O_3 varies proportionally with the amount at various interfacial points.

The amount of mullite on the " kaolin " face was determined by comparison with a sample of pure mullite, the apparent specific gravity of which had been determined previously.

In the " kaolin " zone there was 56% mullite, and 44% of a glassy phase containing approximately 11·6% Al_2O_3. (Composition calculated from an elementary analysis of the Zettlitz kaolin used in the experiment.)

The relatively high proportion of Al_2O_3 in this phase is due to the Zettlitz kaolin containing approximately 1·2% $K_2O + Fe_2O_3$. For the same reason the cristobalite lines do not appear; the silica remains completely dissolved in the glass.

The results of investigations and of calculations for the various surfaces of the reaction zone during the successive grindings are given below. The points refer to measurements on the pellet (see Fig. 8).

mm	Mullite (%)	Glass (%)	α-Al_2O_3 (%)	
5·76	56	44		Same composition as at the external (kaolin) face of the pellet.
5·8	45	39	16	α–Al_2O_3 associated with glass and mullite. Glass assumed to contain 11·6% Al_2O_3
5·84	39·2	22·2	38·5	
5·86	46·7	8·35	45	
5·88		see below		

At 5·88 mm there could be no glass, because the calculated molar ratio between (total $Al_2O_3 - \alpha$-Al_2O_3) and SiO_2 is greater than 3/2.

In Fig. 8, from 5·88 mm on, the A curves are saw-toothed, which can only be explained by the existence of fissures.

The precautions taken to minimize the influence of such fissures have been stressed, but their effect could not be eliminated. Because the calculations are based on the simultaneous use of fluorescence analysis and X-ray crystallography, one must keep in mind that the radiation used for the fluorescence is much less penetrating than that for the X-ray crystallography. Consequently the variations due to shallow fissures are sensitive only to fluorescence. This explains why the curve for the variation of α-Al₂O₃ is more continuous than the one for total Al₂O₃.

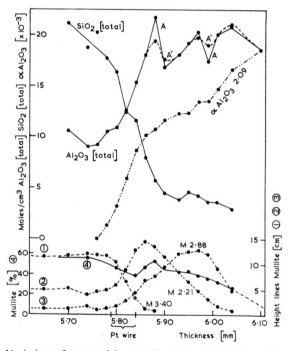

FIG. 8.—Variation of composition (total Al₂O₃, total SiO₂, α-Al₃O₂, cristobalite, mullite) at the interface after heating slabs of kaolin and Al₂O₃ (2 hours 1,600°)

The amount of mullite must therefore be calculated from the amount of SiO₂, assuming that the mullite formed was in the proportion 3Al₂O₃ : 2SiO₂. From this assumption the total Al₂O₃ was calculated by adding combined Al₂O₃ to the α-Al₂O₃.

Curve A′, which shows the results obtained in this way, follows curve A fairly closely. The differences between A and A′ are thought to be explained by the presence of the shallow fissures.

This method of computation gives the following results:

mm	Mullite (%)	α-Al₂O₃ (%)	
		α-Al_2O_3 (%)	
5·88	52·5	47·5	
5·90	44·6	55·4	
5·93	39·1	60·9	(This point seems to be aberrant)
5·95	45	55	
5·97	35·5	64·5	
5·99	36	64	
6·01	33·8	66·2	
6·04	27·3	72·7	

Between 6·04 and 6·10, no mullite is shown by X-ray crystallography, which suggests that a compound was formed in this zone between A and S; it cannot be identified by X-ray crystallography.

4.4 Orientation of Mullite formed in the Presence of α-Al₂O₃

In Fig. 8 are the three characteristic lines of mullite, the height being proportional to their intensity. These lines correspond to $d = 3.4$, $d = 2.21$ and $d = 2.88$Å.

The relative intensity of these lines is (according to the ASTM Powder Data File)

$d = 3.38$ Å   100, corresponding to the planes   2 1 0
$d = 2.20$ Å   75   1 2 1
$d = 2.88$ Å   25   0 0 1

These intensity ratios occur, at least in the same order, in the kaolin zone, but not outside it.

Line 3·4 decreases very rapidly. Line 2·21 first grows, then also decreases from 5·86 mm on, where the line 2·88 becomes dominant. This is a typical orientation phenomenon of the mullite crystals.

Planes 1 2 1 make an angle of about 50° with the c axis of the mullite. From this orientation and from the method of analysis used, it is concluded that the interface is parallel to these planes and that the mullite is formed with its c axis making an angle of 50° with the interface.

Figure 8 shows that line 2·88Å passes through a maximum at 5·97 mm. This line corresponds to the planes perpendicular to the c axis, which is in the direction of the diffusion perpendicular to the interface. This phenomenon is also evident in Fig. 9. In the Al₂O₃ zone the crystals are aligned perpendicularly to the interface.

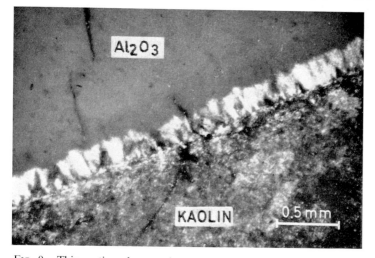

FIG. 9.—Thin section along a plane perpendicular to the reaction face
(polarized light)

5. SUMMARY AND CONCLUSIONS

5.1 SiO₂/Al₂O₃ Reaction 1,600°C. 2 h

Optical investigations were made at the contact of pellets prepared from quartz and bayerite preheated at 1,300°C., and thereby completely converted into cristobalite and α-Al₂O₃.

5.11 Experiment 1

Figure 6 gives the total SiO₂, total Al₂O₃, α-Al₂O₃ and cristobalite at each point of the interface, as determined from fluorescence analyses and from X-ray crystallographic investigations. The percentage of mullite (curve M) (calculated) and the variation of the height of the mullite peaks (3·4Å, 2·21Å, 2·88Å) were plotted. From these data and from the Figs. 1 and 2 the following conclusions are drawn:

(1) SiO₂ diffuses into Al₂O₃, and Al₂O₃ into SiO₂. However, if Al₂O₃ has not been sintered for a long time, the penetration of SiO₂ into the Al₂O₃ zone is much more considerable than vice versa.

(2) Thin sections cut along a plane perpendicular to the reaction zone show that it consists essentially of two zones laying one each side of the reference wire.

(3) On the SiO₂ side is a layer of about 0.2 mm depth consisting of cristobalite and glass.

(4) Starting from the reference wire in the direction of the Al_2O_3, mullite appeared and attains a maximum at 5·87 mm corresponding to 80·5% of mullite.

(5) Figures 4, 5 and 6 clearly show the orientation of the crystals. At the point of contact the planes 2 1 0 (line 3·4Å) are oriented parallel to the reaction face. Later on the crystals develop perpendicular to plane 1 2 1 (line 2·21Å). In this case the c axis makes an angle of 40° with the direction of diffusion of the SiO_2 into the Al_2O_3 (see Fig. 5).

(6) At greater depth, line 2·88Å, corresponding to plane 0 0 1, becomes dominant. From that point the crystals grow parallel to the c axis in the direction of the diffusion of SiO_2 into Al_2O_3.

5.12 Experiment 2

From the results of experiments 1 and 2 it is concluded that the formation of mullite depends strongly on the degree of sintering of the Al_2O_3. Pressing the testpiece at higher pressure, followed by heating at 1,300°C., reduces the penetration of the SiO_2 into Al_2O_3 by a factor greater than two.

5.13 Experiment 3

From Fig. 8 and the photographs of the thin sections (Fig. 9) it can be concluded that the SiO_2 (probably the SiO_2 contained in the vitreous phase of the kaolin) diffuses into the Al_2O_3 phase. Starting from the kaolin zone (left in the figure) the amount of mullite remains constant up to 5·76 mm, i.e. about up to the position of the reference wire. It is also beyond 5·76 mm that α-Al_2O_3 appears and that mullite and glass are formed from Al_2O_3 and SiO_2 from kaolin and from α-Al_2O_3.

The amount of mullite passes through a minimum at 5·84 mm and then increases, which can be explained by the fact that the importance of unattacked α-Al_2O_3 grows relatively with distance from the kaolin zone and that part of the transformed α-Al_2O_3 has dissolved in the glass and so could not contribute to the formation of mullite.

The situation is different at 5·86 mm, where the amount of glass is very small and practically all the SiO_2 has combined with α-Al_2O_3 to form mullite. At 5·88 mm no more glass forms; all the SiO_2 combines with Al_2O_3 to form mullite, and the amount of mullite is at its maximum. Beyond 5·88 mm mullite decreases slowly with the amount of SiO_2. At 6·06 mm the mullite line is no longer seen, whereas the amount of Al_2O_3 grows and that of SiO_2 decreases, which seems to indicate that in this zone a compound is formed, which is amorphous or at least too poorly crystallized to be identified by X-ray analysis.

5.2 Orientation of Mullite in the Presence of α-Al$_2$O$_3$

As soon as silica penetrates in the Al$_2$O$_3$ zone, line 3·4Å (corresponding to plane 2 1 0) decreases rapidly; line 2·21Å increases. The crystals grow in the c direction, the latter axis making an angle with the interface equal to the angle it makes with the planes 1 2 1 (50°).

The 2·21Å peak then decreases and the 2·88Å peak (planes perpendicular to c) becomes dominant. The crystals grow in the direction of the c axis, which is now the direction of the diffusion of SiO$_2$ into Al$_2$O$_3$.

REFERENCES

1. Etudes Comparatives d'Examens par Microscopie Electronique et par Rayons X dans le Système SiO$_2$. Al$_2$O$_3$. (en coll. avec L. Degueldre) (Symposium Chimie des Solides, Madrid: 1956).
2. L'action de CaO sur les Réfractaires Silico-Alumineux (en coll. avec R. Wollast), *Bull. Soc. Franç. Céram.* (50), janv.-mars 1961.

17—Décomposition à Haute Température des Solutions Solides du Type 2CaO(Al,Fe)$_2$O$_3$

By V. Cirilli et F. Abbattista

Institut de Chimie Générale et Appliqué et de Métallurgie de l'École Polytechnique de Turin (Italie)

RÉSUMÉ

L62

Dans ces solutions solides, la formation de liquide commence à une température plus basse si l'atmosphère est réductrice; ceci résulte de la formation de phases moins riches en oxygène. On fait ressortir le rôle important joué par ces solutions solides dans le développement des propriétés du ciment portland, du ciment fondu et des réfractaires de magnésie. On accorde une attention particulière à la nature de la phase ferrite Ca-Al dans les ciments hydrauliques.

The decomposition at high temperatures of solid solutions of the type 2CaO (Al,Fe)$_2$O$_3$

In these solid solutions liquid formation begins at a lower temperature if the atmosphere is reducing; this results from the formation of phases less rich in oxygen. The importance of these solid solutions in determining the properties of portland cement, ciment fondu and magnesite refractories is emphasized; particular attention is paid to the nature of the Ca-Al ferrite phase in hydraulic cements.

Die Hochtemperaturzersetzung von festen Lösungen des Typs 2CaO(Al,Fe)$_2$O$_3$

Bei diesen festen Lösungen bildet sich die Flüssigkeit bei tieferen Temperaturen aus, wenn die Atmosphäre reduzierend ist. Der Grund dafür ist die Bildung einer an Sauerstoff armen Phase. Die Wichtigkeit dieser festen Lösungen für die Bestimmung der Eigenschaften von Portlandzement, Schmelzzement und Magnesitsteinen wird hevorgehoben. Besondere Aufmerksamkeit wird der Ca-Al-Ferrit-Phase in hydraulischen Zementen gewidmet.

1. INTRODUCTION

Lorsqu'on considère les constituents du clinker des ciments Portland, on indique avec la dénomination de " phase ferrique " la solution solide dont la composition est comprise de règle entre les limites 4CaO.Al$_2$O$_3$.Fe$_2$O$_3$ et 6CaO.2Al$_2$O$_3$.Fe$_2$O$_3$.

En réalité les limites de composition d'une telle phase sont bien plus étendues et, à partir du composé 2CaO.Fe$_2$O$_3$, elles arrivent jusqu'à une solution solide du type 2CaO.(Fe,Al)$_2$O$_3$, dans la quelle le pourcentage de Fe$_2$O$_3$ substitué par Al$_2$O$_3$ est à peu pres du 70%.[1] De phases de composition analogue peuvent être retrouvées comme constituents des ciments alumineux; en outre le ferrite bicalcique

259

est usuellement présent dans le matériel intergranulair qui ciment les grains de périclase.

La température de fusion du ferrite bicalcique correspond à 1435°C.; la phase de composition $4CaO.Al_2O_3.Fe_2O_3$ présente une température de commencement de formation de liquide à 1395°C., tandis qu'en augmentant la quantité d'alumine cette température décroît ultérieurement.

Pour la composition $6CaO.2Al_2O_3.Fe_2O_3$ le liquide commence à paraître à 1365°C.[2]

Ces températures de fusion ont été déterminées en présence de l'air, dans les conditions d'expérience normales; si l'on travaille en atmosphère réductrice on peut en effet remarquer que les températures de commencement de formation de liquide sont bien inférieures.

Dans de travaux précédents[3] exécutés dans notre Institut, on a eu la possibilité d'établir que la température de commencement de fusion descend, pour le ferrite bicalcique, jusqu'à 1070°C., et, pour le solide $4CaO.Al_2O_3.Fe_2O_3$ (brownmillerite), jusqu'à 1160°C.; cette température s'élève jusqu'à 1175°C. pour la solution solide plus riche en Al_2O_3, en proximité de la composition limite.

La diminution de la température à laquelle paraît du liquide en atmosphère réductrice est évidemment référable à la formation de phases différentes, ayant une téneur d'oxygène plus petite et se formant pour altération des constituents du clinker de Portland, des ciments alumineux et des matériaux intergranulaires des réfractaires magnésiques.

La littérature donne des renseignements à propos de la possibilité de perte d'oxygène dans le réchauffement à l'air du ferrite bicalcique,[4] tandis que rien de semblable a été référé pour les solutions solides ternaires. Du problème nous allons nous intéresser dans les lignes suivantes, dans lesquelles il sera nécessaire, pour claireté d'exposition, de rappeler quelques résultats de nos travaux précédants.

2. ÉQUILIBRE DE RÉDUCTION DU FERRITE BICALCIQUE

La réaction de réduction du ferrite bicalcique jusqu'à la température de 1050°C. est bien connue, comme il résulte des travaux publiés par R. SCHENCK et al[5] et par nous-mêmes:[6] Elle peut être écrite dans la façon suivante.

$$2CaO.Fe_2O_3 + 3CO \rightleftharpoons 2Fe + 2CaO + 3CO_2$$

La réaction procède, c'est-à-dire, sans formation de phases contenants du fer à l'état ferreux. Le pourcentage d'anhydride carbonique dans la phase gazeuse d'équilibre se modifie avec la température, comme on a indiqué dans la troisième colonne du Tableau 1.

Tableau 1

Composition de l'Atmosphère Gazeuse ($CO_2 \%$) pour les Équilibres: Wüstite–Fer, Ferrite Bicalcique–Fer, Solution Solide entre Chaux et Wüstite–Fer.

Température (°C)	FeO/Fe	$2CaO.Fe_2O_3/Fe$	(FeO + CaO)/Fe
800°	34,8	—	34,0
900°	31,0	22,2	29,3
1000°	27,5	21,6	24,2
1050°	—	21,2	21,6
1100°	25,2	—	20,1

Dans le même tableau (deuxième colonne) on a indiqué la variation du pourcentage de CO_2, en fonction de la température, pour la réaction d'équilibre:

$$FeO + CO \rightleftharpoons Fe + CO_2$$

Avec ces valeurs on a tracé les graphiques (*a*) et (*b*) de la Fig. 1.

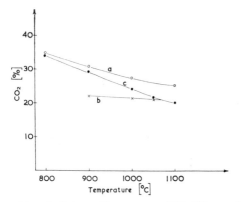

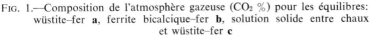

FIG. 1.—Composition de l'atmosphère gazeuse ($CO_2 \%$) pour les équilibres: wüstite–fer **a**, ferrite bicalcique–fer **b**, solution solide entre chaux et wüstite–fer **c**

De l'allure des deux courbes on doit déduire que le ferrite bicalcique a une tension d'oxygène inférieure à celle de l'oxyde ferreux (wüstite) et que la formation de telle phase n'est pas possible au cours de la réduction du ferrite bicalcique.

Une série de recherches que nous avons exécutées [7] a démontré que la wüstite à la limite inférieure de l'oxydation peut dissoudre la chaux en quantités croissantes avec la température.

La solution saturée en chaux a naturellement une tension d'oxygène inférieure à celle de la wüstite, comme on déduit des valeurs du pourcentage de CO_2 en équilibre (quatrième colonne du tableau 1).   La courbe c de la Fig. 1 a été tracée sur la base de ces valeurs et, par conséquent, elle se trouve plus en bas que celle qui si réfère aux conditions d'équilibre du système FeO–Fe.

La courbe b rencontre la courbe c à 1070°C.; on déduit qu'à cette température peuvent coéxister en équilibre avec la phase gazeuse les suivantes phases solides: ferrite bicalcique, solution solide saturée de chaux en wüstite, fer et chaux.

Plus exactement la chaux contient en solution de petites quantités de wüstite.   Coéxistant quatre phases solides et une phase gazeuse le dégré de liberté du système est zéro; la wüstite, en équilibre avec le fer, se trouve évidemment au dégré inférieur de l'oxydation.

On remarque cependant par voie expérimentale qu'à la température de 1070°C. le pourcentage de CO_2 est bien plus élevé qu'on ne puisse déduire par extrapolation et qu'on a provoqué dans le solide de très évident processus de fusion.

On peut expliquer ce phénomène en admettant qu'à la température de 1070°C. se vérifie la formation d'un liquide eutectique dans lequel il peut se dissoudre tout au moins une partie du ferrite bicalcique, avec une conséquente augmentation de la tension d'oxygène.   Le fer, par conséquent, va naturellement disparaître. Cette hypothése est en accord avec la courbe isothermique de réduction qui peut être déterminée en expérimentant à température supérieure à 1070°C.

L'isotherme de la Fig. 2 correspond aux valeurs du Tableau 2, se référant à un expériment exécuté à 1100°C.

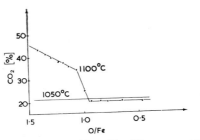

FIG. 2.—Composition de l'atmosphère d'équilibre au cours de la reduction du ferrite bicalcique à 1050°C. et à 1100°C.

L'isotherme montre un trait initial avec une certaine inclinaison, un deuxième bien plus incliné, dans les environs du rapport $O/Fe=1$, et en suite une ligne horizontale jusqu'à la fin de la réduction.

Tableau 2

Composition de l'Atmosphère d'Équilibre au Cours de la Réduction du Ferrite Bicalcique à 1100°C.

O/Fe	$CO_2(\%)$	O/Fe	$CO_2(\%)$
1,40	43,1	0,99	24,9
1,34	41,4	0,93	20,1
1,29	39,7	0,84	20,2
1,22	37,9	0,78	20,0
1,18	37,6	0,65	20,2
1,13	35,6	0,46	19,9
1,06	34,3	—	—

On peut expliquer l'ensemble des phénomènes dans la façon suivante: le premier trait doit correspondre à perte d'oxygène de la phase liquide, dont la tension d'oxygéne va diminuer en proportion avec la quantité du fer ferrique qui disparaît; le deuxième trait, tout de même incliné, se réfère à la réduction d'une solution saturée de chaux en wüstite au dégré maximum de l'oxydation; le trait horizontal regarde l'équilibre entre le fer à l'état métallique et la solution solide entre la wüstite à la limite inférieure de l'oxydation et la chaux.

A température plus élevée, le phénomène est tout-à-fait analogue, mais le premier trait se trouve déplacé en correspondence de quantités plus élevées de CO_2, tandis que le trait horizontal est déplacé en correspondence de plus hautes quantités de monoxoyde de carbone.

En prenant en considération le pourcentage de l'anhydride carbonique des points posés aux extremités du trait incliné intermédiare, on obtient les valeurs du Tableau 3, qui indiquent la composition de la phase gazeuse en équilibre avec la solution saturée de chaux en wüstite à la limite supérieure de l'oxydation et celle en équilibre avec la solution saturée de chaux en wüstite au dégré d'oxydation minimum.

Si l'on considére les solutions de chaux et de wüstite à la limite supérieure de l'oxydation, pour la composition qu'ici nous intérese (50% moléculaire FeO), aux températures supérieures à 1100°C. doivent prendre origine de quantités croissantes de liquide; le diagramme de Fig. 3, exécuté sur la base des valeurs des Tableaux 1 et 3, a été par conséquent indiqué en partie avec des hachures.

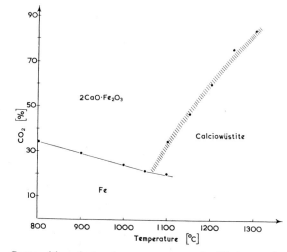

Fig. 3.—Composition de la phase gazeuse en équilibre avec les solutions saturées de chaux en wüstite

Tableau 3

Composition de la Phase Gazeuse en Équilibre avec la Solution Solide Saturée de Chaux en Wüstite à la Limite Supérieure et Inférieure de l'Oxydation

Wüstite à la limite supérieure de l'oxydation		Wüstite à la limite inférieure de l'oxydation	
Température ($^\circ$C)	CO_2 (%)	Température ($^\circ$C)	CO_2 (%)
1100°	34	800°	34,0
1150°	47	900°	29,3
1200°	60	1000°	24,2
1250°	76	1050°	21,6
1300°	84	1100°	20,1

Le graphique, dans son ensemble, représente les rapports de coexistence entre les solutions de chaux et wüstite, le ferrite bicalcique et le fer.

Des mesurations de tension d'oxygène et des observations röntgénographiques exécutées dans notre Institut, dont il serait trop long référer en détail, nous ont permis de définir les limites de solubilité de la chaux dans la wüstite au dégré d'oxydation minimum: à 800°C. le 2,5% mol. de CaO; à 900°C. le 4,5%; à 1000°C. le 6,7%, à 1100°C. le 9,8%. L'oxyde de calcium, à son tour, est capable de dissoudre de petites quantités de wüstite. Au dessous de 700°C. la solubilité de la chaux dans la wüstite est tout-à-fait négligeable.

Entre les solutions solides de chaux et de wüstite à la limite inférieure de l'oxydation il y a un eutectique à la température de 1120°C., en correspondence à peu près du 30% mol. de CaO.

Pour ce qui regarde les solutions solides de chaux dans la wüstite à la limite supérieure de l'oxydation, on ne retrouve jusqu'à présent dans la littérature des valeurs exactes. Sur la base de déterminations très récentes[10] on peut admettre que la solubilité soit bien plus élevée, peut-être plus que le double de la solubilité qui se vérifie pour la wüstite pauvre en oxygéne.

On déduit du graphique de la Fig. 3 qu'une solution solide saturée de chaux en wüstite riche en oxygène, au cours de refroidissement, doit se résoudre avec ségregation de ferrite bicalcique.

Les rapports de coexistence entre les oxydes de fer, le fer, la chaux et le ferrite bicalcique peuvent être indiqués comme dans la Fig. 4, dans laquelle on a simplifié quelques détails. On n'a pas pris en consideration, en effet, la formation du composé CaO.3FeO. Fe_2O_3, dont l'existence est limitée dans un petit champ de température et de pression d'oxygène,[8] et celle du ferrite monocalcique, dont l'existence est conditionnée par une très élevée tension d'oxygène.

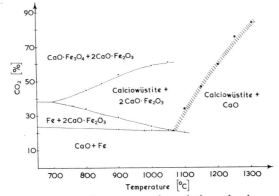

FIG. 4.—Rapports de coexistence entre les solutions de chaux et wüstite, le ferrite bicalcique et le fer

3. ÉQUILIBRES DE RÉDUCTION DES SOLUTIONS SOLIDES 2CaO.(Al,Fe)$_2$O$_3$.

Le problème qu'on a traité jusqu'à ici se réfère au ferrite bicalcique, c'est-a-dire à l'un des termes posés à l'extrémité du champ de solutions solides en examen.

Nous allons maintenant pendre en considération la réduction, à différentes températures, d'un des termes intermédiaires de la série des solutions, dans lequel la moitié des atomes de fer a été substituée par des atomes d'aluminium, par conséquent de composition 4CaO. $Al_2O_3.Fe_2O_3$. Du sujet l'un de nous[6] et A. BURDESE[7] se sont occupés, il y a quelques années.

Jusqu'à la température de 1100°C. la réduction amène directement à fer métallique, sans formation de phases intermédiaires contenant du fer bivalent; dans la solution solide ternaire, la quantité d'alumine augmente par conséquent jusqu'à rejoindre la valeur limite, tandis que l'excès de chaux est mis en liberté. Par ultérieure réduction c'est l'aluminate tricalcique qui va se mettre en liberté. Les valeurs de la composition de la phase gazeuse ($CO_2\%$), en équilibre avec le solide à 1100°C., sont indiquées dans le Tableau 4.

La marche de la réduction change complètement pour des températures plus élevées, par exemple 1160°C.; les résultats obtenus à cette température ont été résumés dans le même tableau.

Tableau 4

Équilibres de Réduction de la Solution Solide de Composition $4CaO.Al_2O_3.Fe_2O_3$

Température (°C)							
1100°				1160°			
O/Fe	*CO_2 (%)*	*O/Fe*	*CO_2(%)*	*O/Fe*	*CO_2(%)*	*O/Fe*	*CO_2 (%)*
1,47	16,8	0,74	16,1	1,39	31,8	0,98	20,1
1,09	16,3	0,64	15,9	1,32	30,1	0,93	18,2
1,00	16,3	0,53	16,1	1,15	29,3	0,75	18,0
0,91	16,0	0,43	16,0	1,04	28,0	0,58	17,9

Avec les valeurs du Tableau 4 on a tracé le graphique de la Fig. 5. L'allure de la courbe obtenue avec les valeurs mesurées a 1160°C.

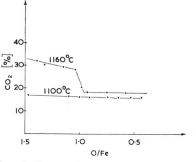

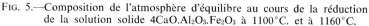

FIG. 5.—Composition de l'atmosphère d'équilibre au cours de la réduction de la solution solide $4CaO.Al_2O_3.Fe_2O_3$ à 1100°C. et à 1160°C.

se présente qualitativement analogue à celle observée pour le ferrite bicalcique à températures supérieures à 1070°C.; elle peut être expliquée d'une façon semblable si l'on prend en considération le graphique de la Fig. 6.

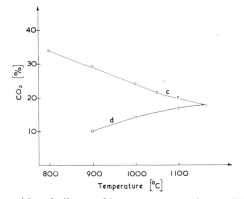

FIG. 6.—Composition de l'atmosphère gazeuse pour les equilibres: solution solide entre chaux et wüstite et le fer **c**, et entre les solutions solides $2CaO.(Al,Fe)_2O_3$ et le fer **d**

La courbe **c** représente la composition ($CO_2\%$) de l'atmosphère en équilibre avec le système $(FeO + CaO)$–Fe, tandis que la courbe **d** représente la composition de la phase gazeuse en équilibre avec les solides $2CaO.(Fe,Al)_2O_3$–Fe. Pour le dernier équilibre la composition de l'atmosphère gazeuse varie en fonction de la température, comme on a indiqué dans le Tableau 5.

Tableau 5

Composition de la Phase Gazeuse en Équilibre avec les Solutions Solides $2CaO.(Fe, Al)_2O_3$ et le Fer.

Solution solide avec 50% de Al_2O_3		Solution solide avec 70% de Al_2O_3	
Température (°C)	CO_2 (%)	Température (°C)	CO_2 (%)
900°	10,2	900°	8,2
1000°	14,3	1000°	13,3
1100°	16,8	1100°	16,0

Les courbes **c** et **d** se rencontrent à la température de 1160°C., à laquelle il serait possible avoir coexistence de la wüstite à la limite inférieure de l'oxydation, de la solution solide ternaire, de la chaux et du fer. En réalité on a formation d'un liquide eutectique qui présente, à cause de la dissolution de fer ferrique, une tension d'oxygéne bien plus élevée qu'on ne puisse admettre pour le solide en équilibre.

L'atmosphère gazeuse est par là plus riche en CO_2; en effet la valeur obtenue par extrapolation (et se référant au solide) devrait être à peu près correspondente à 18% de CO_2, tandis qu'on trouve expérimentalement, une valeur de 32% de CO_2.

Pour la solution solide limite (70% d'oxyde ferrique substitué par alumine) la température de commencement de formation de liquide est bien proche à 1175°C. La composition de l'atmosphère gazeuse ($CO_2\%$) en équilibre avec les solides $2CaO.(Al,Fe)_2O_3$–$3CaO.Al_2O_3$–Fe est indiquée dans le Tableau 5.

Jusqu'ici nous avons pris en considération l'allure de la réduction des solutions solides $2CaO(Fe,Al)_2O_3$ pour différentes compositions et pour différentes températures. On a tout de même indiqué les raisons pour lesquelles en atmosphére réductrice les températures de fusion sont bien plus basses que l'on n'observe en conditions oxydantes. Mais il est de remarquable intérêt de déterminer quelle est la variation avec la température de la tension d'oxygène du liquide qui peut prendre origine des solutions à différentes compositions.

La mesuration directe résulte tout à fait problématique, tandis qu'on peut aisément exécuter une mesuration indirecte, à l'aide de la détermination du rapport CO_2/CO de l'atmosphère d'équilibre.

Par extrapolation du premier trait incliné des isothermes de réduction jusqu'au rapport $O/Fe = 1,5$ il a été possible d'évaluer la composition de la phase gazeuse d'équilibre au commencement de la réduction: les valeurs ont été indiquées dans le Tableau 6.

Tableau 6

Composition de la Phase Gazeuse et Tensions d'Oxygène des Solutions Solides $2CaO.(Fe, Al)_2O_3$ au Commencement de la Reduction

2CaO.Fe$_2$O$_3$			Solution solide avec le 50% de Fe$_2$O$_3$ substitué par Al$_2$O$_3$			Solution solide avec le 70% de Fe$_2$O$_3$ substitué par Al$_2$O$_3$		
Temp. (°C)	$CO_2(\%)$	p_{O_2} (atm.)	Temp. (°C)	$CO_2(\%)$	p_{O_2} (atm.)	Temp. (°C)	$CO_2(\%)$	p_{O_2} (atm.)
1100°	46	$2,5.10^{-13}$	1200°	38	$3,2.10^{-12}$	1200°	28	$1,5.10^{-12}$
1150°	52	$2,3.10^{-12}$	1250°	55	$6,8.10^{-11}$	—	—	—
1200°	65	$3,5.10^{-11}$	1300°	80	$3,0.10^{-9}$	1300°	55	$2,8.10^{-10}$
1250°	82	$9,5.10^{-10}$	1350°	89	$4,5.10^{-8}$	1350°	82	$1,4.10^{-8}$
1300°	90	$2,5.10^{-8}$						

Avec les valeurs de la pression d'oxygène en fonction de la température on a exécuté le graphique de Fig. 7.

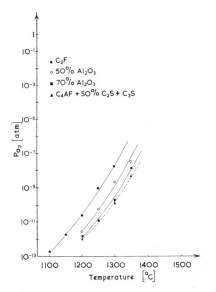

FIG. 7.—Tensions d'oxygène des solutions solides $2CaO.(Al,Fe)_2O_3$ au commencement de la réduction

En extrapolant ces courbes, ou bien les courbes équivalentes : logarithme de la pression d'oxygène versus le réciproque de la température absolue, jusqu'à la température de 1500°C. on peut déduire qu'à cette température la tension d'oxygène du ferrite bicalcique devrait être bien proche à une atmosphère, celle de la solution avec le 50% de Fe_2O_3 substitué par Al_2O_3 (brownmillerite) à 0,01 – 0,1 atm. et quelque peu inférieure la tension d'oxygène de la solution solide plus riche en alumine.

4. STABILITÉ À HAUTE TEMPÉRATURE DES SOLUTIONS TERNAIRES

Ce qu'on a dit explique avec claireté l'allure de la réduction par laquelle il y a la possibilité de formation de phases avec du fer bivalent dans les ciments alumineux, dans lesquels la quantité de FeO—libre ou combiné—est de quelques unités pour cent, et même dans le clinker du ciment Portland, où la quantité d'oxyde ferreux est de règle de quelques parties pour mille.

Dans la marche industrielle de cuite du ciment le contenu d'oxygène dans les fumées est en effet de quelques unités pour cent et la pression paritiale d'oxygène est par conséquent inférieure à un dixième d'atmosphère.

Dans le cas des ciments on peut avancer l'objection qu'on est en présence, outre que de phase ferrique, même de silicate de calcium et de composés contenants de la silice et que ces derniers, pouvant se dissoudre dans le liquide, devraient en diminuer la tension d'oxygène. Les valeurs indiquées dans le Tableau 7 ont été obtenues en rechauffant en atmosphère réductrice la solution solide $4CaO.Al_2O_3$. Fe_2O_3 à laquelle on avait ajouté un poids correspondent d'un mélange des silicates $3CaO.SiO_2$ et $2CaO.SiO_2$, en parties égales. On peut en déduire que la tension d'oxygène est diminuée, mais pas de façon telle qu'on doit modifier substantiellement les interprétations qu'on a données aux phénomènes ci-dessus décrits.

Tableau 7

Composition de la Phase Gazeuse et Tension d'Oxygène de la Solution Solide $4CaO.Al_2O_3.Fe_2O_3$ Mélangée avec un Poids correspondant de $3CaO.SiO_2 + 2CaO.SiO_2$

	Température ($^\circ C$)			
	1200°	1250°	1300°	1350°
CO_2 (%)	25	34	51	76
p_{O_2} (atm.)	$1,1.10^{-12}$	$1,2.10^{-11}$	2.10^{-10}	$6,8.10^{-9}$

Avec les valeurs du Tableau 7 on a tracé la courbe de Fig. 7, indiquée avec des hachures.

Ce qu'on a dit à propos de la possibilité de décomposition des solutions solides $2CaO.(Al,Fe)_2O_3$ nous rend raison des changements de couleur qu'on peut provoquer dans un clinker de ciment Portland, losqu'on le soumit à de différents traitements thermiques.

On devrait se référer, plus opportunément, à un clinker obtenu à partir de SiO_2, Al_2O_3, Fe_2O_3, CaO de haute pureté, à fin d'éliminer l'interférence d'autres oxydes, par exemple des oxydes de manganèse. La quantité de Fe_2O_3 doit être tout de même limitée, par exemple 1%, puisque les transformations qu'on prendra en examen ne sont pas probablement complètes et un excès de phase ferrique rendrait plus difficile évaluer les différences de couleur.

Un mélange des quatre oxydes en rapports correspondants à un clinker normal avec 1% de Fe_2O_3 est nettement rouge. Si le solide est rechauffé longtemps à 1500°C. en atmosphère gazeuse avec 2 ÷ 3% d'oxygène et trempé en eau sa couleur tend légèrement au vert. Ça dépend de la formation d'oxyde ferreux qui, certainement en très petite quantité, peut se dissoudre dans les composants du clinker, ou bien, avec plus de probabilité, donne origine à une phase vitreuse. On doit naturellement prévoir que tout au moins une partie de la wüstite peuve se retrouver libre, finement dispersée. L'oxyde ferreux, prévu son méchanisme de formation, est plus exactemente une solution solide de chaux en wüstite oxydée. Par effet du procédé de trempe, cette solution est, à température ordinaire, bien plus riche en chaux et en oxygène qu'il ne puisse correspondre aux conditions d'équilibre. En effet si le clinker est rechauffé au près de 1000°C. en absence totale d'oxygène et successivement refroidi, jusqu'à la température ordinaire, la couleur tendante au vert aura changé en couleur rose pâle.

C'est-à-dire que l'excès de chaux et d'oxygène a été ségrégé sous forme de ferrite bicalcique, ce qui correspond à la courbe hachée de Fig. 4, ou bien plus difficilement sous forme de solution solide ternaire.

Le diagramme d'état postule qu'à températures inférieures à 700°C. la phase contenant du fer bivalent se décompose complètement en ferrite bicalcique (ou en solution solide ternaire) et en fer, ou bien en calcium–magnétite en dépendance de la pression d'oxygène dans l'atmosphère au contact avec les solides. En présence d'air évidemment la phase contenant du fer bivalent se transformerait complètement en phase ferrique. Mais on observe que la tendance spontanée à la décomposition, en absence d'oxygène, à températures rélativement basses est très petite et la chaux agit par conséquent comme stabilisateur de la wüstite. Encore plus petite est la tendance à la décomposition de la partie d'oxyde ferreux qui est éventuellement dissoue dans les autre composants du clinker et qui est devenue un constituant de la phase vitreuse.

Ce qu'on a écrit ci-dessus à propos de la stabilité à haute température du ferrite bicalcique joue un rôle très important dans le comportement des réfractaires en magnésie.

Le ferrite bicalcique, ou éventuellement la solution solide ternaire pauvre en alumine, est l'un des matériaux intergranulaires que plus fréquemment cimente les grains de périclase.

A température très élevée, à cause de la perte d'oxygène se forme un liquide eutectique chaux–wüstite qui, en présence d'excès de magnésie, se transforme rapidement en un mélange de chaux et de solution solide wüstite–magnésie. Considérant absents des autres oxydes, à cause de la dissociation du ferrite bicalcique, on pourra obtenir une remarquable amélioration de la réfractariété. Dans le système CaO–MgO la température minimum de formation de liquide est à peu près de 2300°C.

Lorsque le réfractaire est utilisé en procédés dans lesquels se forment des gas réducteurs, l'altération du ferrite bicalcique peut avoir lieu en façon imposante même à des températures rélativement non élevées, selon le schéma que nous avons indiqué. Du point de vue pratique c'est d'intérêt particulier l'influence que les conditions d'usage, dans les procédés basiques d'affinage de la fonte, peuvent avoir sur le réfractaire.

Dans ce procédé le réfractaire travaille à température très élevée, de règle comprise entre 1600° et 1800°C., et dans le même temps, étant soumis à l'action du metal liquide, se trouve, tout au moins dans la période initiale de l'affinage, en contact avec des gas riches en oxyde de carbone.

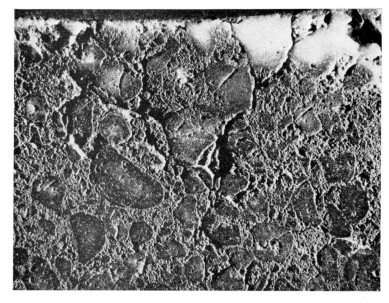

Fig. 8—Section d'un creuset de magnésie contenant à peu près 8% de ferrite bicalcique

Dans la zone tout proche au metal liquide se forme une couche très réfractaire, tandis que dans la zone immédiatement inférieure le matériel est partiellement fondu. Ou peut observer un tel phénomène dans la photographie de Fig. 8 (×8) obtenue sur la section d'un creuset de magnésie contenant chaux et oxyde ferrique en quantité correspondante à peu près à 8% ferrite bicalcique.

La température du bain métallique pendant l'affinage exécuté dans notre laboratoire était proche à 1750°C. En contact avec le métal on a eu formation d'une couche blanche constituée par oxyde de magnésium contenant de la wüstite en solution et de petites quantités d'oxyde de calcium dispersées dans la masse.

La zone immédiatement au dessous correspond à une couche où

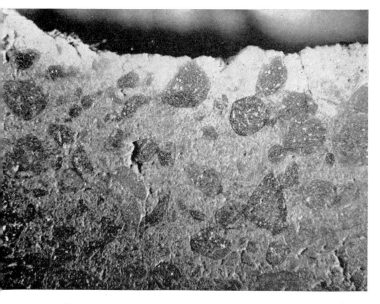

FIG. 9.—Section d'un creuset de magnésie contenant une quantité de ferrite bicalcique inférieure à 3%

le ferrite bicalcique est en train de se dissocier. On a remarqué un comportement analogue sur un réfractaire obtenu à partir de magnésie précipitée de l'eau de mer et avec une quantité de ferrite bicalcique de quelque peu inférieure à 3% (Fig. 9; ×8). On peut voir la couche blanche en contact avec le métal; la couche intermédiaire montre un commencement de décomposition des matériaux intergranulaires.

On doit conclure qu'un traitement réducteur à température élevée produit une remarquable amélioration de la réfractariété des réfractaires de magnésie, où les matériaux intergranulaires sont constitués de quantités prévalentes de ferrite bicalcique. Le processus se déroule par une remarquable transformation des matériaux intergranulaires, ce qui peut en altérer les caractéristiques liantes.

BIBLIOGRAPHIE

1. Swayze, H. A., *Amer. J. Sci.,* **244,** 1, 1946; Cirilli, V., et Burdese, A., *Ric. Scient.,* **21,** 1185, 1951; Malquori, G., et Cirilli, V., " Proc. 3rd Symposium on the Chemistry of Cement " (Londres: 1952).
2. Swayze, H. A., loc cit.
3. Cirilli, V., *Ric. Scient.,* **17,** 942, 1947; Cirilli, V., et Burdese, A., " Proc. Int. Symposium on the Reactivity of Solids " (Gothenburg), **2,** 867, 1954.
4. Kühl, H., et Rasch, R., *Zement,* **20,** 812, 1931; White, J., *J. Iron Steel Inst.,* **27,** 1, 1938.
5. Schenck, R., Franz, H., et Willeke, H., *Z. anorg Chem.,* **184,** 1, 1929.
6. Cirilli, V., *Ric. Scient.,* **17,** 942, 1947.
7. Cirilli, V., et Burdese, A., " Proc. 3rd Symposium on the Reactivity of Solids " (Gothenburg), **2,** 867, 1954.
8. Cirilli, V., et Burdese, A., *La Metallurgia Italiana,* **44,** 371, 1952.
9. Burdese, A., *Atti Accad. Sci. Torino,* **88,** 233, 1953–54.
10. Burdese, A., *Atti Accad. Sci. Torino,* **97,** 1962–63.

18—Reactions and Decomposition of Foreign Inclusions in Pottery Bodies

By R. JOHNSON

Amstan Overseas Ltd., Paris 8e

ABSTRACT
E6/D7

Deals with the reactions and decomposition of certain materials present, intentionally and unintentionally, in pottery bodies, which result in the evolution of gas during firing, and indicates how these gases can be troublesome if the reactions and decompositions are not completed before the maximum firing temperature is reached.

Réactions et décomposition d'inclusions étrangères dans les pâtes de céramique fine

Les réactions et la décomposition de certaines matières présentes, intentionnellement ou non, dans des pâtes de céramique fine, et qui provoquent un dégagement de gaz au cours de la cuisson, sont étudiées. Les difficultés provenant de ces gaz, lorsque les réactions et la décomposition ne sont pas terminées avant que ne soit atteinte la température de cuisson maximale, sont exposées.

Reaktionen und Zersetzung von Fremdeinschlüssen in Töpfereimassen

Reaktionen und Zersetzung einiger Minerale, die absichtlich oder unabsichtlich in Töpfereimassen vorhanden sind, werden besprochen. Sie ergeben eine Gasentwicklung während des Brandes, und es wird gezeigt, wie dieses Gas zu Fehlern führen kann, wenn die Reaktionen und Zersetzungen nicht abgeschlossen sind, bevor die maximale Brenntemperatur erreicht ist.

1. INTRODUCTION

Certain manufacturing faults, sometimes attributed to overfiring, may be due to the evolution of gases from chemical decompositions or reactions, at temperatures when the porosity and permeability of bodies are so small that the gases cannot escape very easily. With the high temperatures involved, and the body softening, these gases can exert pressures sufficient to blister or bloat the body.

The gases may originate from impurities associated with the raw materials or from certain materials specially added so that the casting-slip may have satisfactory rheological properties.

Concerning these impurities with raw materials, Cornish Stone is likely to contain a small amount of fluorspar. Whether it acts as a flux or not, this fluorspar can react with silica to produce silicon tetrafluoride and its decomposition is likely to be incomplete at normal firing-temperatures.

Wet-ground materials—Cornish stone, felspars, flint or quartz, are quite likely to contain a small amount of calcium carbonate, intentionally added during the grinding, to help to keep the material in suspension. This is not likely to be a source of trouble, because the calcium carbonate will be completely decomposed, well before the maximum firing-temperature of most bodies.

The biggest source of trouble is probably sulphates, and the treatments carried out to counteract their effects on the rheological properties of slips in order to get a slip with acceptable properties.

Clay casting-scrap added to a body mix is quite likely to be slightly contaminated with tiny pieces of plaster pulled away from the mould, and also by the plaster which has been dissolved from the surface of the moulds by the electrolytes in the casting-slip. Some ball clays may also contribute towards the sulphate content of a body. The sulphate from these sources can be reduced by filter pressing—but some techniques of body preparation do not filter-press.

Other sulphate in the casting-slip can come from the cobalt additions which are made to whiten the fired body. This can take the form of precipitating cobalt from a cobalt sulphate solution by the addition of sodium carbonate and adding the resulting suspension of precipitated basic cobalt carbonate in sodium sulphate solution to the blunger.

In the preparation of casting-slip, in addition to the normal sodium carbonate and sodium silicate additions, a barium compound—the carbonate, chloride or hydroxide—may be added to precipitate the sulphate as barium sulphate, in order to get better fluid properties.

The result is that a body can contain substances such as calcium sulphate and barium compounds which may still be decomposing at the maximum firing-temperature.

2. TESTS AND RESULTS

To get some idea of the relative importance of these factors in connection with bloating, the evolution of gases was followed by measuring the losses in weight, on firing, to various temperatures, of specimens prepared from contaminated slips.

Specimens were prepared from the following slips:

(1) Normal vitreous china (no scrap additions)
(2) Normal v.c. $+5\%$ CaF_2
(3) Normal v.c. $+2\cdot5\%$ $CaSO_4$
(4) Normal v.c. $+4\cdot25\%$ $BaSO_4$
(5) Normal v.c. $+2\cdot5\%$ $CaSO_4 + 6\%$ $BaCO_3$
(6) Normal v.c. $+2\cdot5\%$ $CaSO_4 + 4\cdot5\%$ $BaCl_2.2H_2O$

The percentage additions are based on the weight of dry body and were intentionally larger than ever likely to be encountered in practice, in order to follow their decompositions gravimetrically using an ordinary balance. 2·5% $CaSO_4$ and 4·25% $BaSO_4$ are approximately chemically equivalent, and on total decomposition evolve approximately the same quantity of gas. The quantity of barium chloride is that needed theoretically to precipitate the sulphate. The quantity of barium carbonate is purposely in excess of that theoretically required to precipitate the sulphate, but is in proportion to that recommended in practice, because of its comparative insolubility and slowness of reaction. 5% CaF_2 can theoretically cause a loss of weight greater than the others, but the reaction with silica is unlikely to go to completion and this excess of CaF_2 was a guess, to give a loss in weight comparable with the others.

Samples made from these slips were fired to various temperatures and the evolution of gas was indirectly followed by measuring losses in weight. These results, plotted in Fig. 1, show that constant weight has been reached for:

(1) The v.c. body at about 1,150°C.,
(2) The v.c. body with $CaSO_4$ at about 1,200°C.,
(3) The v.c. body with $CaSO_4 + BaCl_2$ between 1,250 and 1,300°C.,

indicating that the decompositions or reactions evolving gases have finished.

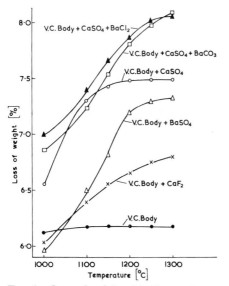

FIG. 1.—Loss of weight of bodies on firing

The other bodies have not reached constant weight, suggesting that chemical reactions and decompositions are continuing.

The results given in Fig. 1 have been used to calculate the percentage decomposition of the materials added to the v.c. body. The method of calculation was as follows:

102·5 parts of body No. 3 consist of
100 parts v.c. body + 2·5 parts of $CaSO_4$
Dividing by 1·025 we get
100 parts of body No. 3 consist of
97·563 parts of v.c. body + 2·437 parts of $CaSO_4$
Loss in weight from 2·437 parts $CaSO_4$ = Loss from 100 parts body No. 3 – Loss from 97·563 parts v.c. body

% Decomposition =

$$\left[\frac{\% \text{ Loss from body No. } 3 - \% \text{ Loss of v.c.} \div 1·025}{\text{Total possible loss from 2·437 parts } CaSO_4} \right] \times 100$$

For the body containing CaF_2, the total possible loss in weight was considered to be due to the evolution of SiF_4 and, for the others, to the loss of SO_3 from the sulphates and CO_2 from the carbonates. For the samples from the slip containing calcium sulphate treated

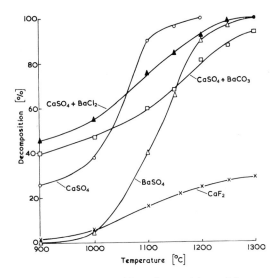

FIG. 2.—Decomposition of materials on firing

with barium chloride, the percentage decomposition curve was compiled, assuming that the decomposition was complete at 1,300°C. The total loss of these samples will be less than theoretically calculated because of the loss of calcium chloride in solution when "dewatering" the slip to form the specimens.

The results in Fig. 2 indicate that of the additions made to the vitreous china body:

(1) The $CaSO_4$ is completely decomposed at 1,200°C.

(2) The $BaSO_4$ is just completely decomposed at 1,300°C.

(3) The $CaSO_4 + BaCO_3$ was not quite completely decomposed at 1,300°C.

(4) The CaF_2 is only about 30% decomposed at 1,300°C. and the rate of decomposition is much less than that of the sulphates and carbonates.

3. DISCUSSION AND SUGGESTIONS

As to the practical significance of this information, the sulphate content of a body can easily be of the order of 0·01%. Sodium carbonate and barium carbonate additions can be of the order of 0·1% each, so that a considerable quantity of gas can be given off on firing. With these quantities about 30 cm³ of SO_3 and 300 cm³ of CO_2 can be generated per kilogram (approx. 400 cm³) of body. These volumes are N.T.P. volumes. Considering that some of this gas can be evolved near to the maximum firing-temperature, at which the decreasing porosity and permeability of the body and the molten glaze make it difficult for these gases to escape, it is not difficult to imagine that the pressures set up at these temperatures by gas trapped in a confined space are sufficient at times to cause blistering and bloating.

If there is a tendency for such trouble, it seems desirable to keep the sulphate content as low as possible and, if possible, to eliminate the barium salt additions. With these additions, the sulphate becomes fixed in the body as $BaSO_4$. Without them, some of the sulphate can be absorbed by the plaster during casting and some will migrate to the surface of a piece while drying and be removed when cleaning, resulting in a decreased quantity of sulphate in the body. With a body containing Cornish stone, it should be safer to use defluorinated stone or felspar.

It is not being implied that it is impossible to make a nearly vitreous body when it contains such impurities, but that these incomplete decompositions evolving gases are one of the several factors contributing towards an occasional small amount of loss.

ACKNOWLEDGMENT

Thanks are due to Mr. L. A. Baines, my Director of Research, for permission to give an account of this small study; the experimental work was done at the Ideal Standard, Laboratoire de Recherches at Le Blanc-Mesnil, S. & O. France, by Mr J. Abegg and Mme N'Guyen.

19—Influence de Quelques Substances Volatiles Présentes dans le Haut-fourneau sur la Désintégration des Réfractaires par Dépôt de Carbone

Par J. P. Kiehl et P. Lakodey

Société Générale des Produits Réfractaires, Paris, France

RÉSUMÉ

K12—D71

La désagrégation des produits réfractaires par la dissociation de l'oxyde de carbone est étudiée sous l'angle apport de catalyseurs en provenance des charges du haut-fourneau. A côté du mécanisme classique de la réaction de Boudouard qui peut être catalysée non seulement par les impuretés ferrugineuses des produits réfractaires mais également par des dépôts de fer provenant de sels ou d'alliages zinc-fer, on peut également démontrer que les réactions de réduction du CO peuvent intervenir pour expliquer des dépôts de carbone dans des zones de températures supérieures à 600°. Le zinc métallique ainsi que les métaux alcalins peuvent être, entre autres à l'origine de ces réactions.

The influence on carbon monoxide attack of volatile substances present in a blast-furnace

The disintegration of refractories by the dissociation of CO is studied from the point of view of catalysts originating in the blast-furnace charge. Besides the classical mechanism of the Boudouard reaction, which can be catalysed not only by the ferruginous impurities of refractories but also by deposits of iron deriving from salts or zinc-iron alloys, it can be shown that reduction reactions of CO can be responsible for the deposition of carbon in regions where the temperature is above 600°C. Metallic zinc and the alkali metals, amongst others, initiate these reactions.

Der Einfluss flüchtiger Substanzen in einem Hochofen auf die Zersetzung von Kohlenmonoxid

Die Zerstörung feuerfester Erzeugnisse durch Dissoziation von Kohlenmonoxid kann durch Katalysatoren hervorgerufen werden, die aus der Hochofencharge stammen. Nach dem durch die Boudouardgleichung gegebenen klassischen Mechanismus können nicht nur eisenhaltige Verunreinigungen feuerfester Produkte katalytisch wirken, sondern auch Anreicherungen von Eisen, das sich aus Salzen oder Zink-Eisen-Verbindungen gebildet hat. Deshalb kann man beweisen, dass die Reaktionen für die CO-Reduktion die Anreicherung von Kohlenstoff in Temperaturzonen oberhalb 600°C erklären. Metallisches Zink kann ebenso wie Alkalimetalle u.a. die Ursache solcher Reaktionen sein.

1. GÉNÉRALITÉS

Depuis longtemps, on sait que la désintégration des matériaux réfractaires sous l'action de l'oxyde de carbone figure parmi les phénomènes importants qui limitent la durée de vie de ceux-ci dans les cuves de haut-fourneau, surtout pour ceux de L'Est de la France dans les conditions actuelles de marche.[1]

En effet, l'oxyde de carbone s'autoxyde suivant le schéma:

$$2\,CO \Longleftrightarrow CO_2 + C \quad . \quad . \quad . \quad . \quad (1)$$

connu sous le nom d'équilibre de Boudouard. Ce carbone se dépose sous une forme " active " qui peut provoquer la rupture du matériau au sein duquel la réaction s'effectue.

En réalité, l'évolution suivant le schéma I n'a lieu qu'en présence de catalyseurs appropriés, au premier rang desquels figurent les métaux de la première triade (fer, cobalt, nickel).

Cependant, on ignore encore le mécanisme exact par lequel le carbone rompt le matériau, bien que certaines études [2—6] tendent à éclaircir ce point.

Pendant longtemps, on a admis aussi que les seuls catalyseurs de cette réaction préexistaient dans le réfractaire. En effet, les traces de fer et d'oxydes de fer non combinés sous forme de silicates,[7] amènent incontestablement la destruction des maçonneries, mais les observations faites ces dernières années dans certains hauts-fourneaux ne peuvent plus être expliquées par ces seuls catalyseurs.

En effet, selon les minerais utilisés, la désagrégation des réfractaires par la réaction de Boudouard est d'importance fort variable, parfois même négligeable. Il semble par contre, que l'emploi de minerais riches en zinc et en éléments alcalins, a une nette influence sur ce type de destruction.

Par ailleurs, au cours de nos investigations sur des blocs réfractaires provenant de hauts-fourneaux, hors service, nous avons observé, et MICHAUD et SCHOENDOERFFER [8] viennent de la confirmer tout récemment, qu'à certains niveaux de la cuve, la zone intrados des réfractaires, au contact direct avec les charges du haut-fourneau, était fréquemment désagrégée et chargée de carbone, de zinc et d'éléments alcalins. Or, à ce niveau de température ($700°$–$1,000°$), la réaction de Boudouard ne semble plus possible et l'expérience classique de laboratoire le confirme.[9]

Nous nous sommes donc penchés sur ces apparentes contradictions et au cours de cet exposé, nous nous proposons de présenter quelques remarques et expériences qui montrent:

(1) que la réaction de Boudouard peut être catalysée par du

" fer " venu de l'intérieur du haut-fourneau par diverses voies gazeuses;

(2) qu'à des températures supérieures à celles nécessaires à la réaction de Boudouard, des éléments tels que le zinc et les métaux alcalins peuvent réduire l'oxyde de carbone en provoquant également un dépôt de carbone.

2. POSSIBILITÉ DE TRANSPORT DE " FER " DU HAUT-FOURNEAU DANS LE GARNISSAGE RÉFRACTAIRE

2.1 Influence des Sels Volatils de Fer

L'idée d'un tel transport a été déjà exprimée [10] mais sous des formes peu explicites et peu précises. Une première possibilité d'apport de fer par l'intermédiaire d'une phase gazeuse semble être fournie par les chlorures de fer. La présente de ces composés n'a rien de surprenant. En effet, les minerais de fer contiennent du chlore (de l'ordre de 600 g de chlore par tonne) [11] essentiellement combiné sous forme de chlorures alcalins.

Il peut donc apparaître des chlorures de fer puisque la formation de ceux-ci par action du fer sur les chlorures alcalins est assez aisée. [12] Exemple:

$$2KCl + Fe \underset{900° C.}{\Longleftrightarrow} FeCl_2 + 2K \quad . \quad . \quad . \quad (2).$$

Or, si nous examinons la chimie des chlorures de fer, nous contatons que de nombreuses réactions conduisent, par réduction, autoxydation, hydrolyse, au fer métallique ou aux oxydes de fer. Ce sont autant de voies possibles susceptibles de provoquer la réaction de Boudouard et par suite la désintégration des briques réfractaires. Enumérons quelques unes de ces réactions:

Le chlorure ferreux se sublime aisément (tension de vapeur 12 mm Hg vers 700°C.). Lorsqu'il est pur et sec, sa sublimation reste purement physique. Par contre, si ces conditions ne sont pas remplies, et c'est le cas dans le haut-fourneau, la sublimation s'accompagne d'une autoxydation:

$$3 FeCl_2 \Longleftrightarrow 2 FeCl_3 + Fe \quad . \quad . \quad . \quad (3)$$

d'où résulte une possibilité de dépôt de fer dans le garnissage, surtout dans les zones de température modérée où le chlorure ferrique est relativement stable.

La vapeur d'eau, composé présent dans le haut-fourneau, hydrolyse le chlorure ferreux en l'oxydant:

$$3 FeCl_2 + 4 H_2O \Longleftrightarrow Fe_3O_4 + 6 HCl + H_2 \quad . \quad (4).$$

L'hydrogène conduit au fer metallique :

$$2\,FeCl_2 + H_2 \Longleftrightarrow 2\,Fe + 2\,HCl \quad . \quad . \quad (5)$$

$$2\,FeCl_3 + 3H_2 \Longleftrightarrow 2\,Fe + 6\,HCl \quad . \quad . \quad (6).$$

De nombreux autres réducteurs libèrent le fer. Parmi les princi-paux de ceux présents dans le haut-forneau, citons le gaz ammoniac, les métaux alcalins et le zinc.

Par exemple, le zinc seul, ou en présence de charbon, réduit aisé-ment le chlorure de fer :

$$FeCl_2 + Zn \longrightarrow ZnCl_2 + Fe \quad . \quad . \quad . \quad (7).$$

Le mélange des chlorures de fer et de sodium attaque vivement le zinc fondu :

$$FeCl_2 + Zn_{fondu} \xrightarrow{\substack{\text{présence} \\ \text{NaCl}}} ZnCl_2 + \text{alliage fer-zinc} \quad . \quad (8).$$

Ces deux dernières réactions nous semblent très importantes car, de tout temps, on avait observé une concomitance entre la destruc-tion du réfractaire et la présence du zinc.

En pratique on arrive à trouver, et nous l'avons observé à plusieurs reprises, des pièces réfractaires présentant des zones de condensation, parfois larges de 15 à 20 mm, contenant des sels et oxydes solubles à l'acide sulfurique $1/2$ N. Les extraits secs de ces solutions titrent jusqu'a 8 % à 10 % de fer combiné essentiellement sous forme de $FeCl_3$ et Fe_2O_3.

Par là, nous avons donc la preuve que quelques unes des réactions décrites précédemment se déroulent bien dans le haut-fourneau et un essai de CO au laboratoire permet facilement de démontrer qu'un réfractaire ainsi imprégné est complètement désagrégé après une centaine d'heures.

2.2 Influence des Alliages de Zinc et Fer

Parmi les travaux récents au sujet de l'intervention du zinc, citons ceux de KHOLZAKOV et TSYLEV [13] et ceux plus fondamentaux de DECROLY et GHODSI.[14]

Des travaux des premiers auteurs ressortent deux faits im-portants :

(1) L'apparition à 647°C., par réaction péritectique, d'une phase h titrant 10 % de fer dans tous les alliages contenant 1 % à 20 % de fer.

Le dépôt de cette phase h entraîne, par ailleurs, un fort accroisse-ment de volume d'où risque de rupture du matériau dans lequel 'effectue le refroidissement des alliages. De fait, KHOLZAKOV et SYLEV [15] montrent que des briques renfermant des alliages à 3,2% et 11,2% de fer éclatent effectivement à 647°C.

Notons, par ailleurs, au passage que les alliages de zinc et de potassium, métaux existants dans le haut-fourneau, donnent également une dilatation entre 405° et 510°C. pour des proportions de 9% à 32% de potassium.[15]

(2) La grande volatilé et oxydabilité par le gaz carbonique, l'air et la vapeur d'eau de certains alliages de fer et de zinc.

Selon ces auteurs, le CO_2 peut résulter de la catalyse de l'equilibre de Boudouard par ces alliages. La destruction du réfractaire dans e haut-fourneau, par le gonflement dû à la formation de la phase h nous parait peu probable étant donné que le titre des alliages de zinc-fer rencontrés dans les maçonneries est toujours très faible.

Par contre, le second point nous semble extrêmement important car il doit être à la base d'un mécanisme de transport d'agents catalytiques de la réaction de Boudouard.

Nos propres expériences dans ce domaine, ont donc porté sur deux points:

(1) Vérification de la volatilité de quelques alliages de fer et de zinc,

(2) Étude du comportement des alliages dans l'oxyde de carbone.

Nous avons préparé des " alliages " de fer et de zinc vers 580°C. sous un débit de quelques dizaines de litres à l'heure d'hydrogène commercial, pour autant qu'on puisse appeler " alliage " les produits obtenus à aussi basse température.

Un examen sommaire de la volatilité des " alliages " est effectué en portant un poids connu " d'alliages " à température constante, sous un courant d'hydrogène de 5 litres/heure. Une partie de l'échantillon se volatilise et se recondense dans les zones plus froides du tube laboratoire. Nous nous sommes efforcés de recueillir ce distillat et de l'analyser.

Ces expériences permettent de se faire une idée de l'ampleur des volatilisations. C'est dans cet esprit semi-quantitatif que nous donnons le Tableau 1.

On peut en déduire:

(1) La volatilité considérable de certains alliages de fer et de zinc à des températures modérées de l'ordre de 650 à 700°C.,

(2) La possibilité d'une distillation du fer (ou d'un entrainement) à ces mêmes températures.

Tableau 1

Echantillon initial	Traitement	Perte de poids	Résidu	Distillat
10,65 g. alliage à 9,7% de fer	6 h à 520°C.	0		
10,65 g. alliage à 9,7% de fer	6 h à 700°C.	33%	7,1 g. à 14,8% de fer	1 à 1,5% de fer
9,6 g alliage à 12% de fer	5 h à 520°C.	0		
9,6 g. alliage à 12% de fer	6 h à 660°C.	52%	4,6 g. à 18% de fer	1,5% de fer

Par la suite nous avons exécuté quelques essais destinés à nou
éclairer sur le comportement des alliages de fer et de zinc dan
l'oxyde de carbone.

Les expériences faites avec ces alliages sont résumées dans l
Tableau 2.

Tableau 2

Alliage	Essai CO	Résultats
Zn–Fe à 12% Fe	24 h à 450°C.	Dépôt de carbone dans le creuset; pas de volatilisation.
Zn–Fe à 12% Fe	43 h à 650°C.	Dépôt de carbone dans le creuset; volatilisation des métaux et condensation sur les parties froides avec net dépôt de carbone tout au long du tube.
Distillat renfermant 1,5% Fe et provenant du maintien de 6 h à 660° dans H_2 d'un alliage fer-zinc à 12% Fe.	660°C. durant 175 h	Gain de poids de 7% après 23 h sans dépôt visible de carbone puis perte de poids par volatilisation des metaux tandis que le dépôt de carbone devient abondant. Le résidue titre 6,5% de fer. Le condensat au voisinage de la nacelle contient du zinc, 0,5% de fer et du carbone.

Ces résultats nous permettent donc de conclure que les alliage
de fer et de zinc catalysent l'équilibre de Boudouard dans le domaine
450°–660°C. au moins.

3. RÉDUCTION DE L'OXYDE DE CARBONE PAR LE ZINC

Ainsi qu'il a déjà été signalé au début de cet exposé, nous avons
toujours été fort intrigués par la présence de carbone dans la partie
intrados de certains blocs réfractaires, extraits de hauts-forneaux
mis hors service, c'est-à-dire dans des zones de température où la
réaction de Boudouard n'est plus possible.

Comme autres composés étrangers au réfractaire, nous trouvions fréquemment du zinc, de l'oxyde de zinc, des hydroxydes et des carbonates de sodium et de potassium, ainsi que quelques unes de leurs combinaisons avec les composés silico-alumineux du réfractaire. Il est évidemment difficile de connaître l'état sous lequel ces différents composés existent dans un haut-fourneau en activité.

Nous avons donc émis et vérifié l'hypothèse d'une réduction possible du CO par le zinc métallique d'après les schémas (9) et (10) à des températures de l'ordre de 700° à 900°, réactions qui sont thermodynamiquement possibles :

$$Zn + CO \rightarrow ZnO + C . \quad . \quad . \quad . \quad (9)$$

$$Zn + CO_2 \rightarrow ZnO + CO \quad . \quad . \quad . \quad (10).$$

Au cours d'une première série d'expériences et pensant que, dans un haut-fourneau, le zinc devait essentiellement exister sous forme d'alliage zinc-fer, nous avons opéré à 900° avec des mélanges d'oxydes de fer et de zinc dans des proportions de 10 à 90% de zinc.

Ces expériences nous ont donné les résultats suivants :

(1) Dépôt de carbone abondant dans la nacelle,

(2) Le fer mis en jeu reste pour l'essentiel dans la nacelle,

(3) Le zinc se volatilise plus ou moins et se recondense sur les parties froides du tube de quartz en entraînant toujours une certaine quantité de fer.

L'étude chimique et l'examen qualitatif aux rayons X des condensats obtenus lors de ces essais nous ont conduit à constater que les condensats contiennent, outre du fer et du carbone, du zinc et de l'oxyde de zinc.

Craignant que le dépôt de carbone ait pu se former à l'échauffement et au refroidissement en traversant le domaine de la réaction de Boudouard, nous avons fait un essai spécial, au cours duquel seul le palier de température de 20 h à 900°C. a été effectué sous oxyde de carbone. La montée et la descente de température ont eu lieu sous courant d'azote. Dans ces conditions, nous avons observé :

à l'entrée et à la sortie du four un condensat de zinc, d'oxyde de zinc, de carbone et des traces de fer;

dans la nacelle, un résidu de fer, un peu de zinc et des traces de carbone.

Cette présence d'oxyde de zinc était donc une première confirmation de la réduction des oxydes de carbone par la zinc à certaines températures.

Ces résultats ont été confirmés par la suite par une série d'essai, résumés dans le Tableau 3, et faisant uniquement intervenir le zinc ou son oxyde.

Tableau 3

Essai avec	Conditions	Résultats
ZnO RP + 3 morceaux de mullite entrée, milieu et sortie du four)	900°C., 38 h 5 l/h de CO	Disparition du ZnO mis dans la nacelle. Les échantillons de mullite deviennent violets. A l'entrée et à la sortie du four il y a des "condensats" de carbone, zinc, oxyde de zinc (analyse chimique et rayons X).
ZnO	900°C., 38 h 5 l/h de N_2	Rien, sauf une perte de poids de 0,4%. Le ZnO n'est donc nullement entraîné par le gaz.
Zn	900°C., 24 h 5 l/h de CO	Volatilisation du zinc. Condensats à l'entrée et à la sortie du four (500°C. environ) contenant Zn, ZnO, un peu de carbone à l'entrée du four et dans la nacelle.
Zn	700°C., 10 h 5 l/h de CO	Léger dépôt de carbone dans la nacelle (10 mg env.) condensats grisâtres à l'entrée et à la sortie du four.

L'ensemble de ces expériences tend à montrer que l'oxydation du zinc liquide par le CO à des températures de l'ordre de 700° à 900°C., semble avoid une vitesse faible, sans doute, mais sensible, Les manipulations avec le zinc, qui suppriment toute possibilité de formation de gaz carbonique donc la possibilité de la réaction 10, confirment bien cette hypothèse.

4. RÉDUCTION DE L'OXYDE DE CARBONE PAR LES ÉLÉMENTS ALCALINS

La réaction de réduction des oxydes de carbone par le zinc n'ayant aucune raison de ne pas être possible avec les métaux plus électropositifs tels que les métaux alcalins, nous avons ébauché quelques expériences avec ces éléments.

La présence de sels de sodium et potassium dans les minerais de fer est bien connue.[16] Leur réduction dans le haut-fourneau peut s'effectuer suivants différents processus entre autres selon les réactions du type:

$$2 KCl + Fe \Longleftrightarrow FeCl_2 + 2 K \quad . \quad . \quad . \quad . \quad (2)$$

$$2 KCN + Fe \Longleftrightarrow 2 K + N_2 + \text{Carbure de fer} \quad . \quad (11)$$

Ces métaux alcalins et les oxydes de carbone peuvent donner lieu à des réactions parallèles à celles envisagées pour le zinc (voir les schémas (9), (10)), avec, sans doute, des conséquences possibles analogues

$$2 K + CO_2 \rightarrow K_2 + CO \quad . \quad . \quad . \quad (12)$$

$$2 K + CO \leftarrow K_2O + C \quad . \quad . \quad . \quad (13).$$

En effet, les essais faits par nous à ce sujet, ont permis de mettre en évidence un début de désagrégation de réfractaire avec formation de carbone, lorsqu'on soumet un réfractaire normalement inactif vis à vis le l'oxyde de carbone, à une attaque par le potassium et l'oxyde de carbone entre 700°–900°C. (Fig. 1).

Fig. 1.—Réfractaire desagrégé par l'action simultanée du carbone et du potassium

Ces expériences ont été arrêtées momentanément car les vapeurs de potassium métallique attaquaient, en plus de réfractaire soumis à l'essai, les tubes d'alumine frittée ou de silice fondue dans lesquels devaient s'effectuer les réactions prévues.

Néanmoins, nous pensons que ces réactions sont à la base des phénomènes de désagrégation, dans certaines parties supérieures de cuves de haut-fourneau, sur les faces intérieures des réfractaires. Dans ces zones de températures, la réaction de Boudouard n'est plus possible, et pourtant on trouve, à côté de carbonate, d'hydroxyde et d'aluminate de potassium, de la kaliophilite et des dépôts de carbone.

5. CONFIRMATION DES HYPOTHÈSES PRÉCÉDENTES PAR QUELQUES ESSAIS DANS LE HAUT-FOURNEAU

Pour vérifier l'influence de l'apport de catalyseurs provenant du haut-fourneau sur la désagrégation des réfractaires, nous avons eu l'occasion d'effectuer les essais suivants:

A travers des trous perforés dans le garnissage d'une cuve (à 7,9 m au-dessus des tuyères), nous avons fait introduire, d'après la technique mise au point par SCHOENDOERFFER, MICHAUX et VICENS [17] d'une part un réfractaire à base de silice et d'alumine à

FIG. 2.—Éprouvette réfractaire après un séjour de 2 mois en contact direct avec les charges de haut-fourneau

60% de porosité ouverte mais ne titrant pas plus de 0,4% d'impuretés, dont 0,1% de Fe_2O_3, d'autre part un réfractaire à base de zircone et de corindon à porosité ouverte et perméabilité quasi nulles.

Ces deux réfractaires, préalablement éprouvés à l'essai de CO de laboratoire, n'avaient donné lieu à aucune trace de désagrégation ni même de dépôt de carbone.

Après un séjour d'un mois environ dans le garnissage du haut-fourneau, les éprouvettes d'essai, gainées dans un tube métallique, ont été retirées.

Le réfractaire poreux était déjà désagrégé en de nombreaux endroits et très chargé en carbone de dissociation aussi bien dans la partie frontale que dans la zone arrière correspondant au domaine de la réaction de Boudouard.

Au cœur même des éprouvettes de ce réfractaire poreux, on a pu déceler à côté du Pb, Zn et Sn, une teneur en Fe_2O_3 allant par endroits jusqu'à 1,5%.

Le réfractaire dense par contre n'a subi aucune modification de structure ou même d'aspect au cours de son séjour dans la cuve du haut-forneau (Fig. 2).

6. CONCLUSIONS

Les apparentes contradictions que l'on observe à propos de la corrosion des garnissages réfractaires des hauts-fourneaux, pourraient donc en partie être expliquées par l'influence des substances volatiles introduites avec les minerais et les cokes. La nature et la proportion même de ces substances variant évidemment avec l'origine des matières premières utilisées, expliqueraient, entre autres, les divergences de la tenue des garnissages réfractaires que l'on semble observer selon la localisation géographique des hauts-fourneaux.

D'après le résultat de nos expériences, il semble prouvé que dans les cas défavorables, les garnissages réfractaires peuvent se charger de nombreuses substances volatiles et deviennent de ce fait de véritables supports soit de catalyseurs de la réaction de Boudouard, soit d'agents réducteurs de l'oxyde de carbone.

Parmi ces substances les sels de fer, les alliages zinc-fer, le zinc pur et les métaux alcalins ont incontestablement une action destructrice essentiellement basée sur les dépôts de carbone provenant:

soit de la dissociation de l'oxyde de carbone, par action purement catalytique:

$$2\,CO \Longleftrightarrow CO_2 + C;$$

soit, de la réduction des oxydes de carbone, par action " chimique " avec les métaux très électro-positifs, selon les schémas :

$$2\,Me + CO \longrightarrow Me_2O + C$$

$$2\,Me + CO_2 \longrightarrow Me_2O + CO$$

L'équilibre de Boudouard a lieu dans le domaine de température de 400°–700°C., alors que les réactions chimiques se déroulent à des températures supérieures qui, d'après nos estimations et expériences, pourraient se situer entre 700° et 900°C. tout au moins.

Des essais in-situ en haut-fourneau ont confirmé ces données de laboratoire et ont également permis de démontrer l'immunité des produits réfractaires à porosité et perméabilité nulles ou quasi nulles.

Un essai industriel avec ce type de réfractaire est actuellement en cours. L'avenir nous renseignera sur la validité de nos hypothèses.

Bien entendu, le présent travail ne constitue qu'une ébauche introduisant quelques hypothèses nouvelles pour l'étude de ce problème très discuté qu'est la destruction des réfractaires dans le haut-fourneau et nous remercions notre Directeur Général M. Letort et notre Directeur Général Adjoint, M. Ardouin d'avoir bien voulu autoriser la publication de la présente étude.

Nos remerciements vont également à M. Michaux, Directeur à la Société de Wendel et à Melle Schoendoerffer, Ingénieur au laboratoire de Réfractaires et Minerais de Nancy pour l'aide efficace qu'ils ont bien voulu nous apporter pour la réalisation des essais sur haut-fourneau.

BIBLIOGRAPHIE

1. Schoendoerffer, M. J., " Evolution des problèmes des produits réfractaires de hauts-fourneaux depuis 1959," *Journée de l'A.T.S.F.,* Paris, 21 Mars 62.
2. Davis, W. R., et Rigby, G. R., *Trans. Brit. Ceram. Soc.,* **53**, 511, 1954.
3. Pukall, K., *Ber. Deutsch Keram Ges.,* **22**, 430, 1941.
4. Juillard, A., Rayet, R., et Lude, A., *Disc. Farad. Soc.,* **4**, 193, 1948.
5. Davis, W. R., Slawson, R. J., et Rigby, G. R., *Trans. Brit. Ceram Soc.,* **56**, 67, 1957.
6. Hofer, J. E., Sterling E., et MacCartney, J. T., *J. Phys. Chem.,* **59**, 1153, 1955.
7. Letort, Y., et Schoendoerffer, M. J., *Bull. Soc. Franç. Céram.,* **34**, 29, 1957.
8. Schoendoerffer, M. J., et Michaux P., " Essais de réfractaires dans les cuves de hauts-fourneaux de Patural," *Journée de l'A.S.T.F., Paris,* 2, Jan. 1963.
9. Berry, T. F., Ames, R. W., et Snow, R. B., *J. Amer. Ceram. Soc.,* **39**, 308, 1956.
10. Halm., L., *Rev. Metal,* **58** (2), 109, 1961.

11. Turpin, G., " Contribution à l'étude de la répartition des éléments dans les minerais de fer de Lorraine," *Publication IRSID 1952, Série A,* No. 42.
12. Hackspill, L., et Grandadam, R., *C.R. Acad. Sci.,* **180**, 68, 1925.
13. Kholzakov, V. I. ,et Tsylev, L. M., *Izvestia Akad. Nauk. SSSR. OTN,* 3, 89, 1958.
14. Decroly, C., et Ghodsi, M., *Mem. Sci. Rev. Metal,* **2**, 138, 1961.
15. Roux, A., " Traité de Chimie Minérale " (P. Pascall) (Masson & Co., Paris, 1934), T. XII.
16. Laplace, G., " Dosage de quelques éléments rares dans les minerais de fer de Lorraine," *Publication IRSID 1952, Série A,* No. 41.
17. Schoendoerffer, M. J., Michaux, P., et Vicens, P., " Essais de réfractaires dans les cuves des hauts-forneaux de Patural," de Wendel et Co., *Journée de l.A.T.S.F.,* Paris, 1963.

20—High-temperature Seals on Pure Dense Alumina

By G. H. Jonker, J. T. Klomp and Th. P. J. Botden

Philips Research Laboratories
N.V. Philips' Gloeilampenfabrieken
Eindhoven, Netherlands

ABSTRACT   E76

Difficulties have been met in preparing vacuum-tight seals with high temperature resistance on alumina products of high purity and density, using conventional methods. Excellent seals can be made by melting thin layers of oxides between the parts to be connected: ceramic–ceramic or ceramic–metal. Oxide mixtures with high melting-points (between 1,250° and 1,700°C.) were used first. Owing to reaction with the solid alumina, the softening-point of the seal may be much higher than the melting-points of the oxide mixture originally applied. It is also possible to start with oxides or mixtures which melt only after reaction with the alumina surface. A feature of these seals is their resistance to hot metal vapours such as those of sodium or cesium. A survey of useful mixtures is given on the basis of ternary phase-diagrams.

Scellements résistant aux hautes températures sur alumine dense pure

L'emploi des méthodes classiques pour effectuer des scellements étanches au vide, résistant aux hautes températures, sur des produits d'alumine de pureté et densité élevées, a soulevé des difficultés. On peut réaliser des scellements excellents en fondant des couches minces d'oxydes entre les pièces à joindre: céramique–céramique ou céramique–métal. On a d'abord utilisé des mélanges d'oxydes à points de fusion élevés (entre 1250° et 1700°C.). En raison de la réaction avec l'alumine solide, le point de ramollissement du scellement peut être beaucoup plus élevé que ceux des oxydes du mélange initial. On peut aussi partir d'oxydes ou de mélanges d'oxydes qui ne fondent qu'après avoir réagi avec la surface de l'alumine. Une caractéristique de ces scellements est leur résistance aux vapeurs métalliques chaudes telles que celles du sodium ou du césium. Une étude critique de mélanges utilisables est donnée; elle est basée sur des diagrammes de phases ternaires.

Hochtemperaturbeständige Verschmelzungen mit reinem und dichtem Aluminiumoxyd

Die Herstellung von hochtemperaturbeständigen und vakuumdichten Verbindungen von hochreinen Aluminiumoxydgegenständen grosser Dichte ergab Schwierigkeiten bei der Anwendung bekannter Verfahren. Ausgezeichnete Verbindungen erhält man, wenn man dünne Oxydschichten auf die zu verbindenden Teile, Keramik–Keramik oder Keramik–Metall, aufschmilzt. Es wurden hochschmelzende Mischungen von Oxyden (Schmelzpunkte zwischen 1250°C. and 1700°C.) verwendet. Durch Reaktion mit dem festen Aluminiumoxyd kann die Erweichungstemperatur der Verschmelzung beträchtlich höher sein als die Schmelztemperatur der ursprünglichen Oxyd-mischung. Man kann auch von Oxyden oder Oxydgemischen ausgehen, welche erst nach einer Reaktion mit der Oberfläche des Aluminiumoxyds schmelzen. Neben der Gasdichtheit und Hochtemperaturbeständichkeit ist eine weitere wichtige Eigenschaft dieser Verschmelzungen die Beständigkeit gegen heisse Metalldämpfe, z.B. Na- und Cs- Dämpfe. An Hand von ternären Zustandsdiagrammen wird eine Übersicht über die für die Ver-schmelzung brauchbaren Oxydmischungen gegeben.

1. INTRODUCTION

The sealing of metals on bodies of high alumina content is becom-ing more and more important in the development of gas-discharge lamps and electron tubes. The application of pure alumina, how-ever, has led to serious problems in this respect, as the tensile strength of seals prepared by conventional techniques is found to be much too low.[1, 2, 3]

This paper describes a new sealing-method which has the ad-vantage that the step of metallizing can be avoided. This new method is a one-step process and consists of melting between the bodies a thin layer of suitable oxide mixture with a melting-point between 1,200° and 1,700°C. These oxides layers show a good ad-herence to alumina as well as to high-melting metals.

2. EXPERIMENTAL PROCEDURE

The oxides are mixed with a nitrocellulose binder to form a paste. A small amount of this paste is applied as a thin layer between two blocks of alumina. These are placed on a ceramic plate in a metal cylinder which can be heated by an H.F. coil. The metal cylinder is surrounded by a quartz bell-jar through which a stream of N_2 or $N_2 + H_2$ is passed (Fig. 1). The temperature is raised at a rate of 100°–150°C./min until a temperature about 50°C. above the melt-ing-point of the oxide mixture is reached, kept constant for 5 min, and then decreased at the same rate.

It is not always necessary to apply the oxide paste directly between the blocks. Generally it is sufficient to place a small amount near the joint. On melting, the mixture flows by capillary forces into the contact area (Fig. 2).

Metal–ceramic and metal–metal joints are prepared in the same way.

For determining the strength of the seals, two cylindrical rods of translucent alumina ($> 99 \cdot 8\%$ Al_2O_3) or molybdenum, with a length of 30 mm and a diameter d of 5 mm, are sealed in this way. The connected rods are placed on two knives, at a distance $l = 50$ mm apart, and then an increasing load K is applied to the joint, until

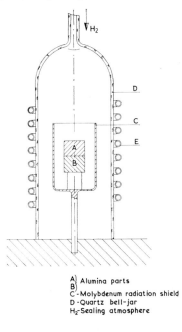

A⟩
B⟩ Alumina parts
C -Molybdenum radiation shield
D -Quartz bell-jar
H₂-Sealing atmosphere

Fɪɢ. 1.—Sealing apparatus: A and B. Blocks of alumina. C. Molybdenum radiation shield. D. Quartz bell-jar. E. Molybdenum cylinder. H₂. Sealing-atmosphere.

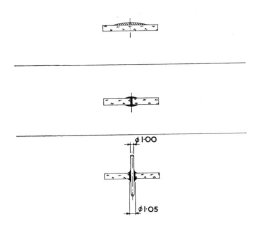

Fɪɢ. 2.—Different forms of oxide paste application

the rod breaks (Fig. 3). The breaking strength σ_B is calculated with the formula

$$\sigma_B = \frac{Kl}{0.4d^3}$$

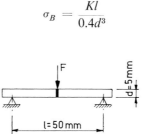

$$\sigma_B = \frac{F.l}{4\left(\frac{d^3}{10}\right)}$$

FIG. 3.—Tensile-strength apparatus

The values of σ_B are compared with σ_B of a single alumina rod, measured in the same way.

A number of oxides and ceramics that were available in the laboratory were investigated. Initial success was obtained with a finely powdered product consisting mainly of $MgSiO_3$, with a melting-point about 1,400°C. After these preliminary experiments, two lines of further research were pursued, with a view to studying:

(1) The variation of the oxide mixture,
(2) The reactions between melt and alumina surface.

The following considerations governed the first line of research:

(a) Only oxides and mixtures melting between 1,200° and 1,700°C. were of interest.
(b) Only non-volatile oxides can be used.
(c) The oxides must be stable, not varying in oxygen content.

Mixtures of oxides from the following list: MgO, CaO, SrO, BaO, Al_2O_3 and SiO_2, were found to satisfy these requirements and other oxides like ZnO, B_2O_3, Na_2O, which may be useful for melting or for better flowing of the melts can be used only as minor additions.

Study of the phase diagrams of these oxides (see Figs. 4–6) indicates a broad field of compositions that melt between 1,200° and 1,700°C. Many of these compositions were investigated, and nearly all of them were found to be useful. The compositions rich in

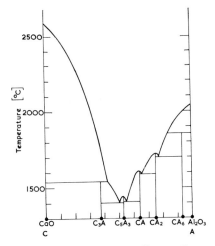

FIG. 4.—Phase diagram of CaO–Al₂O₃ according to RANKIN and WRIGHT. Figure 43 in " Phase Diagrams for Ceramists I ".

SiO₂ were an exception, a certain amount of quartz glass being formed with a very low thermal expansion. It is not possible, however, to draw a sharp boundary between practical and impractical compositions, as the properties of the seal depend to a marked extent on the thermal history of the sealing procedure, which led to the microscopic study of the seals. It was found that there is a certain reaction between the melt and the surface of the alumina body. Nearly all melts attack the surface in such a way that a layer of Al₂O₃ dissolves in the melt, which means that the melt changes in composition and becomes richer in alumina. Now such reactions have different results. The most simple case may be illustrated by the following example. Consider a eutectic mixture of oxides, with alumina as one of the solid phases, e.g. point E in Fig. 5. If this mixture is heated to the eutectic point, there is equilibrium between melt and alumina surface. If we cool directly afterwards, we have a seal which has a softening-point near to this eutectic temperature. But if we heat the mixture to a higher temperature, alumina from the surface starts to dissolve into the melt. If we cool now, we get a certain melting-range which gives the seal a somewhat higher softening-point.

A more complicated example is the case where we start with a eutectic mixture of oxides, e.g. the eutectic in the system CaO–Al₂O₃ (Fig. 4), not in equilibrium with alumina itself, but with a compound richer in alumina than the original mixture. If we now melt the mix-

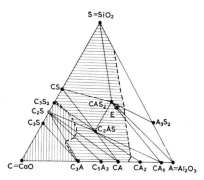

FIG. 5.—Phase diagram of CaO–Al₂O₃–SiO₂ according to GENTILE and FOSTER.[5] Shaded areas denote useful compositions.

ture on the alumina body, a reaction starts between melt and alumina, forming this new compound. How far this reaction goes depends on time and temperature, but it is clear that we obtain higher softening-points. It is even possible, and actually found in some cases, that the reaction with alumina is so fast that the softening-point is even higher than the temperature used for sealing!

More or less the opposite behaviour occurs in the next example, where we start with a pure oxide or a mixture which by itself does not melt at all at the sealing-temperature. Now it is possible that such oxides react in the solid state with alumina to form mixtures which are richer in alumina and have the desired low melting-temperatures. Examples are pure CaO (2,570°C.) and $MgSiO_3$ (1,600°C.) (Figs. 4 and 6); both react readily with alumina at a temperature about 1,400°C. and form mixtures near the eutectic compositions, with much lower melting-points, i.e. 1,400° and 1,360°C. respectively.

For the strength of the seal it is an advantage to have a melt which has dissolved a certain amount of alumina because, during cooling, the surface crystals start to grow into the melt. A microscope study of the seals in fact reveals this behaviour, but the small contrast between these crystals and the rest of the layer makes it very difficult to show in photographs.

The nature of the bonding forces involved in the contact with the metal surface is far more difficult to understand and on this point opinions are widely divergent.

Compositions that have been found useful are given in the Figs. 5 and 6. These diagrams show the compounds that can be formed and the areas in which melting-points are below 1,700°C. In addition, the areas of compositions are shown whose initial melting-points are much too high, but which melt after reaction with solid alumina.

An important point that has not yet been mentioned is, of course, the expansion coefficient of the oxide mixtures, which must not differ too much from that of alumina and the metals. In order to investigate this point we prepared a number of rods from mixtures

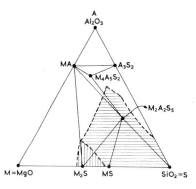

FIG. 6.—Phase diagram of MgO–Al$_2$O$_3$–SiO$_2$ according to RANKIN and MERWIN. Figure 379 in " Phase Diagrams for Ceramists I ".

that had been melted in platinum boats. In Table 1 the expansion coefficients are compared with that of alumina. The differences are small enough to allow for the application of these mixtures in seals. The same Table compares the breaking-strength of the seals at room temperature with the strength of translucent alumina itself.

In conclusion we may say that the results are very promising. We expect that, with further development, these values may even rise considerably.

Table 1

Properties of Ceramic Seals on Translucent Alumina and on Molybdenum

	MgO (M)	CaO (C)	Al$_2$O$_3$ (A)	SiO$_2$ (S)	T_m (°C)	λ 20°–500°C $\times 10^{-6}$	σ_B A—A $\times 1000\ lb/in^2$	σ_B Mo—Mo $\times 1000\ lb/in^2$
CA	—	48	52	—	1,450	5·7	13	22
CAS	—	42	18	40	1,300	9·0	24	11
MAS 1	15	—	35	50	1,500	—	24	19
MAS 2	15	—	44	41	1,600	5·2	—	—
MCS	6	38	—	56	1,400	—	34	—
Alumina	—	—	—	—	—	7·6	~ 40	—

REFERENCES

1. Pincus, A. G., *J. Amer. Ceram. Soc.*, **36**, 152, 1953.
2. Cole, S. S., Jr., and Sommer, G., *J. Amer. Ceram. Soc.*, **44**, 265, 1961.
3. Cole, S. S., Jr., and Hynes, F. J., Jr., *Bull. Amer. Ceram. Soc.*, **37**, 135, 1958.
4. Levin, E. M, McMurdie, H. F., and Hall, F. P., " Phase Diagrams for Ceramists. I " (American Ceramic Society, 1956).
5. Gentile, A. L., and Foster, W. R., *J. Amer. Ceram. Soc.*, **46**, 74, 1963.

Part Four

STRUCTURE AND PROPERTIES
OF PRODUCTS

21—The Nature of the Factors determining the Structure of Polyphase Ceramics

By J. White

*Department of Ceramics with Refractories Technology,
The University of Sheffield*

ABSTRACT   E—A43

The nature of the factors which control the spatial distribution of the phases in polyphase ceramics and the methods developed for the quantitative study of microstructure are described. Recent investigations have shown that in magnesia–monticellite mixtures fired above the melting point of the monticellite, the equilibrium dihedral angle formed in the liquid phase at junctions between periclase grains is increased by additions of Cr_2O_3 and decreased by additions of Fe_2O_3. Consequently Cr_2O_3 decreases the tendency of the silicate to penetrate between the periclase grains, whereas Fe_2O_3 has the opposite effect. It has also been found that the rate of grain growth decreases as the dihedral angle increases. The significance of these findings is discussed from the standpoints of the high temperature properties of refractories and of sintering.

La nature des facteurs qui déterminent la structure des céramiques à phases multiples

On décrit la nature des facteurs qui commandent la répartition dans l'espace des phases dans les céramiques à phases multiples et les méthodes mises au point pour l'étude quantitative de la microstructure. Des recherches récentes montrent qu'au sein de mélanges magnésie–monticellite cuits au-dessus de la température de fusion de la monticellite, l'angle dièdre d'équilibre formé dans la phase liquide aux limites des grains de périclase est accru par des additions de Cr_2O_3 tandis qu'il diminue par des additions de Fe_2O_3. En conséquence, Cr_2O_3 diminue la tendance du silicate à pénétrer entre les grains de périclase tandis que Fe_2O_3 exerce l'effet opposé. On a également constaté que le taux de croissance des grains diminue quand l'angle dièdre augmente. On examine l'importance de ces résultats aux points de vue des propriétés à haute température des réfractaires et du frittage.

Die Eigenschaften der Faktoren, welche die Struktur eines mehrphasigen keramischen Körpers bestimmen

Es werden die Eigenschaften der Faktoren ermittelt, die die räumliche Verteilung der Phasen in einem mehrphasigen keramischen Material bestimmen und es werden Methoden beschrieben, die zur quantitativen Untersuchung der Mikrostruktur entwickelt wurden. Neuere Untersuchungen haben gezeigt, dass in Mischungen aus Magnesia und Monticellit, welche über den Schmelzpunkt des Monticellit gebrannt wurden, der V-Winkel, der sich in der flüssigen Phase an den Berührungsstellen der Periklaskörner bildet, durch Zugabe von Cr_2O_3 vergrössert und durch Zugabe von Fe_2O_3 verringert wird. Infolgedessen verringert Cr_2O_3 die Fähigkeit des Silikates, zwischen die Periklaskörner einzudringen, während Fe_2O_3 den entgegengesetzten Effekt hat.

Ferner wurde gefunden, dass die Geschwindigkeit des Kornwachstums zunimmt, wenn der V-Winkel abnimmt. Die Bedeutung dieses Befundes wird vom Standpunkt der Hochtemperatureigenschaften feuerfester Materialien und des Sinterns erörtert.

1. INTRODUCTION

In selecting a theme that would be suitable for an introductory paper to the section on the structure and properties of ceramics, I thought it might be appropriate to talk about the problem of structure—in the sense primarily of microstructure—of polyphase ceramics and its bearing on their properties. In the metallurgical field the quantitative aspects of structure have received a great deal of attention in recent years, and what has become known as quantitative metallography has developed into a relatively sophisticated technique, or rather group of techniques, for the study of structure in metallic alloys. Essentially, quantitative metallography is concerned with the statistical treatment of measurements made on two-dimensional metallographic sections to obtain parameters which characterize the geometrical features of the structure in three dimensions. Parameters that can be evaluated in this way are the volume proportions of the phases present (including pore volume), the mean grain diameter and grain-size distribution of any phase, the grain-boundary areas between the grains (crystals) of a given phase, the interfacial areas between different phases and the dihedral angle formed at contacts between grains of one phase embedded in another (or of two phases embedded in a third).

The application of the methods of quantitative metallography (other than point-counting) to the study of structure in ceramics is much more recent and few references to this approach are to be found in the literature. This paper indicates some of the techniques employed and shows how they have been used to study the factors which determine the spatial distribution of the phases in polyphase ceramic bodies.

A characteristic of such bodies is that they soften and melt over a range of temperature, which is advantageous in that it is responsible for vitrification and the development of the so-called ceramic bond, but is also disadvantageous, in refractories at least, in that it leads to softening and subsidence under loads at high temperatures. Some years ago in considering this problem ALLISON, BROCK and WHITE [1] pointed out that the spatial distribution of the phases in such a body would be likely to affect materially its high-temperature strength. Thus a body in which the fusible components form a continuous layer round the refractory grains would be likely to have inferior load-bearing properties to one in which the fusible components were present as discrete globules in a continuous refractory matrix. In support of this conclusion it was pointed out that, when bismuth is present as an impurity in copper, it forms thin films round the copper grains, and less than 0·01% causes extreme brittleness at room temperature and complete loss of strength when the bismuth melts. Similarly FeS in steel causes "red-shortness" for the same reason, whereas MnS, which occurs as globules, is relatively harmless in this respect.

The practical importance of the spatial distribution of the phases in refractories was demonstrated a few years later by the commercial development of what has become known as the "direct-bonded" chrome–magnesite brick. This development followed the discovery that, when chrome–magnesite bricks are fired at temperatures in excess of 1,600°C., the silicates normally responsible for bonding the chrome and periclase (magnesia) grains together tend to be displaced into the interstices between the periclase grains, while a "direct bond" is formed between the latter and the chrome.[2, 3] Later FORD et al.[4] showed that the development of direct bonding was accompanied by a marked increase in hot tensile strength.

Figure 1 shows the structure of the normal silicate-bonded brick as seen in thin section between partially crossed nicols. The silicates, which appear bright, are largely distributed as films round the chrome grains and it is evident that they are responsible for a major part of the bonding. The reasons for this are to be found in the method of manufacture, which involves the addition of finely ground

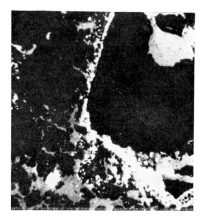

FIG. 1.—Micrograph of "silicate-bonded" chrome–magnesite brick viewed by transmitted light between partially crossed Nicols (×24). Large opaque grains are chrome spinel; small opaque grains are periclase. Pores appear grey and silicate bright.[9, 10]

magnesite to crushed and graded chrome ore to convert the relatively low-melting silicates associated with the latter to forsterite (Mg_2SiO_4) and monticellite ($CaMgSiO_4$), and it is the formation of these compounds *in situ* that is apparently responsible for the distribution observed.

Figure 2 shows the structure developed on firing a brick of similar composition at 1,800°C., as seen in reflected light. It shows a chrome grain surrounded by a continuous polycrystalline layer of periclase which has sintered on to it during the firing. No silicate occurs between the spinel and the periclase, and it appears likely that there is an epitaxial relation between the two.

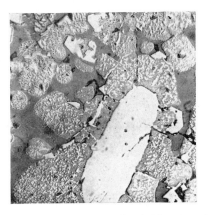

FIG. 2.—Micrograph of chrome–magnesite brick after firing at 1,800°C. Polished section viewed in reflected light (×130) showing a grain of chrome spinel (light) surrounded by a continuous polycrystalline layer of periclase containing precipitated spinel, and angular spinel crystals that have crystallized from liquid silicate during cooling.[9, 10]

2. THE INTERPRETATION OF MICROSTRUCTURE

The fact that the spatial distribution of the phases in the equilibrium structures of polyphase alloys (once the topological requirements of space filling are satisfied) is governed by the geometrical balance of phase-boundary and grain-boundary tensions was first demonstrated quantitatively by C. S. SMITH[5] in a paper which has become something of a classic. The nature of the force balance involved is indicated by Figs. 3 and 4. The former represents a section through a three-grain junction in such a structure, the section being considered to be normal to the edge along which the three grain boundaries intersect. Of the three grains involved, the two

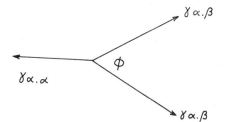

$\gamma \alpha . \beta$

$\gamma \alpha . \alpha$

ϕ

$\gamma \alpha . \beta$

FIG. 3.—Equilibrium between a grain boundary and two equivalent interphase boundaries. ϕ is the dihedral angle. (After SMITH [5])

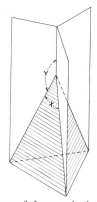

FIG. 4.—Idealized appearance of four-grain junction at which three grains of phase α meet one grain of phase β. α/β interphase boundaries shown shaded, α/α grain boundaries clear. (After SMITH [5])

labelled α are considered to be grains of the same phase, while that labelled β is of a second phase. It is further assumed that, at the temperature we are considering, owing to diffusion or other transport processes the grains can change their shape, however slowly, under the influence of the surface tensions exerted along the boundaries.

When a state of balance has been reached,

$$\gamma_{a.a} = 2\gamma_{a.\beta} \cos \frac{\phi}{2},$$

where $\gamma_{a.a}$ is the energy of the boundary between the two grains of α and $\gamma_{a.\beta}$ is the energy of the interfaces between the grains of α and β. ϕ was termed by Smith the dihedral angle or, more specifically, for the case illustrated, the " β vs α/α " dihedral angle.

It follows that, if $\gamma_{a.\beta} = \gamma_{a.a}$, ϕ will be 120° and all three angles will be equal. This is the situation usually found to exist at three-grain edges in single-phase metals.

If $\gamma_{a.\beta} \leqslant \frac{1}{2}\gamma_{a.a}$, ϕ will be zero, and the second phase will penetrate along the grain boundary indefinitely.

If $\gamma_{a.\beta} > \frac{1}{2}\gamma_{a.a}$, complete penetration will not occur, and ϕ will increase, i.e. the penetration tendency will decrease as $\gamma_{a.\beta}/\gamma_{a.a}$ increases.

Figure 4 shows the situation existing at a four-grain junction. At such a junction, four three-grain edges generated by six boundary surfaces meet at a point. When all the boundary surface energies are equal, which is approximately true in a single-phase metal, the four edges are directed towards the corners of a regular tetrahedron and the angle between any two (e.g. X or Y) will be 109° 20'. The dihedral angle between any two boundary surfaces, measured in a plane normal to their line of intersection, will be 120°.

If, as indicated in the diagram, one of the crystals consists of a different phase from the other two, the surface energies associated with the three phase-boundaries (two of which are shown shaded) will differ from those associated with the three grain boundaries (shown clear). If the phase boundary energy is less than the grain boundary energy, ϕ, the β vs α/α dihedral angle will be less than 120° and will decrease as $\gamma_{a.\beta}/\gamma_{a.a}$ decreases. Remembering that the dihedral angle is measured in a plane normal to the three-grain edge concerned, and that, to a first approximation, the three interphase edges (edges where one β grain meets two α grains) will make equal angles with each other and will be equally inclined to the vertical single-phase edge, it will be seen that, as ϕ decreases, the point of intersection of the four-grain edges will move higher up the diagram, i.e. the apex of the β phase will move upwards. Ultimately, when $\phi = 60°$ and $\gamma_{a.\beta}/\gamma_{a.a} = 1/\sqrt{3}$, the three interphase edges will be three parallel lines perpendicular to the triangular base of the prism, X being then zero and Y 180°. The β pyramid has then become a triangular prism extending without limit along the single phase edge. More precisely, the relationship between ϕ, X, and Y in Fig. 2 is given by the equations:

$$\cos \frac{X}{2} = \frac{1}{2 \sin \phi/2}$$

$$\cos (180 - Y) = \frac{1}{\sqrt{3} \tan \phi/2}$$

It should be noted that the prediction that the second phase will penetrate indefinitely along the grain edges when $\phi < 60°$ is not at variance with the requirement that, for a liquid to penetrate a capillary, the wetting angle θ should be less than 90°. The criterion for the latter is that $\gamma_{s.v} > \gamma_{s.l}$, where $\gamma_{s.v}$ is the surface tension of the solid and $\gamma_{s.1}$ the interfacial tension between the two phases. When $\phi = 60°$, $\gamma_{a.a} = 1\cdot73\,\gamma_{a.\beta}$, where $\gamma_{a.a}$ is the surface tension of the grain boundary and $\gamma_{a.\beta}$ that of the interface. The grain-boundary tension in a metal is, however, considerably less than the surface tension, so that a system which satisfies the criterion that $\phi < 60°$ will also satisfy the criterion that $\theta < 90°$.

Smith showed that the types of equilibrium structure found in multiphase alloys could be accounted for on the basis of these relationships and those derived earlier. Thus consider a two-phase alloy containing a relatively minor quantity of the second phase, β. In general in such an alloy the minor phase will occur between the grains of the major phase rather than as inclusions within the grains, since the former location represents a lowering of the total interface energy relative to the latter. This lowering is greatest when the second phase is located at four-grain corners, since it can then partially replace six surfaces, and is progressively less when it is associated with three-grain edges and two-grain surfaces.

From the foregoing it will be seen that the condition that the second phase should occur as discrete particles at four-grain corners is that the dihedral angle should be greater than 60°. The shape of the particles, it should be noted, will be tetrahedral, i.e., four-cornered, but with the edges and sides in general curved to conform with the requirement that the angle X should achieve its equilibrium value. Thus, as shown above, when $\phi = 120°$, $X = 109°20'$, instead of 60° as in the case of a regular tetrahedron, and the edges and faces will be convex outwards. As ϕ increases towards 180° this convexity will increase so that the particle will become more and more spherical.

As ϕ decreases towards 60° on the other hand, and X decreases towards zero, the edges and faces of the particle will become increasingly concave and the apices of the particle will extend progressively along the three-grain edges. At $\phi = 60°$ or less, as we have seen, it will be capable of extending indefinitely along the grain edges but not along the grain faces. Particles of the second phase at adjacent corners will then join up to give a continuous network, the " strands " of which lie along the three-grain edges of the major phase. Since, in this condition, the grains of the major phase are still joined by their faces, the structure then consists of two interpenetrating phases each of which extends continuously through the alloy.

Finally, when $\phi = 0$, the second phase will penetrate between the faces of the grains of the major phase. The latter will then occur as discrete grains separated from each other by films of the minor phase.

In practice the size of the dihedral angles observed in a micro-section will vary even though the true value is constant. The reason for this is that such a section is a plane cut at random through the three-dimensional structure and the angle between any two planes in the structure as seen in the section can have any value between 0° and 180°, though with different probabilities. The problem of obtaining the true dihedral angle from the measured values in such a section was considered by HARKER and PARKER,[6] who showed that, when a histogram of the measured angles is plotted (frequency of occurrence against size of angle), the true dihedral angle, despite any asymmetry of the histogram, is the one most frequently observed. Poor agreement could be due to the true angles varying due to failure to attain equilibrium or to the lines of intersection of the surfaces defining the angles not being randomly oriented in space.

Harker and Parker applied these principles to studies of grain shape and grain growth in single-phase metals, and Smith used their treatment to obtain the dihedral angles in two- and three-phase alloys. Proof that the dihedral angles measured by Smith were equilibrium angles was obtained by measuring the angles formed by different combinations of interfaces in a three-phase alloy. By determining the appropriate angles, all six of the possible surface energies occurring in the alloy could be related to each other and quantitative values of their ratios obtained by two different routes. These were found to agree with each other within the limits of tolerance of the measurements, indicating that equilibrium angles were being measured.

The heat-treatments used by Smith involved quenching to retain the structures produced by annealing at high temperatures and, with some of the alloys investigated, e.g. Cu–Bi, and Cu–Pb and leaded brasses, in which a liquid phase would be present at the annealing temperature, he was able to examine the equilibrium distribution of the latter. This led him to conclude that, in alloy systems, when the liquid phase contains an appreciable concentration of the solid in solution, the solid/liquid interfacial tension is almost invariably less than half the grain boundary tension in the solid so that $\phi = 0$ and complete penetration of the liquid round the solid grains occurs. One consequence of this is that, when freezing is occurring in the interior of an ingot, the growing crystals will remain separated by a film of liquid until only a small amount of liquid is left. On the other hand, where the compositions of the liquid and solid differ widely, e.g. when liquid immiscibility exists, the solid/liquid inter-facial tension is usually greater than half the grain boundary ten-sion and complete penetration of the liquid does not occur. Similarly he found that in solid alloys the interfacial tension is usually greater than the grain boundary tension in either phase, and in many commercial alloys he found that ϕ lies between $0°$ and $120°$.

Another important generalization that follows from Smith's work is that, as the dihedral angle associated with a minor phase increases (and the ratio of the interfacial energy to the grain boundary energy increases), the less will an inclusion of the material change its shape, and the lower will be the energy change, when it is transferred from the interior of a grain to the grain boundary. Consequently inclusions of large dihedral angle, which will remain nearly spherical when they meet a grain boundary and require little energy to release them from it, should present less obstruction to grain growth than inclusions of low dihedral angle, which spread out when they meet a boundary and which, once collected by it, must move with it.

The first attempt to interpret the microstructure of a ceramic material in terms of surface energy relationships appears to have been by VAN VLACK,[7] who studied the effect of temperature and atmosphere on the dihedral angle in tridymite and cristobalite bodies containing iron oxides. Metallographic examination of quenched specimens showed that in samples containing cristobalite the dihedral angle measured in the iron silicate was about $55°$ at $1,550°C$. and decreased only slowly with rising temperature so that, at all temperatures up to the melting point of the silica, direct contact between silica crystals would be maintained. This, he suggested, provided a possible explanation of the high refractoriness-under-load of silica bricks.

Our own work in this field, which I propose to discuss in the sections below, has been directed primarily towards establishing the nature of the factors which control the distribution of the phases in basic refractories and the development of "direct bonding".

3. MINERALOGICAL CONSTITUTION OF BASIC REFRACTORIES

Since the mineralogical changes which occur in commercial basic refractories during firing are quite complex, it is desirable to discuss this aspect briefly first. One reason for this complexity is the number of components which must be considered significant variables, and it is only within the past few years that we have reached anything like an adequate understanding of the underlying phase equilibria.

The first major step in this direction was the elucidation of the assemblages of solid crystalline phases that can co-exist with magnesia (or magnesio-wustite when FeO is present) in the seven-component system $CaO–FeO–MgO–Fe_2O_3–Cr_2O_3–Al_2O_3–SiO_2$. For a complete description of these phase assemblages reference should be made to RAIT[8] or to a recent paper by the present author.[9] For the present purpose the simplified version shown in Table 1 will suffice. The most significant feature to note is that, in the part of the system covered, the variable that determines the combination of phases that should occur is primarily the CaO/SiO_2 ratio. When the molar value of this ratio is greater than 2, all or part of the sesquioxides will occur in combination with CaO as Ca chromite, ferrite, and aluminates. When it is less than 2, essentially all the sesquioxides occur in the spinel phase combined with MgO and FeO. The latter will then co-exist with magnesio-wustite and two silicates (one at the exact values of the limiting CaO/SiO_2 ratios indicated). Another feature to note is that, due to the prevalence of solid solution (isomorphous replacement), the number of phases co-existing in any one composition is usually only 4 or 5. This simplifies the relationships considerably.

While the phase assemblages have proved extremely useful in predicting the crystalline phases that should occur in a refractory body of any composition, they are to some extent an approximation. One reason for this is that there is appreciable solid solubility

Table 1

Phase Combinations in Basic Refractories

Molar ratio CaO/SiO_2					
0–1·0	1·0–1·5	1·5–2·0	Greater than 2·0		
Magnesio-wustite	Magnesio-wustite	Magnesio-wustite	Magnesio-wustite	Magnesio-wustite	Magnesio-wustite
Spinel	Spinel	Spinel	Spinel	Dicalcium silicate	Lime
Forsterite	Monticellite	Merwinite	Dicalcium silicate	Tricalcium silicate	Tricalcium silicate
Monticellite	Merwinite	Dicalcium silicate	Ca ferrites, aluminates and chromites	Ca ferrites, aluminates and chromites	Ca ferrites, aluminates, and chromites

between many of the phases at high temperatures. Thus monticellite exists over an appreciable range of Mg/Ca ratios at high temperatures. Similarly forsterite, when in equilibrium with monticellite at 1,400°C., has about $\frac{1}{8}$ of its Mg ions replaced by Ca. In both cases the solubility decreases with falling temperature and the permitted departure from the stoicheiometric composition below 1,000°C. appears to be very small.

It has also been shown quite recently that CaO and MgO are appreciably soluble in each other at high temperatures (though negligibly so at low), the solubility of MgO in CaO being 17% by weight and of CaO in MgO 7% by weight at 2,370°C., the eutectic temperature. Since Mg^{2+} is a smaller ion than Ca^{2+}, it is perhaps not unexpected that it should be able to enter the lattice of CaO rather more easily than CaO^{2+} can enter that of MgO.

Another recent discovery is that Cr_2O_3 [10, 11] and Al_2O_3 [12] are appreciably soluble in MgO at high temperatures. It has been known for some time [13] that Fe_2O_3 dissolves in MgO at high temperatures, this being accompanied by a loss of oxygen so that the magnesio-wustite solid solution formed contains both Fe^{3+} and Fe^{2+} cations. Figure 5 shows the solubility limits in the three systems,

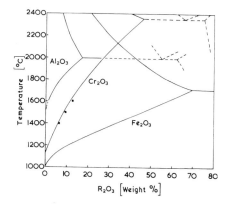

FIG. 5.—Solid solubilities of sesquioxides in periclase at high temperature. that for the system MgO–FeO–Fe_2O_3 being at the oxygen pressure of the atmosphere. It will be seen that at high temperatures the solubility increases in the order Al_2O_3, Cr_2O_3, Fe_2O_3, and that in all three systems it becomes very small at low temperatures. As a consequence, when periclase is heated in contact with the spinel of chrome ore, it will dissolve Al_2O_3, Cr_2O_3, Fe_2O_3 and FeO. Since the only other constituent of the spinel is MgO itself, this means that it can dissolve some of the spinel grain. We shall, for the moment, leave the question of the diffusion mechanism by which this occurs, but it is relevant to note here that the solid solution formed is magnesio-wustite having an MgO-type lattice in which some of Mg^{2+} cations are replaced by Al^{3+}, Cr^{3+}, Fe^{3+}, and Fe^{2+} cations.

Since two trivalent cations will replace three divalent cations, one cation site will also be left vacant for every two trivalent cations introduced. On subsequent cooling, owing to the decrease in solubility with temperature, the solid solution will break down and the sesquioxides will be precipitated in the form of a " mixed " magnesium spinel containing all three. Figure 2 shows the spinel precipitate within the periclase grains of the brick which had been fired at 1,800°C.

While I have referred to the periclase dissolving spinel, this is not an exact description of the solution process, since it is very unlikely that the sesquioxides will dissolve in the periclase in the same proportions as they occur in the spinel. In other words solution will be selective. Figure 5 gives only the solubilities of the individual sesquioxides when each is present alone in the spinel phase and does not tell us how much of each would dissolve from a " mixed " spinel of given composition. We are now trying to establish the boundary surface of the periclase phase in the quaternary system $MgO–Fe_2O_3$–Al_2O_3–Cr_2O_3.

In addition to the precipitated spinel in the periclase grains, Fig. 2 also shows that angular spinel crystals of regular outline have crystallized in the matrix. In some samples similar crystals can be seen growing out from the surface of the chrome grains, and at one time we were uncertain whether they had crystallized from the silicates at the firing temperature, although there were objections to this on thermodynamic grounds, or during cooling. Recently HAYHURST and LAMING [14] have shown that these relatively coarse secondary spinel crystals do not occur in samples quenched from 1,700°C., so that they must crystallize from the silicate matrix during cooling.

As they pointed out, this finding is consistent with the melting relationships indicated by the phase diagram of the system $MgO–MgAl_2O_4$–Mg_2SiO_4–Ca_2SiO_4 proposed by SOLACOLU.[15] The latter shows that, in this system, compositions having an analogous constitution to chrome–magnesite, when cooling from the liquid state, would deposit, in sequence, primary spinel, periclase and spinel, periclase, spinel and forsterite, and finally periclase, spinel, forsterite and monticellite.

In actual chrome–magnesite compositions it is not to be expected that these secondary spinel crystals, as they separate, would have the same composition as the original spinel grains, since selective solution of the various constituents of the spinel will occur during heating, depending on their relative solubilities in the liquid silicate. There is at present no precise information on this point. In the system $MgO–Cr_2O_3–SiO_2$, however, the solubility of $MgCr_2O_4$ in the liquid phase is low up to temperatures approaching 1,800°C., whereas in the system $MgO-Al_2O_3-SiO_2$ the solubility of the spinel in the liquid phase is high. This suggests that in chrome–magnesite refractories at high temperatures preferential solution of Al_2O_3 in the liquid silicate would occur, and this has apparently been confirmed by the work of BERRY, ALLEN and SNOW.[16]

4. IRON OXIDE EQUILIBRIA IN BASIC REFRACTORIES

When refractories contain iron oxides, phase changes, associated with changes in the state of oxidation of the iron, may occur on heating and cooling or when the partial pressure of oxygen in the atmosphere is changed. This is of particular importance in chrome–magnesite refractories and some 14 years ago we started a series of investigations of phase equilibria in spinel-forming systems containing iron oxides, from this standpoint.

The implications of this work on iron oxides is probably best illustrated by Fig. 6, which shows the composition- and phase-changes that occur when mixtures of MgO and Fe_2O_3 are heated under equilibrium conditions in air.[13] In the ternary diagram the compositions of fully oxidized mixtures, which consist of Fe_2O_3 and $MgFe_2O_4$ or $MgFe_2O_4$ and MgO, depending on the MgO/Fe_2O_3 ratio, and represent the stable state of the system at low temperatures, lie along the $MgO-Fe_2O_3$ edge. The dashed lines show the paths along which the mixtures investigated changed as they lost oxygen, and the compositions reached on these at various temperatures are indicated by their intersections with the isotherms (continuous lines with temperatures alongside). The boundaries of the areas where spinel or magnesio-wustite solid solutions exist as single phases are indicated by thick continuous lines. In the areas between these, two solid phases co-exist and the isotherms are straight lines joining the compositions of the two phases which co-exist at the temperatures indicated.

If the course of dissociation on heating is followed, it will be seen that, in mixtures consisting initially of Fe_2O_3 and $MgFe_2O_4$, dissociation of the Fe_2O_3 occurs progressively with rising temperature and is accompanied by solution of the Fe_3O_4 formed in the $MgFe_2O_4$ until the last trace of Fe_2O_3 dissociates, leaving a single spinel phase. In mixtures consisting initially of $MgFe_2O_4$ and MgO, dissociation proceeds with a progressive diminution in the amount of spinel and solution of iron oxide in the periclase until, with the higher MgO contents, a single magnesio-wustite phase is formed. These changes are reversible on cooling, i.e. re-oxidation will occur with separation into two phases.

In the smaller diagram the temperatures at which these transitions are complete are shown plotted against the initial composition before dissociation. The solubility limit of the RO phase with regard to the spinel corresponds to the " Fe_2O_3 " solubility line drawn in Fig. 5, and both correspond to the magnesio-wustite phase boundary in the ternary system.

Similar investigations of the systems $FeO–Fe_2O_3–Cr_2O_3$ and $FeO–Fe_2O_3–Al_2O_3$ have been carried out and the changes which take place when chrome and chrome–magnesite refractories are heated and cooled in an oxidizing atmosphere can be broadly understood in terms of these relationships. Thus in the former, at low

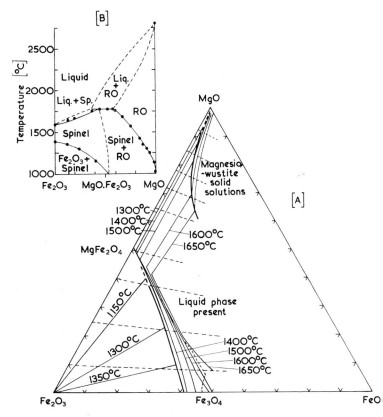

FIG. 6.—Phase-equilibrium relationships in the system MgO–FeO–Fe$_2$O$_3$ up to 1,650°C. in air.[13] Dissociation paths shown dashed, and composition isotherms as thin continuous lines with temperatures alongside. Smaller diagram shows quasi-binary projection of phase boundaries on a temperature/composition diagram

temperatures, oxidation of ferrous iron in the spinel occurs with separation of a sesquioxide phase, which is a solid solution of Fe_2O_3, Cr_2O_3 and Al_2O_3, instead of pure Fe_2O_3 as in Fig. 6. This phase can often be seen in the form of plates within the spinel grains, when oxidized chrome ore is examined by reflected-light microscopy. On subsequently heating to higher temperatures, progressive oxygen loss and re-solution of the sesquioxide in the spinel phase will occur, as in the simpler system.

5. THE STRUCTURE OF BASIC REFRACTORIES

From a consideration of the phase relationships involved it was decided that, in the first instance at least, the work on the structure of basic refractories should take the form of an investigation of the effect of appropriate oxides on the equilibrium structures at high temperatures of bodies consisting of periclase, and silicates which co-exist with it in the fired refractories. The silicate selected for the initial stage of the work which is described in detail in a paper by JACKSON, FORD and WHITE,[17] was monticellite $(CaO.MgO.SiO_2)$, which melts incongruently at 1,500°C. to form a liquid phase saturated with MgO whose composition changes only slowly with increasing temperature. The monticellite was prepared by firing finely ground mixtures of high-purity glass-making sand, A.R. grade $CaCO_3$, and pure grade magnesium carbonate. After grinding to pass a 300-mesh sieve, the product was mixed with the appropriate amount of calcined magnesia and the mixture was then pressed into a pellet.

An initial investigation showed that microstructures suitable for the measurement of dihedral angles and other structural features could be obtained with a monticellite content of 15% by weight. With this content it was found that, at 1,500°C., 2 h firing-time was generally sufficient for the dihedral angles to reach a steady value. All firings were carried out in air, the pellets being supported on platinum foil. After firing they were cooled rapidly to cause rapid freezing of the liquid phase. Prior to grinding and polishing they were impregnated with an epoxy resin.

The mixtures investigated consisted of an 85% periclase : 15% monticellite mixture and four series based on it but containing, (1) additions of Cr_2O_3, (2) additions of Fe_2O_3, (3) 5% Fe_2O_3 with increasing additions of Cr_2O_3, and (4) 10% Cr_2O_3 with increasing additions of Fe_2O_3. In all cases the additions were made as replacements for equal weights of MgO so that the content of monticellite remained constant at 15% by weight, this procedure being adopted to ensure that all the mixtures would have similar liquid contents at the firing temperature. All were fired at 1,550°C. for 2 h.

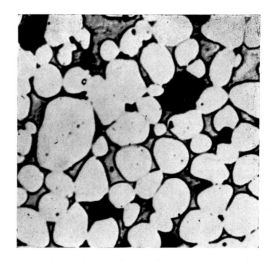

FIG. 7.—Structure obtained by firing a mixture of 85% periclase and 15% monticellite by weight at 1,550°C. for 2 h. Polished section, viewed by reflected light (×400)

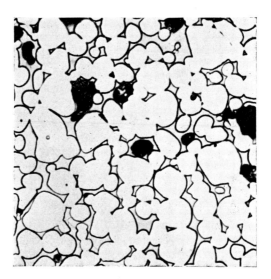

FIG. 8.—Structure obtained by firing a mixture of 80% MgO, 5% Cr₂O₃, and 15% monticellite by weight at 1,550°C. for 2 h. Polished section, viewed by reflected light (×400)

Figure 7 shows the microstructure of a body containing initially 85% periclase and 15% monticellite after firing at 1,550°C. for 2 h. Figure 8 shows a similar specimen containing 5% Cr_2O_3, the initial composition being 80% periclase, 5% Cr_2O_3, and 15% monticellite. Both sections contain rounded periclase grains (crystals) joined together at narrow necks, and set in a matrix of silicate (dark areas are sealed pores which have become rounded during firing). The dihedral angles of interest are the re-entrant angles formed at the necks between the periclase grains. In Fig. 7 the most frequently occurring angle was found to be 25°, whereas in Fig. 8 it was 40°.

In Fig. 9 the dihedral angles of all the mixtures investigated are plotted against their total content of R_2O_3, values for the series of mixtures containing respectively no Fe_2O_3, 5% Fe_2O_3, no Cr_2O_3, 5% Cr_2O_3 and 10% Cr_2O_3, being joined by continuous lines. In addition, values corresponding to series containing 1%, 3%, and 10% Fe_2O_3 are indicated by broken lines. These were obtained by interpolation, this operation being facilitated by the requirement that intersections of curves of constant Fe_2O_3 content with curves of constant Cr_2O_3 content must occur at the same total R_2O_3 content on each curve.

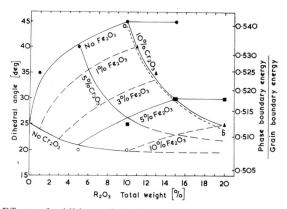

FIG. 9.—Effects of additions of Cr_2O_3 and Fe_2O_3, singly and together, on dihedral angle in periclase–monticellite bodies fired at 1,550°C. for 2 h.

From the occurrence of large, well-formed crystals of spinel in some of the sections it was possible to estimate the solubility limit of the spinel phase in periclase–silicate mixtures at 1,550°C. This as indicated by the dashed line **ab** in Fig. 9. On crossing **ab**, the lines for the 0% and 5% Fe_2O_3 series become horizontal. Since, when saturation was exceeded, the compositions of the phases present would remain constant (only their proportions varying), this provides evidence that equilibrium dihedral angles were being measured. One of the histograms obtained is shown in Fig. 10.

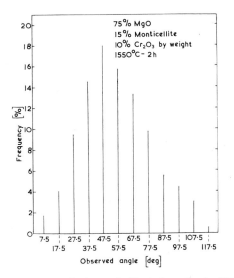

FIG. 10.—Histogram of observed dihedral angles in 75% MgO: 10% Cr₂O₃: 15% monticellite mixture

From Fig. 9 it will be seen that, while Cr_2O_3 increases the dihedral angle, and thus decreases the tendency of the liquid silicate to penetrate between the periclase grains, Fe_2O_3 acts in the opposite direction, causing increased penetration. Even at saturation with Cr_2O_3, however, ϕ is still less than $60°$, so that the liquid silicate will form a continuous phase, rather than discrete globules, within the interstices between the periclase grains. Another significant observation was that, in mixtures in which spinel crystals were present (all of which contained Cr_2O_3), these crystals appeared to prefer to nucleate and grow from periclase surfaces and in many cases to grow between the surfaces of two periclase grains, thus forming a direct-bonded spinel bridge between them.

That the addition of Cr_2O_3 actually does increase the degree of direct contact between the periclase grains is shown in Fig. 11, which shows traces obtained from the micrographs of Figs. 7 and 8, straight lines being drawn between the centres of grains that are in contact with each other in the sections. It is evident that something approaching a continuous network of periclase grains must have existed in the sample containing Cr_2O_3.

The extent of the grain-to-grain contact was also estimated by evaluating the ratio of grain boundary area (neck area) to solid–liquid interface area in the mixtures from the micrographs, using an extension of relationships derived by SMITH and GUTTMAN.[18]

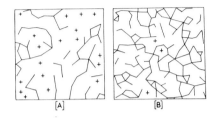

FIG. 11.—Tracings from [A] Fig. 7 and [B] Fig. 8.   Straight lines join centres of grains which are in direct contact in the section.   Crosses denote isolated grains
[A] Without Cr_2O_3 [B] With 5% Cr_2O_3

These authors showed that, if a straight line is drawn at random on the surface of a section through a three-dimensional structure, the total area of the two-dimensional features of the structure (grain- and phase-boundaries) per unit volume, when it consists of contiguous grains, is equal to

$$\frac{2N}{L},$$

where L is the length of the line and N the number of intercepts it makes with the boundaries.   In the case of a dispersed phase α whose grains are not contiguous, their surface area per unit volume of α is given by

$$\frac{2N_\alpha}{L_\alpha},$$

where L_α is the length of the line within the areas of α in the section and N_α the number of α boundaries which it intersects.   Since the ratio of the volume of α to the total volume is L_α/L, it follows directly that, for structures of the type shown in Figs. 7 and 8,

$$\frac{\text{Solid–solid boundary area}}{\text{Solid–liquid boundary area}} = \frac{\text{No. of grain-boundary intersections}}{\text{No. of phase-boundary intersections}}$$

In practice, to ensure large enough counts, it is usual to draw a considerable number of lines at random across the section, when L becomes the total length of all the lines drawn.

Figure 12, which employs the same method of plotting as Fig. 9, confirms that the degree of direct contact between the periclase grains increases with increasing Cr_2O_3 content and decreases with increasing Fe_2O_3 content.

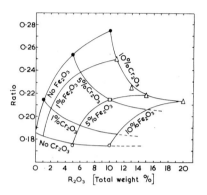

FIG. 12.—Effects of additions of Cr_2O_3 and Fe_2O_3, singly and together, on ratio of solid–solid boundary area to solid–liquid boundary area in periclase–monticellite bodies fired at 1,550°C. for 2 h

Another significant relationship that emerged from this work was that the average size of the periclase grains after 2 h firing decreased as the dihedral angle increased. This is shown in Fig. 13. The average true grain-diameter was obtained from the measured grain-diameters by use of a relation derived by FULLMAN,[19] who showed that, for a random arrangement of equal spherical grains, the average of the diameters observed in a section should be 0·8165 times the true diameter. Alternatively if a random line is drawn in the section, the average of the intercepts of individual grains on the line should be 0·667 times the true grain diameter. The estimates obtained by the two methods were found to agree within 3%. A dependence of firing-shrinkage and fired porosity on the dihedral angle was also found to exist, the former decreasing and the latter increasing as the dihedral angle increased.

These relationships do not appear to have been noted previously. As pointed out in Section 2, Smith concluded that a second phase, when present in small amounts as minute inclusions, would have a greater inhibiting action on grain growth when the dihedral angle was small than when it was large. This is the reverse of the relationship found by JACKSON et al.[17] Smith was, however, considering the effect of small inclusions on the migration of grain boundaries, whereas the present findings relate to grain growth in the presence of a relatively large volume of liquid. This will presumably involve the transfer of material through the liquid phase by solution, diffusion, and re-precipitation, but there are also indications that, in the early stages at least, direct agglomeration of the grains may be occurring. The time dependence of grain growth is now being investigated by Jackson in the hope of elucidating the mechanism involved. One significant result that has emerged is that both grain growth and neck growth continue long after the dihedral angle has reached its equilibrium value.

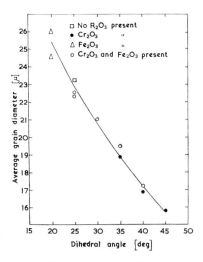

FIG. 13.—Variation of periclase grain-size with dihedral angle in periclase–monticellite bodies after firing for 2 h at 1,550°C.

The effect of temperature on the dihedral angle is also being studied. This work has shown that in the periclase–monticellite-based mixtures so far examined the equilibrium angle decreases by only a small amount up to 1,750°C. This agrees with Smith's findings with metallic alloys and Van Vlack's with silica, but is at variance with observations of HAYHURST and LAMING [14] on commercial chrome–magnesite refractories, since the latter find that the angle is very small at 1,750°C. In chrome–magnesite bricks, however, the silicate is a mixture of monticellite and forsterite and the indications from Solacolu's diagram (see Section 3) are that, while the liquid phase formed at low temperatures will approach the composition of monticellite, it will become increasingly rich in forsterite as the temperature rises, while the solubility of the periclase and spinel in it will increase. This might change the dihedral angle appreciably. Further work may clear up this point.

6. GENERAL CONSIDERATIONS

A condition that the simple treatment of the surface forces indicated in Section 2 should be valid is that the interfacial energies of the crystalline phases involved should be independent of, or only slightly dependent on, their orientation with respect to the crystal axes. An indication that this condition was fulfilled in both the metallic alloys examined by Smith and the periclase-monticellite bodies examined by Jackson *et al.* is provided by the rounded form of the grains. In some ceramic bodies, e.g. bodies containing mullite or corundum and a glass phase, this condition is apparently not fulfilled, since the crystals have well-developed faces. When this occurs, it can be assumed that the faces formed will represent surface orientations of minimum energy and that any rotation of such a surface relative to the crystal axes will be accompanied by an increase in the surface energy. Under these conditions, the forces acting at the intersection point can no longer be assumed to be entirely tangential, since there will be additional forces acting normal to the surfaces concerned and tending to restrain them in their minimum energy orientations. Equations corresponding to this case have been formulated by HERRING,[20] but unfortunately they cannot be generally applied, since they involve no fewer than five unknowns for only two independent equations.

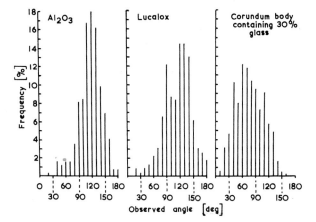

FIG. 14.—Histograms of observed dihedral angles in recrystallized alumina, in Lucalox, and in a body consisting of corundum crystals in a CaO–Al₂O₃–SiO₂ glass[21]

The histogram given by a body prepared from calcined alumina, CaO, and SiO_2, and consisting of corundum crystals in a saturated CaO-Al_2O_3-SiO_2 glass, is shown in Fig. 14.[21] The corundum crystals, which were in the form of plates, formed a practically continuous " direct-bonded " network, with the glass in the interstices. While this appears to be consistent with the fact that the most frequently occurring angle is 60°, the exact interpretation of the histogram is not clear, since plates with parallel faces, intersecting in pairs with a constant relative orientation, would give two dihedral angles, one the supplement of the other. Furthermore, when the same body was prepared using ground crystalline corundum instead of calcined alumina, the fired structure consisted of approximately isometric grains of corundum, mostly separated by films of glass, indicating that the dihedral angle was very small. At the moment it is thought that the latter structure may be the equilibrium one and that the system of interlocking plates represents a non-equilibrium but highly stable structure produced by solution and recrystallization from the liquid state of the calcined alumina. The formation of non-equilibrium structures during crystallization from the liquid state is probably not uncommon. For example, many eutectics, and structures in which dendrites occur, probably do not represent equilibrium, even though they may have considerable stability. Some structures formed by precipitation from metallic solid solutions, e.g. eutectoids and Widmanstätten structures, are also non-equilibrium structures, as is shown by the fact that they can be " spheroidized " by heat treatment.

The other two histograms in Fig. 14 are for single-phase alumina bodies. In both, as in most single-phase metals and alloys, the indicated size of the dihedral angle is 120°. It should be noted that this cannot be construed as indicating that the grain-boundary energy is entirely independent of orientation since, when the dihedral angle has a value of the order of 120°, it is relatively insensitive to differences in the grain boundary tensions, e.g. if we accept a value of 440 dynes/cm for the mean grain-boundary tension of alumina, a change of 30 dynes/cm in the tension in one of the grain boundaries meeting at a three-grain junction would increase the dihedral angle opposite it by 4° only, which would be scarcely detectable on a histogram. On the other hand, when the dihedral angle is small, as in many two-phase bodies, even a small change in the grain-boundary or phase-boundary tension will produce a relatively large change in the angle. A crystalline material may therefore give a dihedral angle of 120° when it is examined as a single-phase body and yet appear with well-developed crystal faces in a polyphase body.

Again, if we assume the grain-boundary tension in periclase to be 400 dynes/cm (consistent with a surface tension of the order of 1,000 dynes/cm), the change from 25° to 45° in the dihedral angle with addition of Cr_2O_3 shown in Fig. 9 would represent a change in the phase-boundary or grain-boundary energy of some 10 dynes/cm only (from 205 dynes/cm to 216 dynes/cm if the change were in the phase-boundary energy). Relatively small changes in the interfacial tensions can, therefore, produce considerable structural changes in polyphase bodies when the dihedral angle is small.

Another significant finding—which has a bearing on sintering-theory, is that, both in alloys and ceramic bodies, a sharp dihedral angle seems invariably to be formed at junctions between two phase-boundaries and a grain boundary. On the other hand, in the sintering of single-phase powders, where an analogous situation exists in the necks between particles, involving the intersection of the particle surfaces with a grain boundary, rounding-off of the angle generally occurs and in fact the assumption of surface curvature in the neck is essential to sintering-theory. A possible reason for this difference in behaviour emerges when the change in surface energy, associated with the change from a sharp dihedral angle to a curved surface, is considered. For this purpose the latter is assumed to be circular in a plane perpendicular to the line of intersection of the three boundaries and is represented by the arc DBC inscribed within the arms of the dihedral angle DAC in Fig. 15. (It may be noted that in such a circular section the interfacial tensions would not be balanced).

The change in surface energy in changing from the dihedral angle to the curved surface (per cm of the line of intersection) is then

$$AB\gamma_{a,a} + \frac{\pi r (180 - \theta)}{180} \gamma_{a,\beta} - 2AC\gamma_{a,\beta}$$

$$= r\gamma_{a,a} \left[\operatorname{cosec} \frac{\theta}{2} - 1 \right] + r\gamma_{a,\beta} \left[\frac{\pi (180 - \theta)}{180} - 2 \cot \frac{\theta}{2} \right]$$

where r is the radius of curvature of arc DBC.

If $\theta = \phi$, the equilibrium dihedral angle, so that $\gamma_{a,a} = 2\gamma_{a,\beta} \cos \frac{\theta}{2}$, this expression becomes

$$r\gamma_{a,\beta} \left[\frac{\pi (180 - \theta)}{180} - 2 \cos \frac{\theta}{2} \right],$$

which is positive for all values of θ up to 180°, i.e. the sharp dihedral angle represents the lower energy state.

If, however, $\theta < \phi$ so that $\gamma_{a.a} < 2\gamma_{a.\beta} \cos \dfrac{\theta}{2}$, the rounded neck represents the lower energy state for all values of θ below a critical value that depends on the value of ϕ. Thus when $\phi = 120°$, this situation holds up to an angle of about $110°$; when $\phi = 60°$, it holds up to about $30°$.

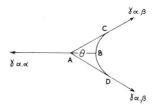

FIG. 15.—Section through neck between two grains of α in contact with a second phase β when a sharp dihedral angle is formed (DAC), and when curvature of the α/β interface occurs (DBC)

The significance of this would appear to be as follows. During the sintering of single-phase powders $\gamma_{a.\beta}$ is the surface tension of the solid and is of the order of $2\gamma_{a.a}$. ϕ is therefore large (of the order of $150°$) and rounding should thus be expected to occur at all points of contact. In two-phase mixtures, on the other hand, $\gamma_{a.\beta}$ is the interfacial tension and is usually much less than $\gamma_{a.a}$. ϕ is therefore usually much smaller, and the curved surface will represent the lower energy only at small values of θ. Further the decrease in energy associated with rounding of the surface will be considerably smaller, at a given value of θ, than when ϕ is large.

REFERENCES

1. Allison, E. B., Brock, P., and White, J., *Trans. Brit. Ceram. Soc.,* **56,** 309, 1957.
2. Richardson, H. M., *Refract. J.,* **35,** 119, 1959.
3. Laming, J., *Refract. J.,* **35,** 116, 1959.
4. Ford, W. F., Hayhurst, A., and White, J., *Trans. Brit. Ceram. Soc.,* **60,** 581, 1961.
5. Smith, C. S., *Trans. A.I.M.E.,* **175,** 15, 1948.
6. Harker, D., and Parker, E. R., *Trans. A.S.M.,* **34,** 156, 1945.
7. Van Vlack, L. H., *J. Amer. Ceram. Soc.,* **43,** 140, 1960.
8. Rait, J. R., " Basic Refractories " (London: Iliffe, 1950).
9. White, J., *J. Iron Steel Inst.,* **200,** 611, 1962.
10. Hayhurst, A., Ph.D. Thesis, University of Sheffield, 1961.
11. Alper, A. M.   Private communication.
12. Alper, A. M., McNally, R. N., Ribbe, P. H., and Doman, R. C., *J. Amer. Ceram. Soc.,* **45,** 263, 1962
13. Woodhouse, D., and White, J., *Trans. Brit. Ceram. Soc.,* **54,** 333, 1954.

14. Hayhurst, A., and Laming, J., *Refract. J.*, **39**, 80, 1963.
15. Solacolu, S., *Ber. Deut. Keram. Ges.*, **37**, 266, 1960.
16. Berry, T. F., Allen, W. C., and Snow, R. B., *J. Amer. Ceram. Soc.*, **33**, 121, 1950.
17. Jackson, B., Ford, W. F., and White J., *Trans. Brit. Ceram. Soc.*, **62**, 577, 1963.
18. Smith, C. S., and Guttman, L., *Trans. A.I.M.E.*, **197**, 81, 1957.
19. Fullman, R. L., *Trans. A.I.M.E.*, **197**, 447, 1957.
20. Herring, C., "Physics of Powder Metallurgy." Ed. W. E. Kingston (McGraw-Hill, 1951), Chapter 8.
21. Buist, D. S. Unpublished work.

22—Development of Connected Porosity in Dense Sintered Oxides at High Temperature

By D. Hayes,* E. W. Roberts, and J. P. Roberts

*Houldsworth School of Applied Science,
University of Leeds*

ABSTRACT   E137—E18/D434

Gas-permeability measurements indicated that tubes of sintered alumina (two materials with initial porosity essentially zero and 5–9% respectively), magnesium aluminate spinel, and " stabilized " zirconia, all of which originally contained no channels through the wall, developed such channels after exposure to high temperature. Microscope examination confirmed the development of connected porosity in some cases, and disclosed secondary phases which were altered by the heat-treatment. Mechanisms of channel formation are discussed.

Développement de pores communicants, dans des oxydes frittés denses, à haute température

Des mesures de perméabilité aux gaz ont indiqué que des tubes en alumine frittée (en deux substances, l'une de porosité en principe égale à 0 et l'autre de porosité comprise entre 5 et 9%) en spinelle d'aluminate de magnésium et en zircone " stabilisée " dont les parois ne contenaient à l'origine pas de canaux, en contenaient après avoir été exposés à une température élevée. Des examens au microscope ont confirmé le développement de pores communicants dans certains cas et ont décelé la présence de phases secondaires altérées par le traitement thermique. Les mécanismes de formation des canaux sont étudiés.

Die Entwicklung einer durchgehenden Porosität in dichtgesinterten Oxiden bei hohen Temperaturen

Messungen der Gasdurchlässigkeit zeigen, dass Rohre aus Sinterkorund (zwei verschiedene Materialien mit einer anfänglichen Porosität von 0 bzw. 5 bis 9%), Magnesiumspinell und stabilisiertem Zirkonoxid, die alle anfänglich keine durchgehenden Porenkanäle hatten, bei hohen Temperaturen solche entwickelten. Mikroskopische Untersuchungen bestätigten die Entstehung von durchgehender Porosität in einigen Fällen und zeigten zweite Phasen, die durch die Wärmebehandlung geändert wurden. Der Mechanismus der Bildung der Porenkanäle wird erörtert.

1. INTRODUCTION

Loss of the imperviousness of dense sintered oxides to gases after prolonged heating at high temperature was reported by Ryshkewitch many years ago.[1] This phenomenon is now being investigated further in the present authors' laboratory, and the development of connected porosity has been directly observed in certain materials.

* Now at Canadian Refractories Ltd., Marelan, P.Q., Canada.

From the practical point of view of making refractory materials having permanently low gas-permeability at high temperatures, prevention of the establishment of channel-flow permeation is the most urgent problem to be solved. An understanding of how and why connected porosity develops in materials initially free of it is therefore required.

Of the available dense ceramics whose permeability has been studied, certain conventional sintered aluminas appear to be the best for low permeability at temperatures reaching up to 1,700°C. However, even with these materials the permeability suddenly increases after tens or hundreds of hours at ~1,700°C. due to the onset of channel flow. The other materials examined have behaved similarly though under less severe conditions.

The term "deterioration" has been used[2] for the onset of channel-flow permeation. The purposes of the present paper are to focus attention on deterioration and to report observations which help to explain the phenomenon in some materials.

2. EXPERIMENTAL OBSERVATIONS AND DISCUSSION

Permeability measurements provide a sensitive and convenient means of investigating the formation of connected porosity in a solid. As the connected porosity develops to give continuous channels through the thickness of a specimen, so the kinetics of any previous gas permeation are replaced by those characteristic of channel flow processes, of which Knudsen (molecular) flow and viscous flow are the most commonly encountered.

The observations on two sintered aluminas, one sintered spinel and one sintered zirconia, now to be reported, were made on tubes whose permeability had been measured at high temperature up to the point in time at which "deterioration" set in. The tubes were closed-ended and of O.D.~20 mm, I.D.~15 mm, and length ~900 mm, except in the case of the sintered alumina tubes of essentially zero porosity, the dimensions of which were O.D. 15 mm, I.D. 10 mm and length 150 mm. The type of apparatus and the technique used in the permeability measurement have already been described.[2, 3] The change in permeation kinetics during deterioration of two sintered-alumina tubes has also been reported.[2]

2.1 Sintered Alumina of Essentially Zero Porosity (Manufacturer H)*

In the course of high-temperature permeability experiments with oxygen, nitrogen, argon and helium, part of one tube, A23(H), was

---

* A code system is used to denote the manufacturers of the various materials whose permeability has been investigated.

maintained at 1,625°C. for 78 h and at 1,700°C. for 44 h, while part of a second tube, A24(H), was maintained at 1,650°C. for 72 h. Both tubes were vacuum-tight before heating. The high-temperature measurements disclosed permeation of oxygen through A23(H) but no definite permeation of nitrogen or argon (this behaviour being similar to that which had been found previously with some sintered aluminas of porosity 4–8%, when it was attributed to a solid-state diffusion of oxygen [2, 3]). This tube was vacuum-tight at room-temperature after the measurements. Tube A24(H), on the other hand, was appreciably permeable to oxygen, nitrogen, argon and helium at 1,650°C., showing that there was connected porosity throughout the wall even before the first measurements were made: presumably it developed during the initial 24-h outgassing period at this temperature. At room temperature after the high-temperature measurements, the permeation kinetics of the same four gases followed closely those expected for Knudsen flow.

Before heating, the microstructure of the material was regular, with ~20μ equidimensional grains, as shown by polished sections (Fig. 1) and thin sections of the unheated ends of the tubes. However, the heating during the permeability work brought about re-

0·5 mm

FIG. 1.—Thermally-etched polished section of the sintered alumina of essentially zero porosity before heating.

markable changes, viz. " rivulet " systems of channels converging on the inner wall surface, extensive grain-growth at the outer wall surface, and a deposit on the inner wall surface (Fig. 2). The section in Fig. 3 disclosed two additional features: channels connecting with the outer wall surface, and giant grains extending almost through the wall (apparently having grown round some of the channels).

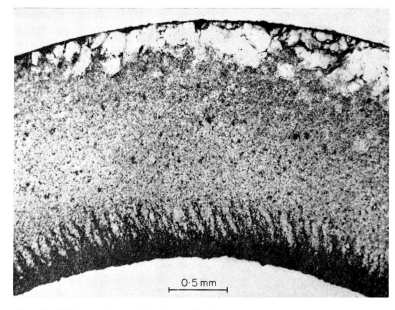

0·5 mm

FIG. 2.—Thin section of the sintered alumina of essentially zero porosity after heat-treatment, showing " rivulet " channels, grain-growth and a deposit (at the inner wall-surface).

There was no doubt that channels were indeed responsible for the "rivulet" patterns. Under high magnification there was a concentration of light down the centre-line of each limb, while under low magnification the patterns appeared dark (cf Figs. 2, 3). This is as would be expected for channels since, with the high refractive index of corundum, parallel rays of light would diverge strongly on traversing channels, and some of the divergent rays would be collected by high-magnification objectives but not by low-magnification objectives.

Figure 4 shows the sub-surface detail disclosed by dark-ground illumination of an area near the inner wall surface in a polished section. The numerous channels which can clearly be seen form

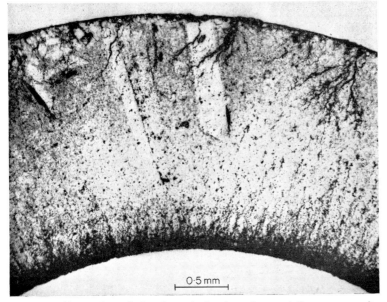

FIG. 3.—Thin section of the sintered alumina of essentially zero porosity after heat-treatment, showing "rivulet" channels at both outer and inner wall-surfaces and giant grains.

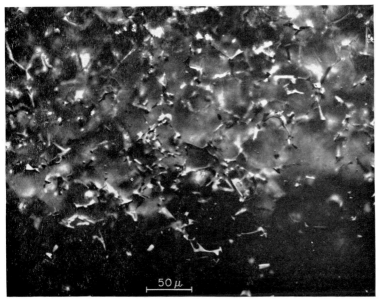

FIG. 4.—Channels near the inner wall-surface of the sintered alumina of essentially zero porosity as shown up by dark-ground illumination.

part of the rivulet system. They are situated in the grain-boundary network, and they appear to follow " three-grain edges ".

Deterioration in these tubes no doubt occurs when the channels extend until they connect the two wall-surfaces, and the channels are almost certainly produced by the volatilization of some impurity.

Throughout the experiments the interiors of the tubes had been pumped continuously (diffusion pump) except during periods of a few minutes when permeation was measured. The exteriors of the tubes had usually been surrounded by the gases chosen for the measurements, at 1 atm. pressure, with only occasional evacuation. The envelope tube was of sintered alumina, purity $\sim 99.7\%$, porosity (closed) $\sim 7\%$. There were no thermocouples or foreign material of any kind inside the tubes; in the annular space of the envelope there was a Pt–5% Rh/Pt–20% Rh thermocouple.

The only impurity phase detected by optical microscopy was present as discrete grains and in such small amounts that its removal could not have accounted for the formation of the connected porosity. This phase, which was absent from regions near the wall surface before the heating, appeared to be the spinel impurity referred to by other workers [4-6] with similar material.

Chemical analysis of portions 0·5 cm long cut from the unheated end and from a heated part of tube A24(H) (actually at 3 cm from the closed end, *which was ~2 cm from the section that had been hottest*) gave:

	Weight (%)	
	Unheated end	*Heated part*
SiO$_2$	0·22	0·68
TiO$_2$	<0·01	<0·01
Mn$_3$O$_4$	0·03	0·04
CaO	0·19	0·19
MgO	0·12	0·19
K$_2$O	0·03	0·04
Na$_2$O	0·02	0·02
Li$_2$O	<0·01	<0·01
P$_2$O$_5$	0·06	0·06
Cr$_2$O$_3$	<0·01	0·04

It had been believed that the material was a pure alumina apart from a deliberate magnesia addition, but it can be seen that appreciable amounts of silica and lime were also present. The data for the heated part show a $3 \times$ increase in silica and a $1\frac{1}{2} \times$ increase in magnesia (the increase in Cr$_2$O$_3$ may not be real), and it is believed that these increases are accounted for by the deposit on the inside wall (cf Figs. 2, 3). If this belief is correct, it must be concluded that both " magnesia " and " silica " sublimed *in vacuo* from the hottest part of the tube. It seems likely therefore that the formation of channels in this material was associated with loss of silica, since loss of magnesia has been reported before [4, 6] but channels do not then appear to have been formed. Since the only second phase observed in the present material was spinel as discrete grains and, in particular, no glass could be detected, it is concluded tentatively that the silica was lost from the alumina itself.

2.2 Sintered-alumina Materials with Closed Porosity (Manufacturers B and A)

Investigation of the high-temperature permeability of these more conventional dense sintered aluminas has already been reported.[2, 7, 3] Material B was ~99·7% Al_2O_3, with 5–8% porosity; material A was ~99·4% Al_2O_3, with 7–9% porosity.

The conditions necessary for deterioration varied among tubes but were some tens or hundreds of hours at temperatures around 1,700°C. Before deterioration, i.e. before channel-flow kinetics were detectable, material B showed [2, 3] selective permeation of oxygen which, it is now clear (from accompanying work on single crystals [8]), can be attributed to some kind of grain-boundary diffusion. Material A, in contrast, showed high-temperature permeation of both oxygen and nitrogen, the kinetics always being consistent with those for an activated diffusion process, and it has been postulated that surface diffusion through narrow channels may have been the rate-controlling process.[2]

Work with a carbon-impregnation technique established that the absence of channel permeation in tubes B was due to the presence of " skins " of material adjacent to one or both wall surfaces and containing only closed porosity.[7] The same technique confirmed the presence of connected porosity across the skins after deterioration: the distribution of carbon in the pores in the interior of the tube walls indicated the localities in the skin in which channels had developed but the channels themselves could not be distinguished.

The tubes of material A possessed no skins on delivery, nor did skins develop during the high-temperature work. In fact, the carbon-impregnation technique showed that there was always some connected porosity throughout the wall, but the dimensions and probably the number of the connected pores must have increased rapidly when " deterioration " set in.

The mechanism of deterioration in these materials has not yet been identified With skins, it might be cracking at grain-boundaries under the internal stresses which must increase as the grains in the skins grow: grains of considerable size have been found in these regions. Alternatively new porosity might be produced by the plastic deformation which invariably occurs while the permeability measurements are being made.

Nevertheless it appears that deterioration of some alumina materials of reasonable purity may be brought about by breakdown of an impurity phase. Figure 5A shows a second phase which has been observed locally in considerable quantities in some specimens of material B.[9]   X-ray diffraction has identified it as sodium "β-alumina" (approx. $Na_2O \cdot 11Al_2O_3$).[10, 11]   On thermally etching a polished section in air at 1,600°C. for 10 min, a depression is formed in the position of each β-alumina grain, as can be seen by comparing Fig. 5B with Fig. 5A. This observation suggests that the β-alumina at surfaces loses its sodium during thermal etching and that connected porosity might well be extended in materials containing sodium impurity by the breakdown of the β-phase.

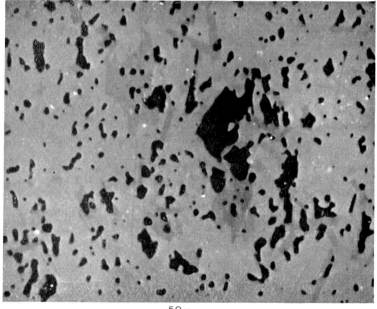

50μ

FIG. 5A.—Polished but unetched section of sintered alumina with closed porosity, showing a second phase.

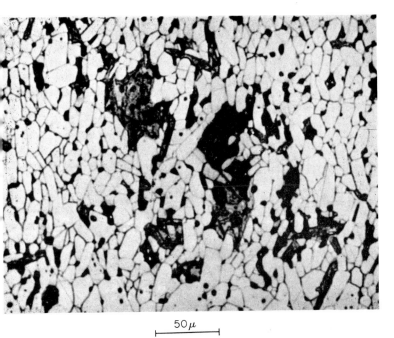

50 μ

FIG. 5B.—The same specimen after thermal etching, showing depressions
where there had previously been grains of the second phase.

2.3 Sintered Magnesium Aluminate Spinel (Manufacturer A)

This material was of density 3·17–3·28 g.cm⁻³. It deteriorated
after only tens of hours in the region 1,500–1,600°C. under the conditions of permeability measurements,[12] i.e. with the interior of
tubes evacuated and the exterior exposed to 1 atm. pressure of gas,
usually oxygen. The distribution of connected porosity in one of
the deteriorated spinel tubes is indicated in Fig. 6. The photograph
was taken with a long exposure during which a high-frequency
discharge probe was passed over the outside of the evacuated tube:
the light patches show where the discharge became concentrated at
the entrances to channels running through the tube wall.

Examination of both thin sections and polished sections of the
unheated end of a tube disclosed two impurity phases between the
~0·5 mm spinel grains: one, present as continuous films, was of
medium birefringence and of reflectivity lower than that of the
spinel; the other, present as discontinuous films and often at " three-
grain edges ", was of very high birefringence and reflectivity. In

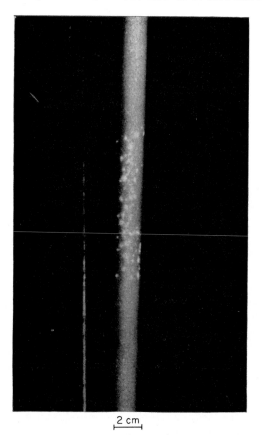

2 cm

FIG. 6.—Distribution of connected porosity in a sintered magnesium aluminate spinel tube after deterioration, as shown up by a high-frequency discharge probe.

the photomicrograph of a polished section shown in Fig. 7A, these two phases can be seen in the " grain-boundaries " of the spinel—the first one appearing dark grey and the second one nearly white.

After deterioration, the phase of low reflectivity was largely missing, leaving gaps along grain-boundaries (Fig. 7B); the gaps could be seen throughout the thickness of the tube wall and were certainly responsible for the deterioration. The highly-reflecting phase appeared unchanged.

Chemical analysis of portions of unheated end and heated zone gave:

	Weight (%)	
	Unheated end	*Heated part*
SiO_2	0·23	0·14
TiO_2	<0·01	<0·01
Al_2O_3	74·30	74·04
Fe_2O_3	0·32	0·34
Mn_3O_4	<0·01	<0·01
CaO	0·27	0·17
MgO	24·62	25·29
K_2O	<0·01	<0·01
Na_2O	<0·01	<0·01
Li_2O	<0·01	<0·01
Loss on ignition	0·14	0·17
	99·88	100·15
ZrO_2 (spectro-graphically)	0·3	0·3 (accuracy within 2 ×)

The microscopy and analysis together suggest that the non-volatile phase was zirconia or some compound containing it. The volatile phase of low reflectivity has not been identified but the analysis indicates that it probably contained calcium and silicon.

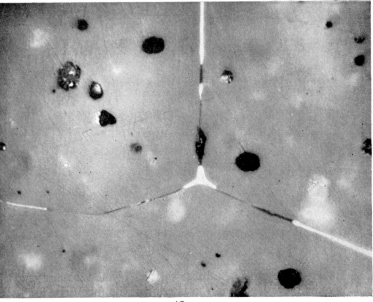

10μ

FIG. 7A.—Polished but unetched section of a sintered magnesium aluminate tube before deterioration, showing two impurity phases at grain-boundaries.

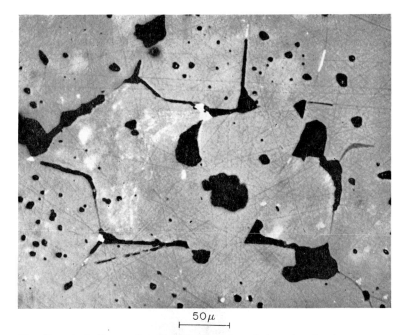

50μ

FIG. 7B.—A similar section after deterioration of the tube, showing gaps at grain-boundaries due to loss of the impurity phase of low reflectivity.

2.4 Sintered " Stabilized " Zirconia (Manufacturer A)

The material contained 91% ZrO_2, 4% MgO, and 3% Al_2O_3 approximately. The overall tube density was 5·03–5·12 g.cm^{-3}. Deterioration was found in one tube after heating at 1,740°C. for 12 h, but other tubes leaked at room-temperature following 12 h exposure at only 1,250°C. or 1,500°C.[12] In the case of the tube that had reached 1,740°C., the leak rate increased markedly at room temperature over the two days immediately following cooling and, on removing the tube from the apparatus, two 8 cm longitudinal cracks extending right through the wall were present in the part of the tube that had been heated to the maximum temperature.

Microscopical examination of this part showed a layer of new phase at both the outer and inner surfaces of the tube and cracks between the outer layer and the interior of the tube (Fig. 8). All the available microscopical evidence is consistent with the hypothesis that the phase is destabilized (monoclinic) zirconia. Destabilization is not unexpected in the light of chemical analyses carried out on the cracked tube:

Weight (%)

	Unheated end	Heated part
SiO_2	0·57	0·20
TiO_2	0·17	0·25
Al_2O_3	3·19	3·58
Fe_2O_3	0·26	0·19
CaO	0·13	0·12
MgO	4·43	3·91
K_2O	<0·01	0·02
Na_2O	0·01	0·03
Li_2O	<0·01	<0·01
ZrO_2	90·72	91·46
Loss on ignition	0·24	0·56
	99·72	100·32

The low magnesia content indicates that the material was not fully stabilized. On destabilization, at the temperatures of the permeability measurements, the tetragonal modification would be produced and then, on cooling, this would invert to the monoclinic modification with an appreciable volume expansion. The cracking away of the layer of destabilized material at the outer surface on cooling to room-temperature is therefore understandable. The compressive

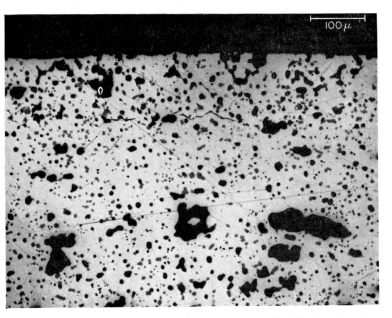

FIG. 8.—Polished but unetched section of a " stabilized " zirconia tube after deterioration, showing cracking between the presumed destabilized region adjoining the outer wall-surface and the stabilized interior.

stress in the layer at the inner surface would not, however, have been able to relieve itself by similar cracking, and it is suggested that the two large longitudinal cracks observed traversing the wall originated in the interior of the wall where tensile stress was at a maximum. The delayed formation of these cracks is consistent with residual stresses produced by destabilization. (It is considered that the cracks could not have had their origin in thermal shock, for such cracks would not be expected to be longitudinal or delayed.)

Thus, it appears that zirconia materials of this type deteriorate by cracking following the beginning of destabilization.

3. CONCLUSIONS

It is clear that connected porosity develops rapidly in several of the presently-available ceramics of high melting-point, impairing their suitability for applications requiring long-term impermeability to gases at high temperatures. In some cases at least the connected porosity is of chemical origin and there are therefore grounds for hoping that deterioration may become a less severe problem as purer materials become available.

ACKNOWLEDGMENTS

The tubes of pore-free alumina and spinel were kindly presented by the manufacturers. The chemical analyses were carried out by Mr. H. Bennett and his colleagues at the British Ceramic Research Association, Stoke-on-Trent. The support of the Atomic Energy Research Establishment, Harwell, is gratefully acknowledged.

REFERENCES

1. Ryschkewitsch, E., *Ber. Deut. Keram. Ges.*, **16**, 111, 1935; see also Ryshkewitch, E., " Oxide Ceramics " (Academic Press, 1960), p. 255.
2. Hayes, D., Budworth, D. W., and Roberts, J. P., *Trans. Brit. Ceram. Soc.*, **62**, 507, 1963.
3. Hayes, D., Budworth, D. W., and Roberts, J. P., *Trans. Brit. Ceram. Soc.*, **60**, 494, 1961.
4. St. Pierre, P. D. S., and Gatti, A., *General Electric Research Laboratory, Schenectady, U.S.A., Reports* 58-RL-1885 and 58-RL-2061, 1958.
5. Coble, R. L., *General Electric Research Laboratory, Schenectady, U.S.A., Report* 59-RL-2212, 1959.
6. Bruch, C. A., *Bull. Amer. Ceram. Soc.*, **41**, 799, 1962.
7. Fryer, G. M., Budworth, D. W., and Roberts, J. P., *Trans. Brit. Ceram. Soc.*, **62**, 525, 1963.
8. Hayes, D., and Roberts, J. P., to be published.
9. Roberts, E. W., unpublished work, University of Leeds, 1961.
10. Nelson, J. B.   Private communication from Morganite Research and Development Ltd., London, S.W.18, 1962.
11. Davidson, J. A. C., unpublished work, University of Leeds, 1963.
12. Roberts, E. W., and Roberts, J. P., to be published.

23—Thermodynamic Order of Phase Transitions in Rock-Salt and Spinel Lithium Ferrites

By J. C. ANDERSON and M. SCHIEBER

*Department of Electrical Engineering,
Imperial College, London, S.W.7*

ABSTRACT

A41

α-LiFeO$_2$, which has a disordered, rock-salt structure at room temperature, and the ordered pseudo-spinel LiFe$_5$O$_8$ have been studied in a high-temperature X-ray camera. LiFeO$_2$ transforms about 420°C. to a b.c. tetragonal structure, β-LiFeO$_2$. The β-phase transforms to a γ-phase, which is ordered, at 530°C. and this, in turn, returns to the disordered α structure at 660°C. The spinel ferrite LiFe$_5$O$_8$ has an order/disorder reversible transition at 750°C., and a magnetic ordering transition at 630°C. These transformations and transitions have been classified for thermodynamic order, by consideration of volume and structure changes, as observed by X-ray methods. A mechanism is proposed for the LiFeO$_2$ transformations, in terms of the requirements for ordering in a close-packed structure.

Ordre thermodynamique des transitions de phase dans le sel gemme et dans les oxydes doubles de fer et de lithium

LiFeO$_2$-α, qui possède une structure de sel gemme en désordre à la température abiante et le pseudo-spinelle LiFe$_5$O$_8$, qui possède une structure ordonnée ont été étudiés à l'aide d'une caméra de rayons X pour hautes températures. LiFeO$_2$ se transforme vers 420°C. en une structure quadratique à faces centrées, LiFeO$_2$-β. A 530°C. la phase-β se transforme en une phase-γ, ordonnée, qui à son tour retourne a la structure-α en désordre réversible à 750°C. et une transition ordonnée magnétique à 630°C. Ces transformations et transitions ont été classées au point de vue de l'ordre thermodynamique ein fonction des modifications de volume et de structure observées par des méthodes de rayons X. Un mécanisme des transformations de LiFeO$_2$, en fonction des nécessités de l'adoption d'une structure étroitement organisée, est proposé.

Die thermodynamische Reihenfolge von Phasenumwandlungen von Kochsalz- und Spinell-Lithium-Ferriten

α-LiFeO$_2$, das eine fehlgeordnete Kochsalzstruktur bei Raumtemperatur hat, und der geordnete Pseudospinell LiFe$_5$O$_8$ wurden in einer Hochtemperaturröntgenkamera untersucht. Bei etwa 420°C. wandelt sich LiFeO$_2$ in eine raumzentrierte tetragonale Struktur β-LiFeO$_2$ um, die sich unwandelt bei 530°C. in eine γ-Phase, die geordnet ist. Die γ-Phase kehrt bei 660°C. in die fehlgeordnete α-Struktur zurück. Der Spinellferrit LiFe$_5$O$_8$ zeigt bei 750°C. eine reversible Ordnung/Unordnungs-Umwandlung und einen Übergang in magnetische Ordnung bei 630°C. Diese Umwandlungen und Übergänge wurden nach ihrer thermodynamischen Reihenfolge geordnet indem Volumen und Strukturänderungen betrachtet wurden, die mit der Röntgenmethode beobachtet wurden. Für die LiFeO$_2$-Umwandlung wurde ausgehend von den Bedingungen der Ordnung einer dichtest gepackten Struktur ein Mechanismus vorgeschlagen.

1. INTRODUCTION

Recent high-temperature X-ray studies on single crystals of LiFeO$_2$ by the authors [1] have shown that the phase transition from a disordered rock-salt structure, α-LiFeO$_2$, to an ordered chalcopyrite structure, γ-LiFeO$_2$, is via an intermediate β-phase. COLLONGUES [2] and FAYARD,[3] in earlier studies of the material, reported a single β-phase having an AuCu face-centred tetragonal structure. It has been established that the α-phase transforms to a β-phase with a body-centred tetragonal structure belonging to the space group I.4. The ordering sequence is proposed as $\alpha \longrightarrow \beta \longrightarrow \gamma$. The experimental technique also provides detail of the volume changes occurring at the transition temperature. It is the purpose of this paper to consider the thermodynamic order of transition of the phase-changes, based on the volumetric and structural information obtained. This is related to the ordering behaviour of the spinel LiFe$_5$O$_8$, which has also been studied.[4]

2. EXPERIMENTAL DETAILS

Full details of specimen preparation and experimental technique have been published elsewhere [1]; only a brief outline is given here.

Both LiFeO$_2$ and LiFe$_5$O$_8$ single crystals were grown by slow cooling, from a ternary melt of Li$_2$O–Fe$_2$O$_3$–B$_2$O$_3$. The X-ray investigation was carried out in a powder camera operating from room temperature to 900 °C., from which the unit-cell dimensions were obtained as a function of temperature. These were calculated, from the powder photography measurements, by means of a least-squares programme on the London University Mercury computer.

The single crystals were mounted in a Weissenberg camera and the resulting photographs, together with powder-diffraction photographs of the crushed crystals, were used to determine the structure of the crystals. Patterson synthesis has been calculated from the corrected intensities of the powder diffraction patterns of the β-phase, with the aid of the computer, in order to ascertain its structure, which was found to be different from that published by other authors.

3. STRUCTURES OF PHASES

Figures 1–3 show the structures of the α, β and γ phases of LiFeO$_2$. The original β-phase, of AuCu structure, proposed by

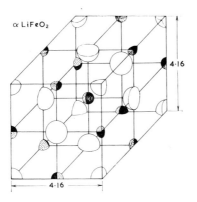

FIG. 1.—Rock-salt type α-LiFeO₂

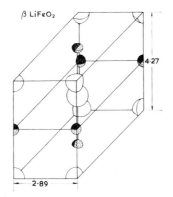

FIG. 2.—Tetragonal body-centred structure for β-LiFeO₂

Collongues and Fayard, did not account for the spots found in Weissenberg single-crystal X-ray photographs, a typical one of which is shown in Fig. 4, which is a photograph taken with un-filtered Cu Kα radiation. The pairing of spots suggests the possibility of two different phases co-existing, the weaker ones corresponding to a phase designated β' and the stronger to the β. With the aid of the Patterson synthesis made on the measured intensities of the powder photographs the two phases have been identified as both belonging to the space group I4, having a body-centred tetragonal structure but with different c/a ratios. This seems improbable and it has been suggested that the pairing of spots is due to special twinning of the β-phase crystals. Details of the deter-

M

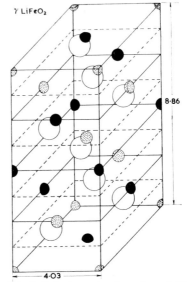

FIG. 3.—CuFeS₂ type structure for γ-LiFeO₂

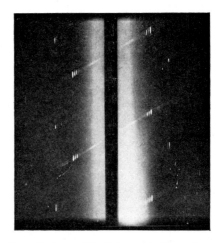

FIG. 4.—Weissenberg single-crystal photograph along the c axis with Cu K$_\lambda$ non-filtered radiation showing the pairing of spots

mination of the structures have been given elsewhere.[1]   Table 1 summarizes some of the structural data for LiFeO₂ together with the approximate transformation temperatures.

Table 1

Structural Data and Transformation Temperatures for LiFeO₂ phases.

	α	β	γ
Symmetry space group	O_R^5 (Fm3m) F.C.C.	I.4 B.C.T.	I.$\bar{4}$.2d B.C.T.
Unit cell dimensions (room temp.) in Å units	$a = 4.1558$	$a = 3.090$ $c = 4.130$	$a = 4.0471$ $c = 8.7273$
No. of LiFeO₂ molecules per unit cell	2	1	4
Transformation temperature (°C)	350*	530	660

* Experimental heat-treatment temperature at which β is formed.

The transformation temperatures are not very definite, owing to the sluggish nature of the phase changes, the α⟶β reaction being particularly slow. The temperature of 350°C. quoted must be treated as a guide only.

On the basis of the results obtained a model may be proposed for the transition mechanisms. A difficulty with the sequence proposed by Collongues and Fayard is that each of the three phases is a close-packed structure, with no vacant sites for migrating ions to occupy during the phase-changes. This difficulty is removed by the body-centred β-phase, since it is not a close-packed structure. The sequence proposed is that the β-phase begins to nucleate from the α-phase in the region of 350°C. The new unit-cell may be formed by taking a face diagonal [110] direction of the f.c.c. α structure as a [100] direction of the β structure, with subsequent migration of ions into vacant sites to form the body-centred configuration. Half of the [110] dimension of the α-phase is $\sqrt{2} \times 4.16 = 2.93$ Å, which corresponds quite well with the figure of 3.09 Å for the a dimension obtained from measurements of the β-phase. The β⟶γ transition is an ordering phase-transition from the b.c.t. β structure to the closer-packed γ structure.

Again the new (γ) phase corresponds to taking a face diagonal of the β-phase as the a dimension of the new phase. The diagonal of the β-phase has a length of $2.89 \times \sqrt{2} = 4.07$ Å, agreeing well with $a = 4.05$ Å in the γ-phase.

For the γ⟶α transition, which occurs at 660°C., the fact that the

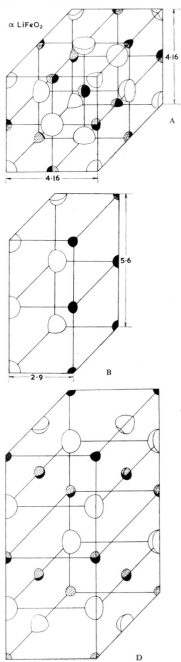

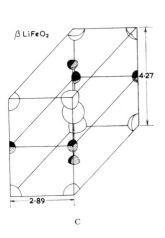

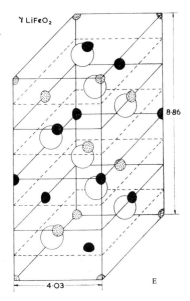

Fig. 5.—Transformation sequence
for LiFeO₂ phases:
A. α;   B. ½ α on [110] direction;
C. β;   D. 4 β on [110] direction;
E. γ.

γ unit cell is twice the volume of the α unit cell suggests that the γ cell simply breaks in two and the metal atoms attain disorder by the solid-solution mixing process of diffusion throughout the crystal. Although γ-LiFeO$_2$ is also body-centred, the co-ordination of metal nearest neighbours is 12, as in face-centred lattices, and not 8, as required for body-centred lattices.

The disordering is necessarily a sluggish process and, although 660°C. is quoted as the transition temperature, faint γ-lines may still be observed in X-ray photographs obtained at temperatures up to 1,000°C. This is supported by the observation, by Fayard, of a "memory" effect in which, in successive cycles of heat-treatment, it was found that ordering proceeded more rapidly each time. It would appear that sufficient of the ordered phase remains to provide ready nucleation sites for the phase changes.

In terms of BUERGER'S[5] classifications the α–β and β–γ transitions are of the reconstructive (sluggish) type involving a change of co-ordination.

Figure 5 gives a schematic representation of the ordering mechanism suggested for LiFeO$_2$. For LiF$_5$O$_8$ the reversible order–disorder transition occurs at 750°C. and, owing to the presence of many ionic vacancies in the spinel structure, the mechanism of order–disorder is quite simple, the ions migrating to their new positions via vacant lattice sites.

4. THERMODYNAMIC ORDER OF TRANSFORMATIONS

In Fig. 6 is given the variation of volume with temperature, at constant density, for the three phases of LiFeO$_2$, together with the

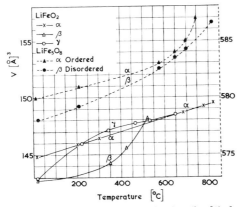

FIG. 6.—Variation of volume at constant density (in Å^3) for LiFeO$_2$ and LiFe$_5$O$_8$ phases

data for $LiFe_5O_8$, the spinel ferrite. From these curves the change in volume of a phase, as a function of temperature, may be calculated and the results for $LiFeO_2$ are shown in Fig. 7 and for $LiFe_5O_8$ in Fig. 8. In addition to this, the coefficient of dilatation $\dfrac{\Delta V}{\Delta T}\dfrac{1}{V}$ and volume changes between the two sequential phases at constant temperature $(V_1 - V_2)_{T = const.}$ for both $LiFeO_2$ and $LiFe_5O_8$ are given in Figs. 9–12 as a function of temperature.

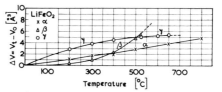

FIG. 7.—Volume changes $\Delta V = V_t - V_0$/temperature (°C.) of $LiFeO_2$ phases

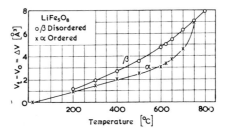

FIG. 8.—Volume changes $\Delta V = V_t - V$ /temperature (°C.) of $LiFe_5O_8$

Transitions between phases are classified thermodynamically according to the degree of the lowest derivative of the free energy which shows a discontinuity. The condition for two phases to be in equilibrium at the transition temperature is that they have the same free energy G, given by

$$G = U - TS + PV \quad . \quad . \quad . \quad . \quad (1)$$

where U is the internal energy, S the entropy, P the pressure and V the volume. For a first-order transition, the first derivative of free energy will show a discontinuity. With respect to pressure and temperature, these are:

$$\left(\frac{\partial G}{\partial T}\right)_P = -S \text{ and } \left(\frac{\partial G}{\partial P}\right)_T = V \quad . \quad . \quad . \quad (2)$$

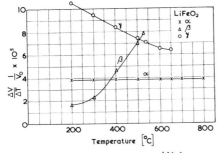

FIG. 9.—Coefficient of volume dilatation $\alpha = \dfrac{\Delta V}{\Delta T}\dfrac{1}{V_0}$ /temperature (°C.) of LiFeO$_2$ phases

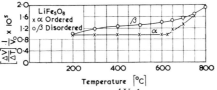

FIG. 10.—Coefficient of dilatation $\alpha = \dfrac{\Delta V}{\Delta T}\dfrac{1}{V_0}$ /temperature (°C.) of LiFe$_5$O$_8$

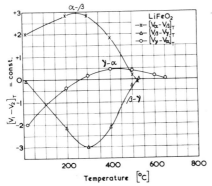

FIG. 11A.—Volume change at constant temperature between contiguous phases in LiFeO$_2$

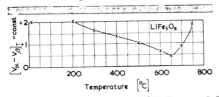

FIG. 11B.—As in Fig. 11A, but for LiFe$_5$O$_8$, α and β phases

so that a first-order transition will be characterized by an abrupt change in entropy and/or volume, as it passes through the transition temperature.

If both S and V are continuous at the transition temperature, the simplest singularity which can occur will be in the second derivatives, so that

$$\left(\frac{\partial^2 G}{\partial T^2}\right)_P = \left(\frac{\partial S}{\partial T}\right)_P = -\frac{C_p}{T} \quad . \quad . \quad . \quad . \quad (3)$$

where C_p is the specific heat at constant pressure, or

$$\left(\frac{\partial^2 G}{\partial P^2}\right)_T = \left(\frac{\partial V}{\partial P}\right)_T = -\beta V \quad . \quad . \quad . \quad . \quad (4)$$

where β is the compressibility. Thus a second-order transition is marked by discontinuities in specific heat and compressibility, the volume and entropy being continuous functions of temperature.

On the basis of these definitions the classification of the $\alpha \longrightarrow \beta$ transformation in $LiFeO_2$ is straightforward. It is obviously a first-order phase change involving a discontinuous change in volume. The $\beta \longrightarrow \gamma$ transformation requires more careful consideration, since it involves ordering of the metal ions. The volume change is zero in the region of the temperature of 530°C., taken to be the transformation temperature. According to GUTTMAN,[6] ordering transitions based on a b.c.c. structure are often of second degree whereas those in which one of the structures is close-packed are invariably of first degree. It can also be shown that for a second-degree transition the two phases never co-exist, but only one or the other is present, according to whether the temperature is above or below T_c. Experimentally the β-γ transition is a complete one, there being no evidence of the β-phase at temperatures above the transition temperature once sufficient time has been allowed for the transformation to complete. It is therefore concluded that the transition is of second degree (second-order).

A similar difficulty arises in the case of the $\gamma \longrightarrow \alpha$ transition, in which the metal ions are disordered. Again the measured volume change appears to be zero at the transformation temperature. In this case, however, one of the structures (α) is close-packed. In addition, traces of the γ phase are found at temperatures well above that of the transformation. It is therefore assumed that there is in fact a small discontinuity in volume involved which, as mentioned above, was not detected in the transformation, and that it is of first degree.

In the case of $LiFe_5O_8$ the low-temperature phase is ordered and becomes disordered at 750°C. The ordered phase is labelled β and the disordered is labelled α. The transition is reversible and occurs rapidly. There is little change in crystal structure and, as seen from Fig. 6, there is a small finite volume change at the transition temperature. This is a typical first-degree order–disorder transition. At the Curie point $\sim 630°C$. it can be readily seen that the volume change is continuous and no change in crystal structure is involved. Therefore for both the α and β phase, the Curie point is a second-order transition.

5. HEATS OF TRANSITION

In a normal order–disorder transition in a binary alloy it is possible to make an approximate calculation of the transition energy (latent heat of transition) for a binary alloy, using the methods due to BETHE [7] or FOWLER and GUGGENHEIM.[8] If $LiFeO_2$ is treated as a binary alloy LiFe, the oxygen atoms being neglected, the calculation may be made for the order–disorder $\gamma \longrightarrow \alpha$ transition. It should be noted that, treating the metal atoms alone, there is no change in co-ordination number for the metal ions in the $\gamma \longrightarrow \alpha$ transition. According to Fowler and Guggenheim, assuming perfect order at $0°K$., the change in configurational energy from $0°K$. to some temperature $T = T_c$ will be given, for an AB alloy, by

$$E_{T=T_c} - E_{T=0} = NkT_c \frac{Z(Z-2)}{4(Z-1)} \log \left(\frac{Z}{Z-2} \right) . \quad \quad (5)$$

where N is the number of atoms, k is Boltzmann's constant, and Z is the co-ordination number, i.e. each atom is surrounded by Z nearest neighbours. For the γ and α lattices, $Z = 12$ for the metal ions and, taking $T_c = 920°K$., Equation (5) gives an energy change of 0.0525 eV or 1.210 kcal/mole. This may be compared with the ordering energy for β brass (CuZn), calculated on the same model, which is given by NIX and SHOCKLEY [9] as $0.492\ kT_c$, whilst the above result is $2.18\ kT_c$.

In the case of $LiFe_5O_8$, the ordering reaction presumably takes place only in the octahedral sites, where we have an AB_3 alloy, ($LiFe_3$). As an approximation to calculation of the transition energy one may use the expression obtained by COWLEY [10] for an AB_3 alloy. In this the critical temperature is given by

$$T_c = \frac{3}{2k} \left(V_1 - \frac{3}{2} V_2 + \ldots \right) . \quad \quad (6)$$

where $V_1, V_2 \ldots$ are the ordering interaction energies between pairs of atoms separated by first, second $\ldots$ shortest distances.

Taking $T_c = 1023$ and $V_2 \doteq -\dfrac{V_1}{10}$, we obtain $V_1 = 0.069$ eV or 0.159 kcal/mole. This is an order of magnitude smaller than the energy obtained for $LiFeO_2$. In view of the many uncertainties in the calculation, little significance can be attached to this result, save to point out that the interaction energy in the spinel crystal would be expected to be lower than that existing in a close-packed structure such as $LiFeO_2$.

6. CONCLUSIONS

The phase-transitions in $LiFeO_2$ are considered to be founded on the necessity for the close-packed structure to " open up " before ordering can take place. No similar difficulty exists in the spinel structure $LiFe_5O_8$, as the spinel crystal provides plenty of vacant sites for migrating ions.

By means of high-temperature X-ray measurements, first-order transitions can be identified unambiguously. It is always more difficult to identify second-order transitions, and the power of the X-ray method is demonstrated by the case of the γ–α transition in $LiFeO_2$. From simple volumetric measurements it might be concluded that the transition is second-order, but the knowledge of mixed phases, obtained by use of X-rays, enables it to be identified as first-order.

In a ternary system rigorous statistical thermodynamic calculations are difficult to make. An order of magnitude calculation of the transition energy for the order/disorder transition may be made by neglecting the oxygen atoms. The results appear to be reasonable.

ACKNOWLEDGMENTS

It is a pleasure to acknowledge advice from Professor J. S. Rowlinson and Professor H. W. Paxton on the interpretation of the results.

REFERENCES

1. Anderson, J. C., and Schieber, M., *J. Phys. Chem. Solids,* **67**, 1838, 1963.
2. Collongues, E., *Compt. Rend.,* **241**, 1577, 1955.
3. Fayard, M. Thesis, Paris 1962.
4. Anderson, J. C., and Schieber, M., to be published.
5. Buerger, M. J., " Phase Transformations in Solids " (Wiley, New York, 1951, pp. 183-212.

6. Guttman, L., " Solid State Physics ", Seitz and Turnbull (Eds.) (Academic Press, New York, 1956), Vol. 3.
7. Bethe, H., *Proc. Roy. Soc.*, **A150**, 552, 1935.
8. Fowler, R., and Guggenheim, E. A., " Statistical Thermodynamics " (Camb. Univ. Press, 1956), p. 576.
9. Nix, F. C., and Shockley, W., *Rev. Mod. Phys.*, **10**, 1, 1938.
10. Cowley, S. M., *Phys. Rev.*, **77**, 669, 1950.

24—Aspects of the Surface Energy of Ceramics
I—Calculations of Surface Free Energies

By R. H. BRUCE

The British Ceramic Research Association

ABSTRACT   A71

Some simple calculations are made for the surface free energy of 14 oxides and β-SiC from a consideration of crystal structure and sublimation energy, and the reversible effect of temperature is calculated; for some the solid-liquid transformation is considered, enabling values of surface free energy from absolute zero to the critical temperature to be obtained. The method used and the results are compared with theoretical and experimental work in the literature.

I. Quelques aspects de l'énergie de surface des céramiques

Quelques calculs simples sont faits pour l'énergie libre de surface de 14 oxydes et de β-SiC en se fondant sur leurs structures cristallines et leurs énergies de sublimation, et l'on calcule dans chaque cas l'effet réversible de la température. On examine pour certains de ces matériaux la transformation solide-liquide, ce qui permet d'obtenir les valeurs pour l'enérgie libre du surface de zéro absolu à la température critique. On compare la méthode utilisée et les résultats avec d'autres travaux théoriques et experimentaux déjà publiés.

I. Berechnung der Oberflächenenergien

Einige einfache Berechnungen für die freie Oberflächenenergie von 14 Oxiden und β-SiC werden ausgehend von der Betrachtung ihrer Kristallstrukturen und der Sublimationsenergien gemacht, und der reversible Effekt der Temperatur wird berechnet; für einige Materialien wird die fest-flüssig-Umwandlung berücksichtigt, wodurch ist es möglich, Werte für die freie Oberflächenenergie vom absoluten Nullpunkt bis zur kritischen Temperatur zu erhalten. Die angewandte Methode und die Ergebrisse werden mit anderen Theorien und experimentellen Arbeiten in der Literatur verglichen.

1. INTRODUCTION

Surface energy is a property of condensed phases and is due to the imbalance between forces acting on atoms in the surface and the forces acting on similar atoms in the centre of the phase, where it is homogeneous and without imperfections. It can be manipulated by the methods of bulk thermodynamics, provided care is taken in the definition of the terms used. Surface free energy, γ, should be defined as the reversible free-energy change involved in the formation of unit surface area under carefully defined conditions of temperature, pressure, concentration and orientation. Surface enthalphy, ε, may be similarly defined, as below, where T is the absolute temperature:

$$\varepsilon = \gamma - T\frac{d\gamma}{dT} \quad . \quad . \quad . \quad . \quad . \quad (1).$$

Occasionally ε is called the " total surface energy ", but it would seem preferable to reserve this term for the surface energy per unit weight of, say, a granular material exhibiting a variety of crystal faces, and possibly of large surface area. The decrease in the total surface free energy of a system is the driving force for such phenomena as sintering and grain growth.

Where there are no polymorphic changes, the surface enthalpy is practically independent of temperature.[1] By an extension of the Nernst Heat Theorem

$$\mathop{Lt}_{T \to 0} \frac{d\gamma}{dT} \to 0,$$

thus at absolute zero $\varepsilon° = \gamma°$. In the region of the critical temperature, T_c, γ becomes zero, thus, as a first approximation for solids:

$$\frac{d\gamma_s}{dT} \doteq -\frac{\varepsilon°}{T_c} \quad . \quad . \quad . \quad . \quad (2).$$

For liquids an equation of the van der Waals' type has been found most generally applicable:

$$\gamma_L^T = K(1 - T/T_c)^n \quad . \quad . \quad . \quad . \quad (3)$$

where K and n are constants: LÖVGREN[2] found n to have a value in the region of 1·2 for many unassociated liquids.

With respect to the definition of concentration, the effect of adsorption on the surface free energy of liquids is well known: as the surface free energy of solids is larger, adsorption is even more important. If a solid surface of 10^{15} molecules/cm² adsorbs a fluid with a heat of adsorption of 20 kcal/mole, a coverage of about 70% will lower the surface enthalpy by about 1,000 erg/cm². This order of decrease in surface free energy is found in practice: for silver, the surface free energy is reported[3] to be lowered from 1,140 erg/cm² to 350 erg/cm² by measurements in He and in air respectively; for mica in vacuo a value of 4,500 erg/cm² was found,[4] and in air it was only 375 erg/cm²—the first value is about four times too high, but the ratio of these figures suggests the importance of excluding from the system all adsorbable fluids such as air.

The effect of pressure on the surface energy is not known to be great, apart from the pressure of an adsorbed phase. The effect of the shape of the surface on the pressure difference across it is important in capillary phenomena and in the mathematical treatment of sintering and grain growth: this effect is expressed in Equation (4):

$$RT \ln (p/p_o) = \gamma M \rho^{-1} (1/r_1 + 1/r_2) \qquad . \quad . \quad (4)$$

where M is the molecular weight, ρ is the density and r_1 and r_2 are the principal radii of curvature. This effect is well known, but it is not generally realized that a pressure difference also occurs between two flat faces of a material with different crystallographic orientations and hence with a difference in the surface free energies ($\Delta\gamma$):

$$RT \ln (p/p_o) = - \Delta\gamma N^{1/3} V^{2/3} J^{-1} \qquad . \quad . \quad . \quad (5)$$

where N is Avogadro's number, V is the molar volume and J is Joule's equivalent. Applying Equation (5) to MgO at 1,500°K. with a difference in free energies between the (111) and (100) planes of 880 erg/cm^2 (see below), the ratio of vapour pressures above these planes will be 19. Thus the effect of orientation is of utmost importance and will be discussed in detail.

In the application of surface thermodynamics it is important that we should know the actual value of the surface free energy of ceramics. In this part, calculations are shown of this parameter for a number of simple crystalline and liquid materials.

2. PREVIOUS WORK AND THE PRESENT METHOD

Wave mechanical calculations have been made by several different methods from LENNARD-JONES onwards.[5] Objections have been raised (e.g. by BENSON and McINTOSH[6]) to these methods, and caution must be exercised before accepting their results. Miss DENT [7] made some corrections to Lennard-Jones's figures to allow for polarization, and her figures have been used, wrongly in the author's opinion, in connection with quite different methods of calculation. For example, for the (100) face of NaCl values from 77 to 188 erg/cm^2 at 0°K. have been found. Heat of solution figures [8] at 25°C. are in the region 300–400 erg/cm^2 for this material, and extrapolation, as shown below, from a measured value [9] for liquid NaCl gives a surface free energy at 25°C. of 296 erg/cm^2, so these theoretical results seem to be too low. Empirical calculations by LIVEY and MURRAY [10] were based on rather uncertain values for the surface free energy for MgO and CaO. FRICKE [11] was one of the first to use a treatment based on sublimation energy; his method yielded a result for the (100) face of NaCl of 152 erg/cm^2 at 0°K., which also seems low; however, a simple method involving the sublimation energy will be used here.

Table 1

Thermochemical Data

	$T_m(^\circ K)$	$T_b(^\circ K)$	$T_c(^\circ K)$	L_f	H_s
				kcal/mole	
MgO	3075	3600	5470	18·5	129
CaO	2860	3800	5770	19·0	142
FeO	d 1644	d 3400	5170	7·4	126
BeO	2820	4390	6680	17·0	155
SiC	d 3000	—	(5500)	—	205
*SiO$_2$	1986	d 3200	4800	1·85	168
TiO$_2$	2400	d 3200	4800	15·5	135
Al$_2$O$_3$	2300	d 3700	5180	26·0	470
Cr$_2$O$_3$	2710	d 3300	4620	—	399
Fe$_2$O$_3$	d 1730	—	(5000)	—	389

* β-cristobalite.
d Decomposition or dissociation at or below this temperature.

The surface free energy may be described in terms of the bonding of atoms. When a bond between two atoms is broken, it is assumed that half the energy supplied applies to each atom—thus the bond energy, β, is defined as $\beta = \frac{1}{2} H_s J/CN$, where H_s is the molar heat of sublimation, and C is the number of bonds per molecule. Thus $\gamma = \beta e$, where e is the number of bonds per cm^2 for the plane under consideration, and is easily obtained by inspection of a model of the crystal.

To estimate the surface entropy of a solid, a knowledge of T_c is required. A literature survey [12] yielded some empirical equations which were applied to some oxides to yield ratios T_c/T_b. For lack of a better criterion the oxides were grouped according to their valency as below:

MO, $T_c/T_b = 1·52$;   MO$_2$, $T_c/T_b = 1·50$;   M$_2$O$_3$, $T_c/T_b = 1·40$.

Boiling-temperatures were obtained from the literature [13] and are shown in Table 1 with the critical temperatures for some ceramic materials. Difficulty was experienced in obtaining the sublimation energy for some materials; several references were consulted [13, 14] and the Born–Haber cycle was used to calculate H_s in each case to give self-consistent values. The latent heat of fusion is also included in Table 1 from the same sources [13, 14] except for cristobalite, which was obtained from FÖRLAND.[15]

At the melting point the surface of a solid will consist of those faces with the lowest possible free energy; this will be considered in detail in Part II. On melting, the latent heat of fusion (L_f) will contribute to a decrease in surface free energy:

$$- \Delta\gamma = BL_f / AN \qquad . \quad . \quad . \quad . \quad (6)$$

where A is the surface area per molecule and B is the ratio of "free" bonds to normal co-ordinate bonds for one molecule, in this surface. BONDI[16] quoted a similar equation and found $B = 1$ for some metals. Equation (3) may be used for the liquid material, and so it is possible to estimate the surface free energy of some materials from absolute zero to the critical temperature.

3. EXAMPLE OF CALCULATION: NaCl

All the crystal parameters were taken from DONNAX and NOWACKI.[17]

The sublimaton energy is 56 kcal/mole and there are six complete bonds per molecule, giving $\beta = 3\cdot243 \times 10^{-13}$ erg/bond. In the (100) plane there are four bonds per unit cell of side $a = 5\cdot639$Å $\therefore e_{(100)} = 4/a^2$ and $\gamma^\circ_{(100)} = 408$ erg/cm². T_c is estimated (c.f. ratio for MO) to be 2,600°K.,

$$\therefore \frac{d\gamma}{dT} = -\frac{\gamma^\circ}{T_c} = -0\cdot1557 \text{ erg/cm}^2/°\text{C. and } \gamma^T_{(100)} = 408 - 0\cdot1557T$$

At 25°C. this gives a surface free energy of 352 erg/cm², which is in good agreement with the heat of solution values quoted above. At the melting point (801°C.) the value is 241 erg/cm² and the (100) plane has the minimum surface free energy (see Part II): a is then 5·657 Å, B is 1/6 and $L_f = 6\cdot9$ kcal/mole; thus from Equation (6), $\Delta\gamma = -57\cdot8$ erg/cm² and $\gamma_L^{801} = 183$ erg/cm². From Equation (3) $\gamma_L^T = 567 (1 - T/2,600)^{1\cdot2}$.

At the melting point the value for the liquid (183 erg/cm²) is higher than that of JAEGER[9] (114 erg/cm²) but the difference may be attributed to the effects of impurity and adsorption on the experimental value.

If B were taken as unity in Equation (6), a negative surface free energy would result for the liquid.

In these calculations it may seem preferable to use the lattice energy instead of the sublimation energy. The lattice energy of NaCl is about 185 kcal/mole, thus values would be derived more than three times those quoted above, and would be far too high. In addition, the use of the lattice energy does not seem to be justifiable from atomistic consideration of the production of a new surface.

Table 2

Calculated Surface Free Energies (erg/cm²)
for some Ceramic Materials

	Plane x	Minimum surface free energy (γ_x)	Average surface free energy (γ_A)	γ_A^{1723}	γ_L^{Tm}	K	$T_c(°K)$
			Solid			*Liquid*	
MgO	(100)	$1680 - 0·308T$	$2600 - 0·476T$	1750	515	1387	5470
CaO		$1420 - 0·246T$	$2200 - 0·381T$	1525	—	—	—
FeO		$1580 - 0·306T$	$2440 - 0·472T$	(1600)	987	1562	5170
BeO	(0001)	$2140 - 0·321T$	$2400 - 0·359T$	1760	1013	1955	6680
β-SiC	(110)	$2030 - 0·370T$	$3000 - 0·546T$	2030	—	—	—
SiO₂	(110)	$616 - 0·128T$	$925 - 0·193T$	580	346	657	4800
TiO₂	(110)	$426 - 0·089T$	$800 - 0·167T$	505	—	—	—
Al₂O₃	(10$\bar{1}\bar{4}$)	$1120 - 0·216T$	$1200 - 0·232T$	790	566	1144	5180
Cr₂O₃		$857 - 0·186T$	$925 - 0·200T$	570	—	—	—
Fe₂O₃		$807 - 0·161T$	$870 - 0·174T$	(560)	—	—	—
M.A.	(100)	$2340 - 0·451T$	$3000 - 0·577T$	1975	—	—	—
Fe₃O₄		$1890 - 0·379T$	$2450 - 0·490T$	1580	—	—	—
M.C.		$1980 - 0·397T$	$2570 - 0·510T$	1660	—	—	—
F.C.		$1940 - 0·388T$	$2520 - 0·504T$	1625	—	—	—
C₂AS	(001)	$1460 - 0·325T$	$1600 - 0·356T$	990	624	1180	4500

Notes: Col. 1: SiO₂ refers to β-cristobalite; M.A. refers to MgO.Al₂O₃; M.C. and F.C. are self-evident; C₂AS = gehlenite.
Col. 5: The bracketed figures are for unstable phases.
Cols. 7 and 8 refer to the general equation $\gamma_L^T = K (1 - T/T_c)^{1·2}$

4. CALCULATIONS FOR CERAMIC MATERIALS

From visual examination of an expanded model of a crystal structure it is quite easy to determine bond densities for any plane, and also to determine which plane has the minimum surface free energy. This was done for some ceramic materials and the surface free energies are given in Table 2. Surface free energies for several planes were calculated for each structure, and an assessment was made of an average value (columns 4 and 5 in Table 2): a definition of this parameter is given in Part II.

In some cases, values for the liquid were calculated, due correction being made to the lattice parameter for thermal expansion.[17, 18] It is assumed that the structure of the liquid is very similar to that for the solid crystal plane of minimum surface free energy, although the order is necessarily of short range, and that the liquid does not show abnormal behaviour with temperature change, as is found for some silicates.[19]

For SiO_2 the values quoted for the solid only refer to β-cristobalite, although it is expected that those for the α form would be close: tridymite has a lower density than cristobalite, so one would expect a lower average surface free energy (870 erg/cm²?); similarly the value for quartz would probably be higher ($1,000$ erg/cm²?).

The heat of formation of spinels is about 2–3% greater than that of their constituent oxides, so the bond strength for each type of metal/oxygen bond was arbitrarily increased by $2\frac{1}{2}\%$ to calculate the surface free energies for this class. Owing to lack of data on gehlenite, no such increase was made, so the figures might be 1–2% greater.

5. COMPARISON WITH PREVIOUS WORK

Magnesia (MgO). The wave mechanical results were discussed by BENSON and MCINTOSH[6] and were considered to be unreliable. FRICKE'S result[11] for $\gamma^{\circ}_{(100)}$ is $1,459$ erg/cm². A heat of solution value [20] includes the effect of temperature, and an extrapolation leads to a critical temperature in the region $5,500°$–$5,800°$K., very similar to that found here ($5,470°$K.): although possibly fortuitous, this does afford some confirmation of this method of estimating the surface entropy.

Calcia (CaO) Fricke finds $\gamma^{\circ}_{(100)}$ to be 979 erg/cm², which seems low in view of a heat-of-solution value [22] of $1,310 \pm 200$ erg/cm² at $23°C$., which is in good agreement with the present value of $1,346$ erg/cm² at this temperature. It would seem difficult to prevent the adsorption of water, and so the experimental result would not be expected to be high.

Ferrous Oxide (FeO) The best previous figure would seem to be that of KOSAKEVITCH[23] for the liquid at $1,420°C$. of 585 erg/cm²; the figure presently suggested is 970 erg/cm². It was admitted [23] that the wüstite contained as much as 5% Fe_2O_3, which has a much lower surface energy in the solid. No data are available for L_f for Fe_2O_3, so assuming a value of about 20 kcal/mole, γ^{1693}_L for Fe_2O_3 was calculated to be 540 erg/cm²; this is in good agreement with the supposition that the slag of Kosakevitch was almost completely covered with Fe_2O_3.

Silica (SiO₂) By extrapolation of some values[19, 23] for siliceous slags to 100% SiO_2, values in the region 180–273 erg/cm² are found:

it is likely that there is an upward slope in the concentration curve near the SiO_2 end, so these values are probably low, and extrapolation for such associated liquids is not very reliable. On a "quartz" fibre at 1,100°C. a value [24] of 290 erg/cm² was measured. Heat of solution of amorphous SiO_2 gave a value [22] of 259 erg/cm² at 23°C. From crushing-experiments with quartz, figures in the region of 100,000 erg/cm² are reported,[25] which are at least two orders of magnitude too high. The best experimental values [22, 24] are about half that in Table 2.

Alumina (Al_2O_3) From heat of solution at 25°C., FRICKE obtained a value [26] of 560 erg/cm²; and from dihedral angle measurement at 1,850° C., KINGERY[27] obtained a value of 905 erg/cm²: the present value is rather lower than the latter figure. For the liquid, values of 577 and 700 erg/cm² are reported [28]; the former is in good agreement with the present value from Table 2, whereas the latter is higher and may indicate the presence in the surface of the liquid of some proportion of high-energy configurations.

Ferric Oxide (Fe_2O_3) A heat of solution value[26] of 350 erg/cm² at 25°C. is again lower than the present value.

Gehlenite From the work of KING [19] on the $CaO–Al_2O_3–SiO_2$ system, it is estimated that the liquid surface free energy for the gehlenite composition would be about 500 erg/cm² at 1,570°C.— i.e. about 75% of the present figure, and may indicate dissociation, with excess surface concentration of a low-energy species.

Silicon Carbide (SiC) The thermochemical data for this substance are the least satisfactory of those considered, so it is not surprising that values found for other carbides by LIVEY and MURRAY [10] should be about half that shown in Table 2.

6. CONCLUSION

Although the methods used here to calculate the surface free energy have several theoretical limitations, they are simple to apply and yield results at least as reliable as any other theoretical method yet developed. In comparison with experimental work, the present values are generally higher, which is attributed chiefly to adsorption, and the great difficulty of keeping experimental surfaces clean. The trend in experimental work is to find higher values as the experiment becomes more refined, giving some measure of support to the present work.

REFERENCES

1. Frenkel, J., "Kinetic Theory of Liquids" (Clarendon, Oxford, 1946), p. 308.
2. Lövgren, N., *Svensk Kem. Tid.*, **53**, 359, 1941; *Amer. Chem. Abstr.*, **36**, 3077, 1942.
3. Udin, H., Funk, E. R., and Wulff, J., *J Metals*, **3**, 1206, 1951.
4. Orowan, E., *Nature*, **154**, 341, 1944.
5. Lennard-Jones, J. E., and Taylor, P. A., *Proc. Roy. Soc., A* **109**, 476, 1925; *A* **117**, 230, 1926; Biemüller, J., *Z. Physik*, **38**, 759, 1926; Shuttleworth, R., *Proc. Phys. Soc., A* **62**, 167, 1949.
6. Benson, G. C., and McIntosh, R., *Canad. J. Chem.*, **33**, 1677, 1955.
7. Dent, B. M., *Phil. Mag.*, 7th Series, **8**, 530, 1929.
8. Lipsett, A. G., Johnson, F. M. G., and Maas, O., *J. Amer. Chem. Soc.*, **49**, 1940, 1927; **50**, 2071, 1928; Harkins, W. D., *J. Chem. Phys.*, **10**, 268, 1942; Benson, G. C., and Benson, G. W., *Canad. J. Chem.* **33**, 232, 1955.
9. Jaeger, F. M., *Z. anorg. Chem.*, **101**, 1, 1917.
10. Livey, D. T., and Murray, P., *J. Amer. Ceram. Soc,.* **39**, (11), 363, 1956.
11. Fricke, R., "Handbuch der Katalyse", IV (Springer-Verlag, Vienna, 1943), p. 1.
12. Guldberg, C. M., *Z. physik. Chem.*, **5**, 374, 1890; Lewis, D. T., *J. Chem. Soc.*, p. 261, 1938; Meissner, H. P., and Redding, E. M., *Ind. Eng. Chem.*, **34**, 521, 1942; Herzog, R., *Ind. Eng. Chem.*, **36**, 997, 1944.
13. Brewer, L., *Chem. Rev.*, **52**, 1, 1953; Kubaschewski, O., and Evans, E. Ll., "Metallurgical Thermochemistry" (Pergamon Press, London, 1956).
14. Bichowski, F. R., and Rossini, F. D., "Thermochemistry of Chemical Substances" (Reinhold, New York, 1936); Cotrell, T. L., "The Strength of Chemical Bonds" (Butterworth, London, 1954); Herzberg, G., "Molecular Spectra and Molecular Structure. I. Spectra of Diatomic Molecules" (New York, 1950).
15. Förland, T., *J. Amer. Ceram. Soc.*, **41**, 524, 1958.
16. Bondi, A., *Chem. Rev.*, **52**, 417, 1953.
17. Donnax, J. D. H., and Nowacki, W., "Crystal Data" (Geol. Soc. of America, mem. 60), 1954.
18. Rigby, G. R., *Trans. Brit. Ceram. Soc.*, **50**, 175, 1951; Rigby, G. R., Lovell, G. B. H., and Green, A. T., *Trans. Brit. Ceram. Soc.*, **45**, 251, 1946; Whitmore, O. J., and Ault, N. N., *J. Amer. Ceram. Soc.*, **39**, 433, 1956; International Critical Tables, vol. III, p. 83.
19. King, T. B., *Trans. Soc. Glass Technol.*, **35**, 241, 1951.
20. Jura, G., and Garland, C. W., *J. Amer. Chem. Soc.*, **74**, 6033, 1952.
21. Jura, G., *J. Chem. Phys.*, **12**, 1335, 1949.
22. Brunauer, S., Kantro, D. L., and Weise, C. H., *Canad. J. Chem.* **34**, 729, 1956.
23. Kosakevitch, P., *Rev. de Mét.*, **46,** 505, 1949.
24. Parikh, H. M. Sc.D. Thesis, Massachusetts Institute of Technology, 1953; see Kingery, W. D., *Bull. Amer. Ceram. Soc.*, **353**, 108, 1956.
25. Johnson, J. F., Axelson, A., and Piret, E. L., *Chem. Eng. Prog.*, **45**, 708, 1949; Schellinger, A. K., *Trans. A.I.M.E.*, **179**, 379, 1952.
26. Fricke, R., *Kolloid Z.*, **96**, 213, 1941.
27. Kingery, W. D., *J. Amer. Ceram. Soc.*, **37**, 42, 1954.
28. von Wartenberg, H., Welmar, G., and Saran, E., *Nachr. Göttingen, Math. Phys. Kl., Fachgruppe* 2 (N.F.), **2**, 73, 1936; Kingery, W. D., *Bull. Amer. Ceram. Soc.*, **35**, 108, 1956.

II—Calculation of the Average Surface Free Energy and the Effects of some Variables

ABSTRACT

An attempt is made to define theoretically an average surface free energy, and this parameter is calculated for a number of simple crystal systems. The irreversible effect of temperature on the average surface free energy of isolated single crystals is briefly considered. The effect on the total surface free energy of some departures from perfection, such as dislocations and grain boundaries, is shown to be negligible.

II. Calculs pour une énergie libre moyenne de surface et les effects de quelques variables

On tente de définir de façon théorique une énergie libre moyenne, et on calcule ce paramètre pour un certain nombre de systémes de cristaux simples. On examine brièvement l'influence irréversible de la température sur l'énergie moyenne de surface de cristaux isolés. On constate que les effets sur l'énergie libre totale de quelques écarts par rapport au cas idéal, tels que les joints des grains et les dislocations, sont négligeables.

II. Berechnung der mittleren freien Energie der Oberfläche und die Einflüsse einiger Abweichungen.

Es wird ein theoretischer Versuch gemacht, eine mittlere freie Energie der Oberfläche zu definieren, und dieser Parameter wird für eine Angahl einfacher Kristallsysteme berechnet. Eine kurze Betrachtung betr. die irreversiblen Effekte der Temperatur auf die mittlere freie Energie der Oberfläche von isolierten Kristallen wird durchgeführt. Der Einfluss einiger Abweichungen vom idealen Verhalten auf die gesamte freie Energie der Oberfläche wie Korngrenzen und Versetzungen erweist sich als vernachlässigbar.

1. INTRODUCTION

Several equations have been developed [1] to describe the rate of various mechanisms involved in sintering; each contains a surface free energy term, and it is generally a poorly defined parameter. The term used in these equations is an average surface free energy, generally for curved solid surfaces containing a grain boundary. A curved liquid surface presents no difficulties, as the molecules are mobile and all elements of a given liquid surface are equivalent in structure and surface free energy, except perhaps close to a boundary. The curved surface of a solid cannot be uniform in structure or surface free energy, unless it may be described as vitreous, when it is more correctly treated as a viscous liquid. Some experimental values are available for curved crystalline surfaces, derived from creep rates near the melting point,[2] and from dihedral angle measurements,[3] but these few results cannot as yet be related to the surface free energy of particular crystallographic faces, which is easily obtained for a large number of solids as was shown in Part 1.

The only estimate which has been made of this type of relationship, to the author's knowledge, was by FREIDEL, CULLITY and CRUSSARD [4] in connection with the surface energy of grain boundaries in a metal.

It is proposed to examine the average surface free energy of some members of the cubic system, as they are fairly accessible to mathematical analysis.   An irreversible temperature effect and the effect of some departures from perfection will also be considered, in a more general way.

In the first instance let us consider a convex spherical surface. Such a surface may be formed from a cube of {100} faces by removing edges and corners, without causing any lattice imperfections, to give 26 faces of the three families {100}, {100} and {111}, in such a manner that they are all equal in area.   This process of edge and corner removal is repeated until a sphere results whose surface consists of all possible planes, all equal in area.   If this sphere is finite, say 1 mm diam. and the limiting size of each face is taken as 4 Å^2, the number of planes formed will be in the region of $\pi \times 10^{14}$: however, this limit will be shown to have no practical significance.

This type of surface can be analysed to yield an average surface free energy which will be directly applicable to spheres and spherical pores, of and in a single crystal, and it will afford a fair estimate of the surface free energy of the material in the neck between two grains sintering together.   The structure of the material in such a neck poses an interesting problem: if the material is crystalline and continues the structure of the contiguous grains, a normal type of grain boundary would exist and one would expect a dihedral angle to form a cusp and prevent this material from assuming a lenticular shape.   Crystalline connective material with a curved surface, and bisected by a clear grain boundary, has been found for metals (e.g. PRANATIS and POUND [5]) whereas, for Al_2O_3, curved or cusped connective surfaces may be found,[6] depending on the atmosphere during sintering.   Thus the average surface free energy should only be used for such connective material when it is known that a curved surface does indeed form.

2. THE SIMPLE CUBIC SYSTEM

In a simple crystal system we may derive a surface energy ratio which involves a consideration of bond densities, and is independent of bond strength and of lattice parameter.   Such a ratio will apply to all members of this system, and will be independent of temperature as long as the surface maintains its identity and the thermal expansion is isotropic.

FRIEDEL et alia [4] derived the following equations involving the Miller indices (h, k and l) of a plane, the bond strength (β) and the lattice parameter (d):

Simple Cubic
$$\gamma_{(hkl)} = \frac{h + k + l}{\sqrt{(h^2 + k^2 + l^2)}} \cdot \frac{\beta}{d^2} \quad \quad \cdot \quad \cdot \quad \cdot \quad \cdot \quad (1)$$

Face-centred Cubic
$$\gamma_{(hkl)} = \frac{4(2h + k)}{\sqrt{(h^2 + k^2 + l^2)}} \cdot \frac{\beta}{d^2} \quad \quad \cdot \quad \cdot \quad \cdot \quad (2)$$

Body-centred Cubic
$$\left.\begin{array}{l} \gamma_{(hkl)} = \dfrac{2[2h\beta_1 + (h + k + l)\beta_2]}{(h^2 + k^2 + l^2)^{\frac{1}{2}}\, d^2} \text{ when } h \geqslant (k + l) \\[4mm] \gamma_{(hkl)} = \dfrac{2(h + k + l)(\beta_1 + \beta_2)}{(h^2 + k^2 + l^2)^{\frac{1}{2}}\, d^2} \quad \text{ when } h \leqslant (k + l) \end{array}\right\} (3)$$

where $\gamma_{(hkl)}$ is the specific surface free energy of (hkl) near absolute zero; the subscripts 1 and 2 on the bond strength in Equation (3) refer to the nearest-neighbour and to the next-nearest-neighbour bond strengths respectively. These equations apply when $h \not< k \not< l$ and each is positive.

Table 1

Partial and Total Average Ratios for the Simple Cubic System

n	R_n'	R_n
1	1·4163	1·4163
2	1·5463	1·5118
3	1·5464	1·5347
4	1·4197	1·4774
5	1·5469	1·5121
6	1·5463	1·5235
7	1·5475	1·5331
8	1·5494	1·5378
9	1·5180	1·5318
10	1·5470	1·5353
11	1·5442	1·5378
12	1·5473	1·5395
13	1·5468	1·5413
14	1·5450	1·5419
15	1·5491	1·5432
16	1·5471	1·5438
17	1·5477	1·5446
18	1·5463	1·5448
19	1·5469	1·5452
20	1·5463	1·5453

In the simple cubic system, $\gamma_{(100)}$ is the lowest surface free energy, and we may define the surface energy ratio for this system as:

$$R_{(hkl)} \equiv \frac{\gamma_{(hkl)}}{\gamma_{(100)}} = \frac{h + k + l}{\sqrt{(h^2 + k^2 + l^2)}} \qquad . \qquad . \qquad . \qquad (4).$$

If we divide the planes into n groups, such that $n = h$, and the number of planes in each family is f, we may define the average ratio, R_n, for all faces up to and including those of group n, as:

$$R_n = \frac{\sum\limits_{1}^{n} (f_{(hkl)} \times R_{(hkl)})}{\sum\limits_{1}^{n} f_{(hkl)}} \qquad . \qquad . \qquad . \qquad . \qquad (5).$$

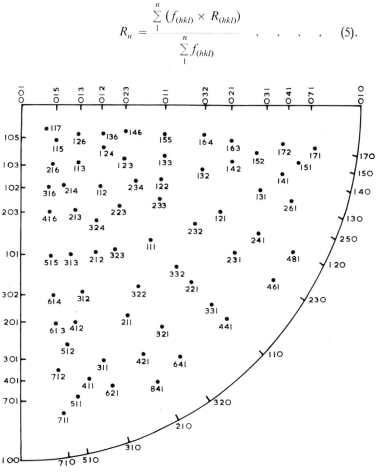

FIG. 1.—The positive quadrant of a stereographic projection of a cubic crystal with some planes indicated by their Miller indices.

Further limitations are imposed in that no plane may be included if it does not contain any atoms, or if it is parallel to a pair of planes already considered. Then as n tends to ∞, the average factor tends to the value for a sphere, for which the average surface free energy is $R_\infty \gamma_r$, where γ_r is the surface free energy of the reference plane (in this case it is $\gamma_{(100)}$).

As an aid to extrapolation, a partial average, R'_n, was calculated derived only from members in the group n. Table 1 shows the results of these calculations up to $n = 20$, involving some 57,000 planes, which number is far less than that mentioned in the above section ($\pi \times 10^{14}$), and yet R_∞ may be estimated as 1.546 ± 0.001.

It was found possible to plot the surface energy ratios as smooth contours on a stereographic projection: the positive quadrant of such a projection is shown in Fig. 1, giving the position of some

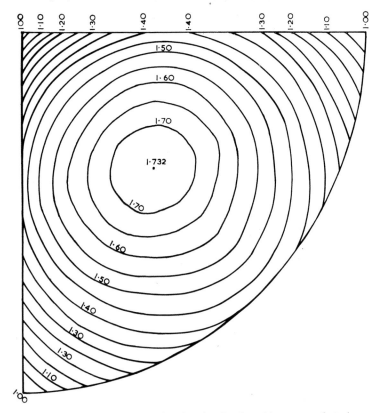

FIG. 2.—The surface energy ratios for the simple cubic system plotted on a stereographic projection.

planes. Figure 2 shows the contours of the surface energy ratios for the simple cubic system: this ratio changes continuously with orientation. From Fig. 2 the surface free energy near $0°K$., for any given plane and any given material in this system, can be obtained by multiplying the indicated ratio by $\gamma°_{(100)}$ for this material.

From Fig. 2 a graphical integration was attempted to derive R_∞. The ratios were weighted by factors proportional to the areas on the projecting sphere, and a figure of 1·497 resulted: this is some 3% lower than the ratio found above but, as the error in plotting the contours was about 5%, the agreement is considered to be satisfactory.

3. THE FACE-CENTRED CUBIC SYSTEM

For the face-centred cubic system Equation (2) was used in its corrected form [7] as above. In this case the (111) plane has minimum surface free energy, and the surface free energy ratio is:

$$R_{(hkl)} \equiv \frac{\gamma_{(hkl)}}{\gamma_{(111)}} = \frac{2h + k}{\sqrt{(h^2 + k^2 + l^2)}} \qquad . \qquad . \qquad . \qquad (6).$$

Partial and total averages were calculated as before and are shown in Table 2.

Table 2

Partial and Total Average Ratios for the
Face-centred Cubic System

n	R_n'	R_n
1	1·1397	1·1397
2	1·2083	1·1903
3	1·2085	1·2022
4	1·2083	1·2052
5	1·2085	1·2069
6	1·2086	1·2074
7	1·2085	1·2078
8	1·2086	1·2080
9	1·2083	1·2081
10	1·2083	1·2083

The limit appears to emerge with a much smaller number of planes than for the simple cubic system: it is $R_\infty = 1·2083 \pm 0·0003$. Figure 3 shows the contours of the surface energy ratio plotted as before. The figure is more complex than that for the simple cubic, with a marked minimum at (111), surrounded by maxima of 1·291 for the {210} planes, and there are inflexions at {100} and {110} planes.

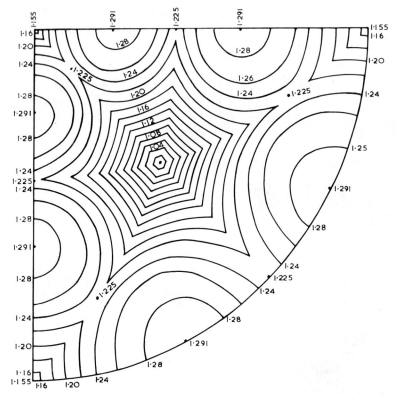

Fig. 3.—The surface energy ratios for the face-centred cubic system plotted on a stereographic projection.

4. THE BODY-CENTRED CUBIC SYSTEM

As is seen from Equation (3), this system introduces the complexity of two different bond strengths. It is inconvenient to use β_1 and β_2 separately, so we may put $\beta_1/\beta_2 = x$ and eliminate β_1 for any chosen value of x. In the face-centred cubic system the (110) plane has minimum surface energy, so we derive Equations (7) with this plane as reference:

$$
\left.
\begin{aligned}
R_{(hkl)} &= \frac{(2x + 1)\,h + k + l}{\sqrt{2}\,(h^2 + k^2 + l^2)^{1/2}\,(x + 1)} &&\text{when } h \geqslant (k + l) \\[2ex]
R_{(hkl)} &= \frac{h + k + l}{\sqrt{2}\,(h^2 + k^2 + l^2)^{1/2}} &&\text{when } h \leqslant (k + l)
\end{aligned}
\right\} \quad (7).
$$

Table 3

**Partial and Total Averages for
the Body-centred Cubic System**

		n									
		1	2	3	4	5	6	7	8	9	10
$=1\cdot269$	R_a'	1·0930	1·1530	1·1539	1·1543	1·1541	1·1600	1·1542	1·1541	1·1543	1·1543
	R_a	1·0930	1·1372	1·1482	1·1512	1·1527	1·1541	1·1547	1·1545	1·1544	1·1544
$=1\cdot300$	R_b'	1·0939	1·1533	1·1545	1·1548	1·1547	1·1605	—	—	—	—
	R_b	1·0939	1·1376	1·1488	1·1518	1·1533	1·1547	1·1553	1·1550	1·1550	1·1549
R_b/R_a		1·0009	1·0004	1·0005	1·0005	1·0005	1·0005	1·0005	1·00045	1·0005	1·0004

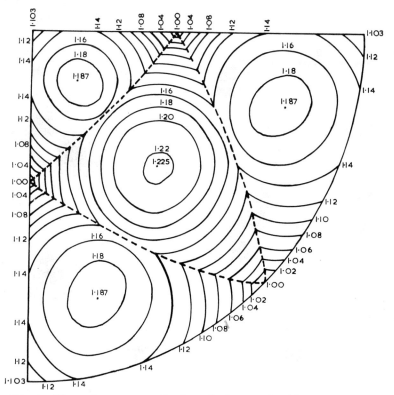

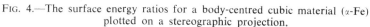

Fig. 4.—The surface energy ratios for a body-centred cubic material (α-Fe)
plotted on a stereographic projection.

From these equations it is seen that the ratio is independent of x when $h \not> (k+l)$. For a suitable value of x, α-Fe was chosen for which [4] $x = 0.99/0.78 = 1.269$; to estimate the change produced by varying x, it was also taken as 1.300. The results are shown in Table 3, in which the subscript n is replaced by a when $x = 1.269$, and by b when $x = 1.300$.

The average ratio for α-Fe may be taken as 1.1544 ± 0.0003: this ratio increases as x increases, but a change in x of 2.44% produces a change in the average ratio of only 0.045%, so the actual value of the bond energy ratio x is seen to be not very important.

In Fig. 4, the stereographic contour figure, the area inside the dashed lines is invariant: outside it the ratio changes with x and, for any change in x, the change in the ratio increases with the distance of the projection of a given plane from the dashed lines.

5. THE EFFECT OF TEMPERATURE

Significant irreversible changes may take place in a crystalline material well below its melting point. The lowest temperature at which sintering can be detected was first investigated in detail by TAMMAN,[8] and the ratio of this temperature to the absolute melting temperature is described as the Tamman ratio. For oxides the Tamman ratio is usually in the region of $0.5 - 0.6$,[9] though for silicates and silica it may be higher.[10] It is important that these ratios should refer to pure stoicheiometric compounds in the absence of chemical or physical reaction such as dehydration or inversion.[11]

Above the Tamman temperature (T_T) high-energy faces will tend to change to lower energy faces, and so the average surface energy ratio should tend to unity, when only faces of the reference planes will be left. The rate of change of the ratio will depend on the difference between the actual ratio and unity, hence it will change exponentially with time, being asymptotic to unity:

$$R_T = 1 + be^{-ct} . \quad . \quad . \quad . \quad . \quad (8)$$

where R_T is the surface energy ratio at $T\,^\circ K$ $(T_m > T > T_T)$, t is the time and b and c are constants. At T_T the rate of change of R will be infinitely slow and at the melting point it may be assumed to be infinitely fast, so as a first approximation:

$$\frac{dR}{dT} = - k \left(\frac{T - T_T}{T_m - T} \right) . \quad . \quad . \quad . \quad (9).$$

From (8), at $t = 0$, $b = (R_0 - 1)$. On differentiating and substituting in (8):

$$c = -\frac{1}{b}\left(\frac{dR}{dT}\right) = \frac{k(T - T_T)}{(R_0 - 1)(T_m - T)}$$

substituting:

$$R_T = 1 + (R_0 - 1) \exp\left[\frac{-k(T - T_T)t}{(R_0 - 1)(T_m - T)}\right] \quad . \quad (10).$$

In Equation (10) the constant k only applies to one crystalline particle; for more general application we may include a diffusion constant (D cm^2 sec^{-1}) and the particle size (r cm), such that $k = Dk'/r^2$, where k' is a dimensionless constant in the nature of a probability term.[12] D itself is a function of temperature, so, with the usual notation

$$R_T = 1 + (R_0 - 1) \exp\left[\frac{-D_0 e^{-\frac{E}{RT}} k'(T - T_T)t}{r^2(R_0 - 1)(T_m - T)}\right] \quad . \quad (11).$$

It is not easy to suggest representative values for the diffusion constants in Equation (11): for illustration we may put $D_0 = 10^{-7}$ cm^{2}sec^{-1}, with activation energies in the region 20-40 kcal/mole. Choosing $R_0 = 1 \cdot 5$, $k' = 0 \cdot 25$, $T_T = 1,000°$K., $T_m = 2,000°$K., and r in the region 10-1,000μ, Figs. 5, 6, and 7 were drawn. The large effects of activation energy and particle size are clearly seen.

BURTON and CABRERA [13] worked out a critical temperature below which nucleation is required for crystal growth; this temperature varies with the face under consideration. For a simple cubic alkali halide they found temperatures for the (100), (110) and (111) faces to be 1,000°C., 400°C. and -30°C. respectively. It will be noted that these temperatures change in the opposite direction to the surface free energy for these faces, and it is an attractive postulate that the Tamman temperature varies from face to face in such a manner, if nucleation is required for this process. If this is so, the gradual elimination of high-energy faces with time at a high temperature will cause the Tamman temperature to increase. It therefore seems unprofitable to develop Equation (11) any further.

One must also consider the area change as such a spherical crystal changes to an ideomorphic form. In the face-centred cubic system a possible ideomorph would be an octahedron of {111} faces. With unit spherical area, the initial total surface free energy would be $1 \cdot 208 \ \gamma_{(111)}$; an octahedron of the same volume would have a total surface free energy of $1 \cdot 327 \ \gamma_{(111)}$. Thus a sphere of face-centred cubic material would not spontaneously change to an octahedron.

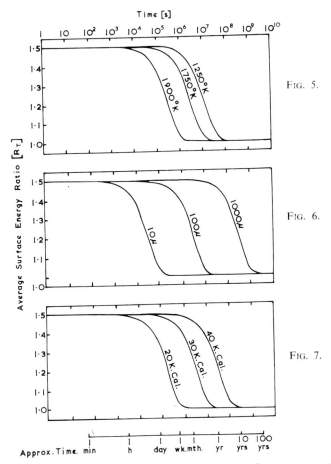

FIG. 5.—The effect of temperature on the average surface energy ratio
($E=30$ kcal; $r=100\mu$)

FIG. 6.—The effect of particle size on the average surface energy ratio
($T=1{,}750°$K; $E=30$ kcal)

FIG. 7.—The effect of activation energy on the average surface energy ratio
($T=1{,}750°$K; $r=100\mu$)

Similar considerations show that a change from a sphere to a cube
is possible for simple cubic material, and a body-centred cubic
sphere may tend to a duodecahedron.

Activation energies for self-diffusion are generally larger than
40 kcal/mole for pure oxides; MgO has a very low activation
energy for sintering, in the region of 43 kcal/mole.[9] Thus it would

seem from Figs. 5 to 7 that little change in the average ratio may be expected within a period of hours except for materials with a low activation energy, of small particle size and near their melting point.

In the literature the only examples of such polygonization of ceramics seem to be for Al_2O_3. KUCZYNSKI, ABERNETHY and ALLAN [6] show a photograph of beautifully clear facet development (their Fig. 11, p. 168) for originally spherical single crystals of 34μ diam., heated in dry H_2 at $1,900°C$. for 35 min; this effect was only observed in dry H_2, so it is probably due to evaporation of the lower oxides and not to a rearrangement of the molecules as is envisaged above.

It must be stressed that the discussion in this section only applies to isolated single crystal particles; the introduction of interparticle contacts and grain boundaries would greatly complicate this discussion.

6. DEPARTURES FROM PERFECTION

The effect of adsorption has been touched upon in Part I. Non-stoicheiometry may give rise to a special type of adsorption, such as was considered for wüstite in Part I, and so it may have a considerable effect on surface free energy. If non-stoicheiometry may be considered to be due to the presence, in small amount, of a second species of molecule, and if this species should tend to have a higher surface free energy than the stoicheiometric species, the second species will tend to be negatively adsorbed and will not greatly raise the surface free energy; on the other hand, the surface free energy may be considerably lowered by a species of lower energy molecule. If the species are present in comparable amounts, new structures may be produced. Examples of such effects are shown in Part I for the oxides of iron.

The effects of crystallographic imperfections would seem to be more generally predictable. It was shown in Part I that surface free energy changes continuously with orientation, and so stepped vicinal faces would tend to lower the surface free energy of high-energy faces and to raise that of low-energy faces. From photographs (e.g. VERMA [14]) these steps are estimated to increase the surface area by about 0.01%. At high temperatures, kinks in these steps become significant in number, about one kink for every four molecules in the region $0.5 - 0.8$ Tm (see reference 15, p. 13): holes and islands may also exist to about the same extent, so the total contribution of these defects may amount to an increase in total surface free energy of about 0.02%.

Dislocations may give rise to terraces, with an effect similar to that mentioned above. However, the centre of a screw dislocation

N

is associated with an excess free energy, as described by COTRELL (see reference 12, p. 38), and the energy associated with an edge dislocation is about 50% greater. With a high shear strength of 10^9 dynes/cm^2, and assuming a dislocation is 1,000Å in radius with a centre radius of 2·5Å, the free energy associated with a screw dislocation in a ceramic may be calculated to be about 2.4×10^{-4} erg/cm, or an average for both types of dislocation of about 3×10^{-4} erg/cm. With a distance between atomic layers of 1·5Å and a high dislocaton density of 10^8 cm^{-2} (see reference 10, p. 102), the excess surface free energy due to dislocations in a ceramic will not be more than about 4.5×10^{-4} erg/cm^2.

Mosaic crystals may be considered as arrays of dislocations with a similarly small effect. Interaction of the dislocations may increase this contribution, but it is not likely to be more than, say, 5×10^{-4} erg/cm^2.

Grain boundaries intersecting a surface may contribute to the surface energy by an amount varying with the mismatch in orientation of the grains and the inclination of the boundary to the surface. They may be described as arrays of dislocations when the angular distortion is small.[12] If we consider an extreme case in which every molecule in a boundary were part of a dislocation, and if the boundary were five molecules wide, the contribution would be $1·5 \times 10^{-3}$ erg per cm of boundary. For a material with grains of 10μ diam., this would amount to an increase in surface free energy of 0·3 erg/cm^2. A similar consideration applied to triple and quadruple points would give another increase of about 10^{-3} erg/cm^2. The magnitude of these effects is quite negligible.

For very small crystals, possibly of colloidal dimensions, the specific surface free energy may be higher than for a large crystal, because polarization deformation may be restricted, resulting in a strain energy contribution. In addition, edges and corners may have a similar effect in some cases (MOLLIÈRE et alia [15]), but it is not easy to estimate these effects; they are probably negligible for material above about 10μ diam.

Apart from adsorption, all these defects would be expected to have a maximum effect of less than 1 erg/cm^2 for a ceramic of 1,000 erg/cm^2 surface free energy.

7. CONCLUSION

The surface free energy of a spherical surface of a crystal may be derived from the structure of the crystal. The average surface free energy ratio, described above, should apply to all surfaces in which every possible plane has an equal probability of occurrence, in particular, to spherical single crystals and to spherical pores in a single crystal. It is difficult to predict the structure of a lens between two particles sintering together, but if this material is crystalline and has a curved surface the average ratio should apply. Similarly it should also apply to any spherical pores in a crystalline material, so an average ratio should be included in any rate equation containing a surface free energy term and applicable in the initial or in the final stages of sintering of solids.

Crystal defects, such as dislocations and grain boundaries, have negligible effect on the specific surface free energy.

ACKNOWLEDGMENTS

These two papers were from the work carried out for a Ph.D. thesis in the Metallurgy Department of the Royal College of Science and Technology (now Strathclyde University), Glasgow. The author desires to thank Emeritus Professor R. Hay, B.Sc., Ph.D., F.R.I.C., F.I.M., and J. Taylor, M.Sc., Ph.D., F.I.M., who freely gave help and useful discussion. Thanks is also due to the Union Carbide and Carbon Corp. for financial assistance during part of this work, and to the British Ceramic Research Association for assistance in preparing this paper.

REFERENCES

1. Mackenzie, J. K., and Shuttleworth, R., *Proc. Phys. Soc.*, **B62**, 833, 1949; Kuczynski, G. C., *J. Metals*, **1**, 169, 1949; Clark, P. W., and White, J., *Trans. Brit. Ceram. Soc.*, **49**, 305, 1950.
2. Udin, H., Funk, E. R., and Wulff, J., *J. Metals*, **3**, 1206, 1951.
3. Kingery, W. D., *J. Amer. Ceram. Soc.*, **37**, 42, 1954.
4. Friedel, J., Cullity, B. D., and Crussard, C., *Acta Met.*, **1**, 79, 1953.
5. Pranatis, A. L., and Pound, G. M., *Trans. A.I.M.E.*, **203**, 664, 1955.
6. Kuczynski, G. C., Abernethy, L., and Allan, J., "Kinetics of High Temperature Processes", ed. W. D. Kingery (John Wiley & Sons Inc. and Chapman & Hall Ltd., 1959), p. 163.
7. Friedel, J. Private communication.
8. Tamman, G., *Z. anorg. Chem.*, **149**, 29, 1925; *Kolloid Zeit.*, **98**, 275, 1942.
9. Clark, P. W., Cannon, J. H., and White, J., *Trans. Brit. Ceram. Soc.*, **52**, 1, 1953.
10. Volmer, M., "Kinetik der Phasenbildung" (Dresden, 1939), p. 56.
11. Taylor, N. W., *J. Amer. Ceram. Soc.*, **17**, 155, 1934.
12. Cotrell, A. H., "Dislocations and Plastic Flow in Crystals" (Clarendon, Oxford, 1953), p. 49.
13. Burton, W. K., and Cabrera, N., "Crystal Growth", *Disc. Faraday Soc.*, No. 5, 1949, p. 35.
14. Verma, "Crystal Growth and Dislocations" (Butterworth, London, 1953), p. 97.
15. Mollière, K., Rathje, W., and Stranski, I. N., *Disc. Faraday Soc.*, No. 5, 1949, p. 21.

25—Strains in Glazed Ceramic Products

By M. F. A. HOENS and J. C. KREUTER

Ferro Enamels (Holland) N.V.

Rotterdam, Netherlands

ABSTRACT   D428—E4—E5—E6—A71

During and after glost firing, strains are set up by differences in expansion, elasticity, thickness and reactivity between the body and the glaze. The properties of the interfacial layer depend on the mineralogical composition and porosity of the body, the composition and fineness of the glaze, and the wetting of the body by the glaze. An apparatus has been developed to measure the strain, the criterion being the deformation of a hanging test-strip in relation to temperature. An advantage is that small flat samples can be tested; special shapes do not have to be made.

Tensions dans les produits céramiques émaillés

Les différences de dilatation, d'élasticité, d'épaisseur et de réactivité entre le tesson et la glaçure créent des tensions pendant et après la cuisson en émail. Les propriétés de la couche interfaciale dépendent de la composition minéralogique et de la porosité du tesson, de la composition et de la finesse de la glaçure, et du mouillage du tesson par la glaçure. Un appareil, basé sur la déformation d'une bande suspendue en fonction de la température, a été mis au point pour la mesure de la tension. Il présente l'avantage de pouvoir se prêter à l'essai de petits échantillons plats; il n'est pas nécessaire de fabriquer des pièces de forme spéciale.

Spannungen in verglasten keramischen Gegenstanden

Während und nach dem Glasurbrand entstehen Spannungen durch Unterschiede in thermischer Ausdehnung, Elastizität, Dicke und Reaktivität zwischen Scherben und Glasur. Die Eigenschaften der Übergangsschicht hängen ab von der mineralogischen Zusammensetzung und Porosität der Scherbe; der Zusammensetzung und Feinkörnigkeit des Glasurschlickers und der Benetzung des Scherbens von der Glasur. Ein Apparat ist entworfen für die Bestimmung des Spannungen nach dem Prinzip der Biegung von einem aufgehängten Prüfstab abhängig von der Temperatur. Ein Vorteil der hier entwickelten Methode ist, dass die Bestimmung an kleine ebene Muster vorgenommen werden kann, sodass spezielle Muster nicht hergestellt brauchen zu werden.

1. INTRODUCTION

Normally the glaze on a ceramic body is under compression at room temperature. This is deliberate, because a glaze resists compressive forces better than it can resist tensile forces. But in any case the differences in thermal expansion between glaze and body set up strains, and these strains determine the thermal shock resistance of the glazed product, the tendency for hairlining or chipping, and the deformation of the product.

N*

In the literature, several methods are mentioned for the direct measurement of the strain of a glazed sample, sometimes in relation to temperature, but a distinction must be drawn between those methods that allow the sample to deform, and those methods in which the sample cannot move freely.

In practice, two methods are used principally. The first one was developed by STEGER,[1] who measured the deformation of a flat sample, partly glazed on one side, in relation to temperature. The second one is the measurement of strain optically,[2] which is only possible with transparent glaze. Since the index of refraction of a glaze also depends on the strain (photo-elastic effect), with this second method the distribution of the strain through the cross-section can also be measured, again provided that the glaze is transparent.

In this paper the strain between glaze and body is discussed in relation to temperature. As a measure of the strain, we use the deformation that has been caused by the differential expansion of body and glaze. The distinction between this method and Steger's is that the equipment used here is designed to measure the strain developed in flat glazed test-bars, either during or after glost firing, whereas Steger's method was more suitable for measuring the strain after the glaze has matured. It also required long bars of special shape to be made, with the attendant disadvantages.

The strain apparatus was constructed to take small flat samples, and so no special shapes had to be made. This is important so that the apparatus can be used for practical problems, e.g. arising with wall-tiles, which are relatively small and for which deformation—particularly curvature—is critical because they are glazed on one side only. With the apparatus to be described, strain can be measured on bars to which glaze has been applied to one side, or to both sides, in different thickness. In this way several variables which are important in the strain phenomena of glazed products can be eliminated. The effect of micro-fissures in the body, which cause disorientation and "hysteresis", and the presence of an interfacial layer between glaze and body, should be mentioned.

2. STRAIN MEASUREMENT BY DEFLECTION

Figure 1 is a diagram of the apparatus. The sample is 15 cm long and 2 cm wide, and its thickness can be varied as required; normally it is 2·5 mm. Bars of suitable dimensions can be sawed from biscuit wall-tiles with a diamond saw. The bar is glazed over a length of 10 cm and, after drying, it (1) is fixed in the water-cooled sample-holder (2). The lower end (3) of the bar guides a

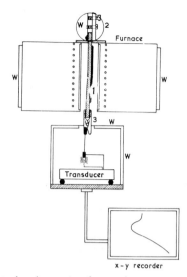

Furnace

Transducer

x - y recorder

FIG. 1.—Apparatus for strain measurement

coil of a transducer and the change in curvature of the bar during glost firing can be recorded with an X-Y recorder.

The furnace and transducer are enclosed in a water-cooled jacket (W), to keep the temperature of the ends of the sample relatively low. The heating- and cooling-cycles of the furnace are regulated by means of a program controller ($20°$–$1,050°$–$20°C.$). The temperature in the furnace is measured by means of a thermocouple which is in contact with the glaze at the middle of the bar; at about $700°C.$ the temperature variation in the furnace is a maximum of $50°$. This variation results in an average systematic deviation in deflection, which is proportional to the deflection corresponding to a temperature range of $5°$–$10°C.$ The apparatus can be used horizontally as well as vertically, and as some bodies tend to sag at the temperature of glost firing, we normally use the vertical position.

Changes in size during heating and cooling have been measured on control bars, and are not generally of great significance ($0·05$–$0·1$ mm). This deviation, of course, determines the sensitivity of the strain measurement. Where necessary, this sensitivity can be improved by using thinner specimens; the measurements are generally comparative and not absolute.

In the strain graphs the deflection of the lower end of the test bar is plotted against temperature. The quantity of glaze is given in grams per 20 cm², e.g. 1 g of glaze corresponds to a fired thickness of about $0·2$ mm.

3. THEORETICAL CONSIDERATIONS

In general the strain between glaze and body is caused by the differences in their expansion, moduli of elasticity, relative thicknesses of the various layers, etc.

3.1 The Interfacial Layer

The reaction between glaze and body enriches the glaze at the interface with quartz, and this interfacial layer generally has a lower coefficient of expansion and a higher softening temperature than the glaze.

The upper example in Fig. 2 is a thick interfacial layer, and is for a reactive and porous body; the lower one is a less reactive combination. X-ray diffraction diagrams showed that the interfacial layer is in fact a glass which is contaminated by the body.

Table 1 gives some physical characteristics of bodies and glazes used in this investigation.

Table 1

Characteristics of Bodies, Glazes and Mixtures

	3α ($\times 10^{-7}$)		T_s ($°C$)	Porosity ($\%$)
	$20°-320°C$ Heating up	$320°-20°C$ Cooling down		
BODIES				
A Feldspathic body	180	161	—	17
B Porous Ca- and Fe-bearing body	246	246	—	22·3
C Wollastonite body	214	214	—	19·1
D Feldspathic body with cristobalite	276	127	—	16·4
GLAZES				
1 Transparent Pb-bearing	153	153	578	—
2 ,, ,, ,,	188	188	605	—
3 White opaque Zr-bearing	153	153	650	—
4 ,, ,, ,, ,,	206	206	580	—
MIXTURES				
80% glaze 1 + 20% body A	144	144	617	—
70% ,, 3 + 30% ,, B	164	164	656	—
70% ,, 4 + 30% ,, D	176	176	645	—

The influence on the strain of differences in expansion (or contraction) of glaze and interfacial layer is shown in Fig. 3. The expansion curves of these two layers are drawn so as to coincide with that of the body at the softening temperatures of the glazes, which are measured with a Leitz expansiometer. The strain, which is proportional to the difference in expansion of body and glaze, will be strongly influenced by the interfacial layer, the cross-section of which will exhibit a strain gradient.

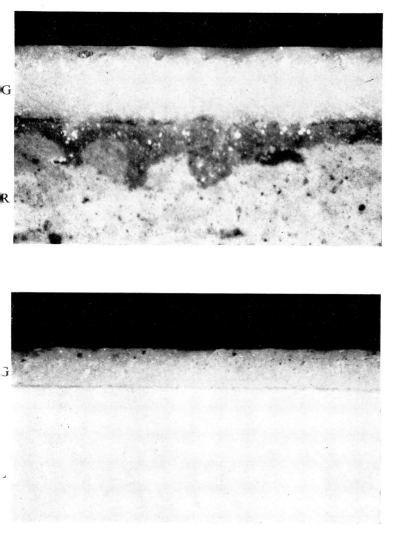

FIG. 2.—Interfacial layers
G = Glaze
R = Reactive body
L = Less reactive body

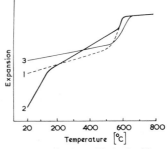

FIG. 3.—Expansion behaviour of: glaze (1), body (2), and interfacial layer (3)

3.2 Strain Distribution in Cross-section

There are several reasons for assuming that the strain due to the relative thermal expansions of glaze and body varies across the section: (1) the two dissimilar layers that constitute the glazed body [4]; (2) the interfacial layer; (3) the body can be regarded as a

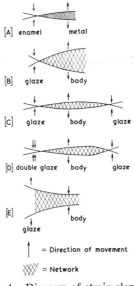

FIG. 4.—Diagram of strain elements
A. Glass on metal (fine network)
B. Glass on coarse network
C. Coarse network, blocked at two sides
D. Asymmetric blocked coarse network
E. Glass under tensile stress on a coarse
    network

coarse network, because it is porous and because it contains micro-
fissures.[5] If this "network" contracts or expands more towards
one face than another, the apparent strain deflection appears to be
greater than if there were no "network" of pores. Moreover, both
strain and the resulting deflection can exhibit hysteresis.

Figure 4 indicates the strain elements from the point of view of
the "network" theory, and Fig. 5 shows the consequences to be
expected for the strain distribution for networks.

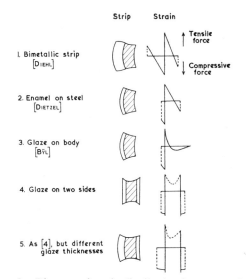

FIG. 5.—Diagram of strain distribution in cross-section

In example (2), the strain gradient of enamelled steel looks
simpler than for example (3) of the glazed body, but in fact this is
not so. Enamelling is a quick procedure which may introduce strain
gradients, since the rim and the outside of the enamelled article
cool down more quickly than the inside. Strain measurements
showed that within wide limits the strain deflection of enamelled
strips is proportional to the applied thickness of the enamel, but
this is not so with the glaze measurements to be described.

Measurements on totally glazed bodies, the body being in tension,
showed a great decrease in expansion, if the expansion of the un-
glazed body exhibited permanent deformation.

3.3 Strain Formulae

Though the calculation from formulae of the strains between
body and glaze due to the differences in expansion or the strain

deflection is only approximate, some of the formulae are given in Table 2.

As the strain deflection at any given rate is proportional to the strain and, because the various properties such as elasticity, expansion, etc., vary across the section, the formulae only have a demonstrative function. In fact we use the deflection as a comparative measure of the strain between glaze and body.

Table 2

Strain formulae

FLAT FIXED SAMPLE

One component $\qquad \sigma = \dfrac{\epsilon E}{1 - \mu}$

Two components $\qquad \sigma_g = \dfrac{\displaystyle\int (\alpha_g - \alpha_b)dT}{\dfrac{1 - \mu_g}{E_g} + \dfrac{1 - \mu_b}{E_b} \cdot \dfrac{d_g}{d_b}}$

FREE-MOVING SAMPLE

Two components $\qquad D = \dfrac{L^2}{2} \cdot \dfrac{\displaystyle\int (\alpha_b - \alpha_g)dT}{\dfrac{d_b + d_g}{2} + \dfrac{E_b}{E_g} \dfrac{Bd_b^3}{6d_g(d_b + d_g)}}$

$\qquad \sigma = \dfrac{2D}{L^2} \left[\dfrac{B(E_g d_g^3 + E_b d_b^3)}{6(d_b d_g + d_g^2)} + \dfrac{E_g d_g}{2} \right]$

σ = Strain
D = Strain deflection
g = Glaze
b = Body
ϵ = Increase of length
E = Modulus of elasticity
μ = Poisson's ratio
T = Temperature
d = Thickness
L = Length of glazed strip
B = Width of glazed strip (in mm)
α = Linear coefficient of expansion

3.4 Multi-component Systems

Actually more than two components are involved: the body, the glaze, the interfacial layer, and, sometimes, the glaze and interfacial layer on the opposite side of the body. As the elasticity of the total system can vary, experiments were made by loading the strips with weights (Table 3). If the strain between glaze and body is not excessive, it can be concluded within wide limits that:

(1) Hook's law is valid for tangential movement.

(2) The Young's modulus of elasticity of the glaze has considerable influence on the bending or deformation of the total system.

(3) The elasticity of a system coated on two sides does not differ greatly from that of the system on one side.

The results of the bend tests are in agreement with the network scheme, for it includes differences in apparent elasticity.[7]

The above conclusions enable the deflection to be used as a comparative measure of strain (Table 3).[8]

Table 3

Elasticity and Strength of Some Materials

MODULUS OF ELASTICITY E

$kg/cm^2 \times 10^3$

Glaze	..	..	..	500–800
Body	..	..	..	400–600
Porcelain	..	..	..	700–800
Steel	..	..	..	~ 1800

"E" TANGENTIAL

$kg/cm^2 \times 10^3$

Body A	..	..	..	103
Body B	..	..	..	68
Body C	..	..	..	74
Body D	..	..	..	75
D + 5% glaze		..	..	79
D + 2 × 5% glaze			..	81
D + 10% glaze		..	..	215
D + 2 × 10% glaze	..		..	230

TENSILE STRENGTH

kg/cm^2

Body	..	..	..	200
Glaze	..	..	..	300–500
Porcelain	..	..	..	240–500

COMPRESSIVE STRENGTH

kg/cm^2

Body	..	..	5800–7900
Glaze	..	..	$\sim 10,000$
Porcelain	..	..	5000–7000

4. STRAIN MEASUREMENTS

4.1 Reactivity

Figure 6 shows strain curves for glaze No. 3 (Table 1) on a very reactive body (B), measured during cooling during the glost firing (20°C./min). 3/0 means 3 g of glaze on one side of the body (which corresponds to a fired thickness of 0·6 mm) and 0 g on the opposite

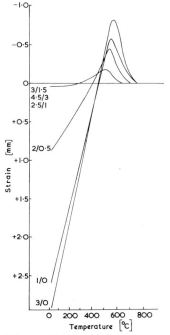

Fig. 6.—Influence of the reactivity on the strain between glaze and body

side. There is considerable strain deflection and the softening temperature is high. From Fig. 2 it was calculated that about 1 g of glaze was necessary to form the interfacial layer.

Curve 1/0 shows the influence of the interfacial layer on strain development, which does not differ much from the 3/0 curve. When glaze is applied to both sides, however, as in the case of 2/0·5, the strain deflection decreases. When more than 0·5 g is applied (e.g. 2/0·7), the deflection decreases until, at 1 g, no further interfacial layer develops (saturation), and low strain and lower softening temperatures result.

The comparative curves 3/1·5, 4·5/3 and 2·5/1 show the same result. This again agrees with the saturation and the differences in tangential elasticities (Table 2).

4.2 Hysteresis Effects

There are several causes for hysteresis.

4.21 Thermal Conductivity

During cooling, when the glaze solidifies, the temperature of the body is higher than that of the glaze; this difference in temperature decreases, but the total contraction of the body is greater than that of the glaze. The slope of the curve for the heating cycle, however, is about 15% steeper than that of the cooling curve. The deviation on the numerical value is proportional to this figure.

4.22 Soaking-time

Some of the bars, the curves for which are shown in Fig. 6, had a longer soaking at 1,050°C. to see if the shape of the curves would be different. However, the reaction layer proved to be saturated and the curves did not show a significant difference.

4.23 Moisture Expansion

Moisture increases the volume of the body and so decreases the compression of the glaze. This effect is not taken into consideration here.

4.24 Hysteresis of the Glaze

The glaze strain tends to decrease with time and the transformation temperature of the glaze is different for heating and cooling. After the glost fire the glaze can be considered as an annealed glass, because cooling is slow. Heating up was also slow, so the influence of hysteresis of the glaze was not great.

4.25 Hysteresis of the Body under Compression

Body B (Table 1) does not show a distinct hysteresis. Indeed the curves in Fig. 6 did not show hysteresis effects during heating up. This is different for Body A (Fig. 7[2]). The curve drawn is for body A glazed on one side with glaze 2 (1g = 0·2 mm). After heating

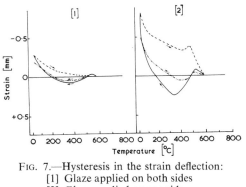

FIG. 7.—Hysteresis in the strain deflection:
[1] Glaze applied on both sides
[2] Glaze applied on one side

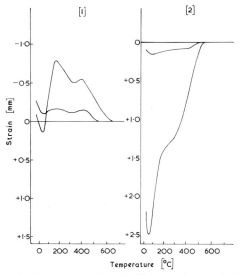

FIG. 8.—Strain curves of glazed bodies containing cristobalite

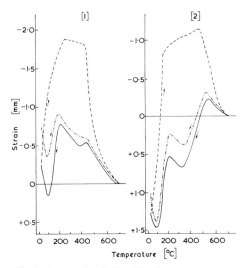

FIG. 9.—Strain hysteresis of glazed bodies containing cristobalite

again (dotted line) the curve shows a strong hysteresis. The second cooling curve looks more like the first, but it indicates that the body is not exactly the same as it was. Apparently in the biscuit firing the components of the body did not react completely. The same phenomenon we see in Part 1 of the figure, where the combination is the same but the glaze is applied to both sides and at different thicknesses. This means that the influence of the interfacial layer has been compensated and we can conclude that this hysteresis is due to the body.

4.3 Cristobalite-containing Bodies

The slope of the expansion curve of a cristobalite-containing body is steep from room temperature until about 200°C. and it indicates large hysteresis (Table 2, Body D). Figure 8 shows great strain variations in the region below 200°C. 8[1] is the cristobalite body, glazed on one side with a glaze of high expansion (glaze no. 4 : 1·5 g = 0.3 mm thickness); 8[2] represents the curve for the same body, but with a glaze of lower expansion (glaze 2). The curve near the zero strain axes in Fig. 8 represent the same glaze applications, but on both sides of the bodies (3 and 1·5 g). It is clear that in this last case a compensation takes place for both interfacial layer and " network " effects. In order to get a glaze that fits well, a compromise had to be made between the expansion of the glaze and the reactivity (interfacial layer) (Fig. 8[1]).

The thermal shock resistance, however, is poor (the reheating curves in Figs. 9[1] and 9[2]). The glaze in 9[1] is again No. 4; the glaze in Fig. 9[2] is a mixture of glaze 4 and 30% of the body, which resulted in a lower-expansion glaze. If the glaze is applied to both sides in different thicknesses, the deflection and the hysteresis effect decrease in the same ratio as in Fig. 7.

4.4 Comparison with Theoretical Values

With the strain formulae of Table 2 the strain and the strain deflection can be calculated approximately. As an example, it is assumed that:

d body = 2.5 mm
d glaze = 0·3 mm (or eventually difference in thickness)
B = 20 mm
μ = 0·25
E glaze = 6,000 kg/mm²
E body = 5,000 kg/mm²
ε = $\int (\alpha_g - \alpha_b)\ dT$

A difference in length of $\varepsilon = 0.0005$ (cristobalite transformation of Fig. 8) gives a strain deflection of 1 mm for a body glazed on one side.

The theoretical deflection, calculated with $\varepsilon = 0.0005$, is 0.07 mm. The corresponding strain is about 4 kg/mm². If the glaze is applied to both sides, but in different thicknesses (difference in thickness 0.3 mm) we do indeed find a low deflection —according to Fig. 8, 0.06 mm. Apparently only in that case can the modulus of elasticity of the body be used in the formulae. For bodies glazed on one side, other factors are responsible for the greater strain deflection (≈ 1 mm):

(1) The relative significance of the modulus of elasticity. Substitution of the tangential modulus of elasticity (Table 3) of the body (ca. 800 kg/mm²) for the Young's modulus of elasticity gives a higher calculated value for the deflection (0.4 mm), which is in agreement with the network scheme.

(2) The influence of the interfacial layer (Fig. 3), which will increase the strain and the strain deflection even more.

5. FINAL REMARKS

The apparatus described enables strain curves to be obtained during glost firing. Subsequent heating-up cycles then show the thermal shock resistance and possible transformations that may occur in the body or the glaze.

The strain distribution is not homogeneous, but concentrated near the glaze-body interface, and can be explained by means of the technique of applying glaze to both sides of the bar.

Different softening-temperatures and strains were observed, which further explain the strain distribution with the interfacial layer and the network theory, which are different from the bimetallic strip and the enamelled strip.

The strain gradient in cross-section of a thin glaze layer can be even more pronounced than supposed by Bijl. This depends on the development of the interfacial layer.

REFERENCES

1. Steger, W., *Keram. Rundschau*, **3**, 29, 1932.
2. Padmos, A. A., *Philips Res. Repts*, **1**, 332, 1948.
3. Bijl, C. L., *Chem. Weekblad*, **48**, 998, 1952.
4. Diehl, M. G. Thesis Delft (Holland), 1948.
5. Kingery, W. D., " Introduction to Ceramics ", p. 481 (1960).
6. Dietzel, A., *Mitt. Ver. Dtsch. Emailfachl.* **10**, 35, 1962; Timoschenko, S. J., *Opt. Soc. Amer.*, **11**, 233, 1925; Lauchner, Cook Andrews, *J. Amer. Ceram. Soc.*, **39**, 288, 1956; Hollenweger, *Sprechsaal*, **60**, 489, 1927.
7. Dekker, P., *Mitt. Ver. Dtsch. Emailfachl.*, **7**, 49, 1959.
8. Henze, W., " Glasuren ", p. 53 (Verlag Wilhelm Knapp, Halle, 1951).

26—Solid Oxide Electrolytes

By C. B. ALCOCK and B. C. H. STEELE

Imperial College of Science and Technology, London

ABSTRACT

H40

Solid solutions of some Group IIa or IIIa oxides in thoria and zirconia possess the fluorite lattice, and contain a large number of vacant anion sites. Consequently the transport number of oxide ions in the solutions is often very nearly unity. The materials can thus be used as solid-state electrolytes and some typical applications are described, such as the measurement of the thermodynamics of oxygen in liquid metals and non-stoicheiometric oxides. The limitations of the range of application of a given solution are determined by the phase equilibria, which are governed by temperature and oxygen potential. Some examples, which have recently been elucidated, are discussed.

Electrolytes d'oxydes solides

Des solutions solides de certains oxydes des groupes IIa ou IIIa dans la thorine et la zircone possèdent le réseau de la fluorine et contiennent un grand nombre de sites d'anions vacants. En conséquence le nombre des transports d'ions d'oxyde dans les solutions est souvent très proche de l'unité. Ces substances peuvent donc être utilisées comme électrolytes à l'état solide et certaines applications typiques, telles que la mesure de la thermodynamique de l'oxygène dans les métaux liquides et les oxydes non stoechiométriques, sont décrites. Les limitations du domaine d'application d'une solution donnée sont déterminées par les équilibres de phases, qui sont régis par la température et le potentiel d'oxygène. Quelques exemples, récemment élucidés, sont étudiés.

Elektrolyte aus festen Oxiden

Feste Lösungen von Oxiden der Gruppe IIa oder IIIa in Thoriumoxid und Zirkonoxid haben Fluoritstruktur und enthalten eine grosse Anzahl von leeren Anionengitterplätzen. Infolge dessen ist der Überführungskoeffizient der Sauerstoffionen in diesen Lösungen häufig nahe bei 1. Die Stoffe können daher als Elektrolyte im festen Zustand benutzt werden. Einige typische Anwendungen werden beschrieben, wie z.B. eine Messung der Thermodynamik des Sauerstoffs in flüssigen Metallen und nichtstöchiometrischen Oxiden. Die Begrenzung des Anwendungsbereiches einer gegebenen Lösung wird durch das Phasengleichgewicht bestimmt, das von Temperatur und Sauerstoffpotential abhängt. Einige Beispiele, die kürzlich aufgeklärt wurden, werden besprochen.

1. INTRODUCTION

In recent years considerable interest has grown in the electrical properties of the solid solutions in zirconia of calcium oxide and certain Group III oxides, such as yttria, which possess the fluorite structure. The X-ray measurements of HUND and co-workers [1] had already established the fact that these solutions contained vacant anion sites, the number being directly proportional to the mole fraction of the lower valency cation. As might be expected, the oxygen ion transport number is nearly unity [2] in the presence of the high defect concentration in the anion lattice, the materials behaving practically as electrolytic conductors.

Analogous electrolytic solid solutions are formed in thoria as solvent, the difference being that, as pure thoria possesses the fluorite lattice, the fluorite solution range is wider than those based on zirconia, where about 10 mole % of calcium oxide or yttria must be added to stabilize the fluorite structure.

The applications of these solid electrolytes include the measurement of oxygen potentials by means of electro-chemical cells, and power generation by high-temperature fuel cells. Examples of such applications will be given, and it will be the object of this paper to consider the relative merits of some zirconia- and thoria-based electrolytes.

2. THE PREPARATION OF MATERIALS

The solid solutions were prepared from Johnson and Matthey spectroscopically pure materials* by dissolution of the requisite amounts of the separate components in triple-distilled water or the minimum amounts of "Analar" nitric acid, followed by evaporation to dryness or co-precipitation with "polarographic-purity" ammonia. The resulting nitrate or hydroxide mixture was dried and ignited finally to 1,400°C. in air for 16 h. The oxide solid solutions were then ground in an agate mortar, mixed with 3–4 wt. % "Cranko" (methyl–methacrylate polymer) and compressed in Vinamold (a polyvinyl chloride gel) to 30 tons/in². The pellets thus obtained were heated *in vacuo*, held in a thoria or stabilized-zirconia crucible, to a temperature of 2,000°C. for 3 h, and then heated in air at 1,400°C. for a further 8 h. During the vacuum treatment the oxides lost oxygen, and the final air-treatment was carried out to restore the original metal/oxygen ratio. The resulting pellets were usually 2–3 mm thick and approximately 1 cm diam.

The faces were polished, finally with 0·25 μ diamond paste, to give mirror finishes to the translucent pellets.

---

* Zirconyl nitrate 99·8% (0–0·2% HfO₂) others < 10 p.p.m., thorium nitrate 99·999%, calcium carbonate 99·995%, yttrium oxide 99·98%, lanthanum oxide 99·995%.

3. ELECTRICAL CONDUCTIVITIES

The conductivities of zirconia–lime and zirconia–yttria solutions have recently been studied by DIXON.[3] It was found that the maximum conductivity occurs at the zirconia-rich end of the fluorite field, the conductivity decreasing continuously as the mole fraction of lime or yttria was increased. The conductivities were measured by the four-point probe d.c. method, and the results are listed in Table 1.

Table 1

Electrolyte	Defect concentration (%)	Specific conductance* (1,000°C) Mhos.cm⁻¹	Conductivity/temperature relationship (Arrhenius Equation)
$Zr_{0.85}Ca_{0.15}O_{1.85}$[3]	7·5	$3·0 \times 10^{-2}$	$\sigma = 2·7 \times 10^3 \exp. \left(-\dfrac{28,000}{RT} \right)$
$Th_{0.85}Ca_{0.15}O_{1.85}$	7·5	$9·2 \times 10^{-4}$	$\sigma = 22 \exp. \left(-\dfrac{25,500}{RT} \right)$
$Zr_{0.75}Y_{0.25}O_{1.875}$[3]	6·25	$5·0 \times 10^{-2}$	$\sigma = 2·8 \times 10^3 \exp. \left(-\dfrac{29,000}{RT} \right)$
$Th_{0.75}Y_{0.25}O_{1.85}$	6.25	$2·4 \times 10^{-3}$	$\sigma = 42 \exp. \left(-\dfrac{24,700}{RT} \right)$

* Conductivity value reported for measurements in air.

(The conductivities of the thoria solid solutions exhibit a small dependence upon oxygen pressure, indicating a finite electronic contribution to the total conductivity.)

It is interesting to note that the pre-exponential factors are practically the same for these two solutions, but the yttria solution is a better conductor than the zirconia–lime solution in the temperature range of the measurements (600°–1,200°C.).

In the present investigation the electrolyte discs were pressed between platinum foil contacts and the conductivities measured with a capacitance-resistance bridge at 1·5 kc/s. These were recorded from 700° to 1,000°C. and the results are shown in Table 1.

Again, the pre-exponential factors are similar, and the activation energies are of the same order as those which are well established for the zirconia solutions. It will be observed, however, that the conductivities of the thoria solutions are some 20–30 times lower than those of the corresponding zirconia solutions. Once again, the yttria solution is a better conductor than the lime solution of approximately the same anion defect concentration.

4. THE MEASUREMENT OF OXYGEN POTENTIALS

It has been pointed out that a useful application of these electrolytes is in the determination of the oxygen potentials of systems at high temperatures. Examples of this are to be found in the pioneering work of KIUKKOLA and WAGNER [4] where the electrodes were compressed pellets of pure metal and the corresponding lowest oxide, such as nickel–nickel oxide, iron–wüstite and copper–cuprous oxide.

Subsequently measurements of activities in copper–nickel alloys were made by MAAK and RAPP [5] using electrodes of pure nickel–nickel oxide on one side of the cell, and of copper–nickel alloys—nickel oxide on the other side.

ARONSON and BELLE [6] first measured the oxygen potential of non-stoicheiometric UO_{2+x} by means of solid electrolyte cells, and PETERS [7, 8] and co-workers have studied CO/CO_2 mixtures using the gas in contact with platinum as the electrode.

In all of these studies, except the last-named, the electrolyte was zirconia–lime, Peters also having used thoria-based electrolytes.

These systems have in common the fact that the oxygen potentials involved were relatively high (greater than -100 kcal/mole O_2), and the results could have been obtained, in principle, by the use of conventional techniques such as gas–solid equilibria. Furthermore the lowest temperature at which results were reported was about 700°C., since the resistance of the electrolyte was too high, at lower temperatures, for accurate results to be obtained with the potentiometric measuring devices which were used.

It is of considerable interest to the metallurgist to have a technique which will allow the direct determination of low oxygen potentials such as those occurring in systems involving the reactive metals, e.g. niobium, vanadium. It was decided then to concentrate in this study on measurements involving the niobium–NbO electrode which has an oxygen potential in the region -150 kcal at temperatures around 1,000°C.

The electrodes were iron–wüstite and niobium–niobium monoxide pellets made by mixing pure Fe, Fe_2O_3 and Nb, Nb_2O_5 in appropriate proportions and pelletizing at 5 t/in². The pellets were annealed in vacuum at 1,000°C. for 24 h to approach metal/oxide equilibrium and the two phases were clearly visible. Before mounting in the cell the faces were ground flat to ensure good electrical contact.

The apparatus in which the measurements were made could be flushed with argon purified by passing through cupric oxide at 550°C., Sofnolite, magnesium perchlorate and finally titanium granules at 900°C. Alternatively, the apparatus could be evacuated to a final pressure of 10^{-5} mm Hg. It was found necessary to incorporate titanium or zirconium getter material in the assembly around the cell in order to obtain useful results. The entirely erroneous results shown in Fig. 1 are probably due to the presence of small amounts of oxygen-containing impurity gases in the argon atmosphere around the cell.

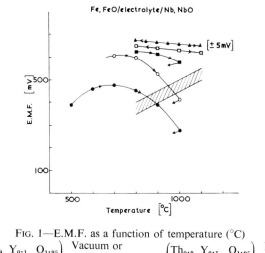

Fe, FeO/electrolyte/Nb, NbO

FIG. 1—E.M.F. as a function of temperature (°C)

▲ $\left. \begin{array}{l} Th_{0\cdot9}\ Y_{0\cdot1}\ O_{1\cdot95} \\ Th_{0\cdot9}\ La_{0\cdot1}\ O_{1\cdot95} \\ Th_{0\cdot85}\ Ca_{0\cdot15}\ O_{1\cdot85} \end{array} \right\}$ Vacuum or purified argon with getters

///// $\left. \begin{array}{l} Th_{0\cdot9}\ Y_{0\cdot1}\ O_{1\cdot95} \\ Th_{0\cdot9}\ La_{0\cdot1}\ O_{1\cdot95} \\ Th_{0\cdot85}\ Ca_{0\cdot15}\ O_{1\cdot85} \end{array} \right\}$ Purified argon without getters

□ $Th_{0\cdot75}\ Y_{0\cdot25}\ O_{1\cdot875}$ (10mm) Vacuum with getters

○ $Zr_{0\cdot85}\ Ca_{0\cdot15}\ O_{1\cdot85}$ (10m) Vacuum with getters

■ $Th_{0\cdot75}\ Y_{0\cdot25}\ O_{1\cdot875}$ Vacuum with getters

● $Zr_{0\cdot85}\ Ca_{0\cdot15}\ O_{1\cdot85}$ Purified argon without getters

Zirconia–lime, thoria–lime, thoria–yttria, and thoria–lanthana electrolytes were used in these cells, and the results are brought together in Fig. 1. The thoria solutions are clearly superior to the zirconia solution in giving higher and reproducible e.m.f's. Moreover the higher values are similar to those obtained by GERASIMOV et al.[9] The results for $Th_{0\cdot9}\ La_{0\cdot1}\ O_{1\cdot95}$, $Th_{0\cdot9}\ Y_{0\cdot1}\ O_{1\cdot95}$ and

$Th_{0.85} Ca_{0.15} O_{1.85}$ were the same in argon or in high vacuum, which is contrary to some observations in the literature.[10]

It is interesting to note that as the temperature was raised in the experiments using the zirconia–lime solution, the e.m.f. first increased and then fell, and on cooling lower e.m.f's were obtained than those at corresponding temperatures during the heating cycle. The same was observed with a 2 mm thick $Th_{0.75} Y_{0.25} O_{1.875}$ electrolyte, but a 10 mm thick electrolyte of the same composition gave reproducible e.m.f's approaching the highest values.

As might be anticipated, it was found that with two electrolytes in series, between these electrodes, one zirconia–lime and the other thoria–lime, the highest values of the e.m.f's were again obtained.

Measurements which were made with Ni–NiO and Fe–FeO or Cu–Cu_2O were the same whether zirconia or thoria electrolytes were used. In the experiments with the Ni–NiO + Cu–Cu_2O electrodes, the temperature of measurement was successfully taken down to 400°C., as against the previous lower limit of about 700°C., by the use of a vibrating-read electrometer having an input impedance of 10^{13} ohms instead of the potentiometer previously employed. The results are shown in Fig. 2.

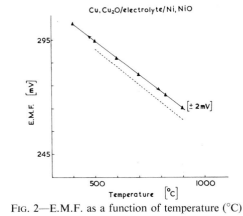

FIG. 2—E.M.F. as a function of temperature (°C)

▲ $\begin{cases} Zr_{0.85} Ca_{0.15} O_{1.85} \\ Th_{0.75} Y_{0.25} O_{1.875} \end{cases}$ ······ $Th_{0.75} Y_{0.25} O_{1.875}$ (heated air/oxygen at 1450°C)

The main differences between these systems and the Fe–FeO + Nb–NbO cell is that the mean oxygen potential of the electrodes is much higher, and the e.m.f's are about one-third of those obtained with the niobium cell. This smaller e.m.f. can be obtained at a low mean oxygen potential by the use of the electrodes Nb–NbO +

NbO–NbO$_2$. For this cell, HOCH and co-workers [11] obtained an e.m.f. at 1,000°C. of 174 mV using a zirconia–lime electrolyte, whereas we obtained 203 mV with a thoria–yttria electrolyte.

All the facts reported above indicate, as has also been demonstrated by SCHMALZRIED [12] for commercial materials, that the electronic contribution to conduction in the zirconia–lime electrolyte is significant at low oxygen potentials. Thus the real electrolyte, as opposed to the ideal one, has a finite electronic conductance, and so a current is flowing continuously in the cell, even on open circuit, resulting in the transport of oxygen from the electrode at the higher oxygen potential to that at the lower oxygen potential. The oxygen so transferred must be absorbed by the electrode and hence the rate at which this oxidation process can occur will be a function of the temperature and the materials in the electrode. If the rate of arrival of oxygen is faster than the limiting rate at which it can be absorbed by the electrode, then a polarization will appear, reducing the net potential across the electrolyte until a steady-state can be achieved. Clearly this was never reached in our experiments with zirconia–lime and a thin Th$_{0.75}$ Y$_{0.25}$ O$_{1.875}$ electrolyte in the niobium cell but was reached with the thick Th$_{0.75}$ Y$_{0.25}$ O$_{1.875}$ electrolyte.

It can be concluded from these experiments that the virtue of thoria-based electrolytes vis-à-vis zirconia-based ones may be due to their lower conductivities as well as their greater thermodynamic stabilities, i.e. their resistance to reduction in the semi-conducting state. We have found, however, that in experiments with high oxygen potential electrodes of very long duration, the e.m.f's of cells with thoria-based electrolytes decrease slowly to lower values than the correct ones. PAL'GUEV and NEUIMIN [13] have also shown that thoria–lime electrolytes give low results with electrodes of oxygen pressures between 10^{-2} and one atmosphere.

5. LIQUID-METAL AND GAS ELECTRODES

Due to the higher rate of diffusion of atoms in liquids than in solids, the former would seem to be a closer approximation to the reversible ideal electrode for the study of conduction in the electrolytes. Thus in a study of the thermodynamics of oxygen dissolved in liquid lead carried out in the temperature range 400–700°C. [14] it has been found possible readily to alter, under controlled conditions, the oxygen content of the liquid lead electrode by coulometric titrations. Steady currents of 200 micro-amps can be passed at temperatures around 700°C. but the value falls to 5–10 micro-amps at 500°C. The material used as an electrolyte was commercial

o

stabilized zirconia in the shape of a crucible containing the liquid
metal. Figure 3 shows a typical titration curve.

One interesting application that has been made with a gaseous
electrode has been in the measurement of the oxygen potential of
our so-called " purified " argon, the preparation of which was described earlier. One electrode was a Ni–NiO pellet, and the other
was a disc of platinum pressed against the other face of the electrolyte. This latter functioned, in the argon atmosphere, as a reversible oxygen electrode, the potential of which was related to the
oxygen impurities in the argon. It was found that between
$800°-1,000°C$. the oxygen potential of argon was equivalent to a
partial pressure of about 10^{-15} atm. This was confirmed by in-
serting an iron strip into the furnace, and finding the temperature at
which wüstite was formed, from which the oxygen potential could
be calculated.

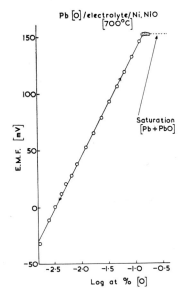

FIG. 3—E.M.F. as a function of logarithm of oxygen content of liquid lead.

The work of PETERS and co-workers [7, 8] and the recent work of
WEISSBART and RUKA [15] amply demonstrates the possibilities of
high-temperature fuel cells with solid electrolytes. For this application where maximum anionic conductivity is required, the zirconia-
based electrolytes are far superior to the thoria solutions (Table 1)
providing that the oxygen potentials employed at the electrodes are

high enough not to induce significant electronic conduction, and where moreover the thoria electrolytes appear to be unsatisfactory for long service (see above).

6. FURTHER DEVELOPMENTS OF SOLID ELECTROLYTES

Additional studies aimed at a proper understanding of the range of stability and oxygen potential dependence of these oxide electrolyte systems would be fruitful. We have indicated some of the limitations of the simple zirconia and thoria-based electrolytes but, even here, much remains to be done. For example, the work of COLLONGUES and co-workers [16, 17] has shown that in some systems e.g. ZrO_2–Gd_2O_3 there is a fluorite–pyrochlore transformation in a certain range of composition near $2ZrO_2.Gd_2O_3$ where the cations become ordered. This would limit the useful range of solid solutions with a large number of random anion defects. Similarly DIETZEL [18] has indicated that ZrO_2–CaO solid solutions may undergo decomposition below 850°C. similar to that observed in ZrO_2–MgO [19] fluorite solid solutions.

It was mentioned earlier that the measurements of electrical conductivity on ZrO_2-based solutions indicate a decreasing conductivity with increasing defect concentration. It has been suggested [20] on the basis of X-ray and neutron diffraction studies that this may be due to ordering of the anion defects with increasing concentration, and if this proved to be a general phenomenon, the useful range of additions to the base oxide in order to increase the specific conductivity for possible fuel cell applications may be severely limited.

Finally, it has been shown that the electron transport number in a given electrolyte clearly depends upon the ambient oxygen potential. Samples of $Zr_{0.85}$ $Ca_{0.15}$ $O_{1.85}$ and $Th_{0.75}$ $Y_{0.25}$ $O_{1.875}$ were heated for 200 h in oxygen and argon (p_{O_2}, 10^{-15} atm) at 1,000°C. and 1,400°C., without showing any marked change in X-ray diffraction patterns of quenched samples. The thoria-based electrolyte however was red coloured after the oxygen treatment at 1,400°C. and yellow after the oxygen treatment at 1,000°C., whereas those heated in purified argon remained white. The coloured samples when used in cells of a high mean oxygen potential (Cu–Cu_2O, Ni–NiO) showed the presence of increased electronic conductivity over the corresponding samples heated in argon.

REFERENCES

1. Hund, F., *Z. phys. Chem.*, **199**, 142, 1952.
2. Kingery, W. D., Pappis, J., Dotz, M. E., and Hill, D. C., *J. Amer. Ceram. Soc.*, **42**, 393, 1959.

3. Dixon, J., LaGrange, L., Merten, U., Miller, C., and Porter, J., *J. Electrochem. Soc.*, **110**, 276, 1963.
4. Kiukkola, K., and Wagner, C., *J. Electrochem. Soc.*, **104**, 79, 1957.
5. Rapp, R., and Maak, F., *Acta. Met.*, **10**, 63, 1962.
6. Aronson, S., and Belle, J., *J. Chem. Phys.*, **29**, 151, 1958.
7. Peters, H., and Mann, G., *Z. Elektrochem.*, **63**, 244, 1959.
8. Peters, H., and Möbius, H-H., *Z. Physik. Chem.*, **209**, 298, 1958.
9. Gerasimov, T. Ia., Leventov, V. I., Kuznetsev, F. A., and Rezuhina, T. N., *Doklady Akad. Nauk. S.S.S.R.*, **136**, 1372, 1961.
10. Rapp, R., *Trans. A.I.M.E.*, **227**, 371, 1963.
11. Hoch, M., Iyar, A. S., and Nelken, J., *J. Phys. Chem. Solids*, **23**, 1463, 1962.
12. Schmalzried, H., *Z. Elektrochem*, **66**, 572, 1962.
13. Pal'guev, S. F., and Neuimin, A. D., *Trans. (Trudy) Inst. Electrochemistry*, No. 1, p. 90 (translation from the Russian by Consultants Bureau, New York 1961).
14. Alcock, C. B., and Belford, T. N., *Trans. Faraday Soc.*, **60**, 822, 1964.
15. Weissbart, J., and Ruka, R., *J. Electrochem. Soc.*, **109**, 723, 1962.
16. Collongues, R., Stocker, J., and Moset, M., " Natl. Colloq. on the Chem. of High Temp. C.N.R.S. Paris, 1957."
17. Perez y Jorba, M., *Ann. Chim.*, **7**, 479, 1962.
18. Dietzel, A., and Tober, H., *Ber. Deutsch. Keram. Ges.*, **30**, 22, 1953.
19. Weber, B. C., Garrett, J., Mauer, F. A., and Schwartz, M. A., *J. Amer. Ceram. Soc.*, **39**, 197, 1956.
20. Carter, R. E., and Roth, W. L., Abstract No. 154, *J. Electrochem. Soc.*, **110**, 66c, 1963

27—Effects of the Method of Preparing Titanium Monoxide on its Electrical Properties

By Malcolm G. McLaren

*School of Ceramics, Rutgers, The State University,
New Brunswick, New Jersey, U.S.A.*

ABSTRACT

D661—E75

Recent literature has indicated that, in its electrical properties, TiO behaves as a metallic compound. It was found that in the high-TiO-phase field stoicheiometric ratios of $TiO_{<1.0}$ showed metallic behaviour, while stoicheiometric ratios of $TiO_{>1.0}$ exhibited semi-conductor conduction. All samples were prepared by sintering techniques in flowing helium atmospheres. Seven sintering treatments were used and in all cases the $TiO_{1.0}$ samples showed lower resistivity curves than $TiO_{0.8}$, $TiO_{0.9}$, $TiO_{1.1}$ and $TiO_{1.2}$. A single crystal of $TiO_{1.19}$ was also tested. Hall measurements were attempted on the range of samples.

Effets de la methode de preparation de l'oxyde de titane sur ses propriétés eléctriques

Des articles récents montrent qu'en ce qui concerne ses propriétés électriques, TiO se comporte comme un composé métallique. On trouve que dans le domaine de la TiO haute température, les proportions stoéchiométriques de $TiO_{<1.0}$ ont un comportement métallique, tandis que les proportions stoéchiométriques de $TiO_{>1.0}$ se comportent comme des semi-conducteurs. Tous les échantillons sont préparés par des techniques de frittage dans des atmosphères d'hélium en circulation. Sept traitements par frittage sont employés et dans tous les cas on trouve pour les échantillons de $TiO_{1.0}$ des courbes de résistivité plus faiblesque pour ceux de $TiO_{0.8}$, $TiO_{0.9}$, $TiO_{1.1}$ et $TiO_{1.2}$. Des essais sont également faits sur un monocristal de $TiO_{1.19}$. Des mesures pratiques sont faites sur l'ensemble des échantillons.

Einfluss der Präparation von Titanmonoxid auf seine elektrischen Eigenschaften

Neuere Literatur zeigt, dass TiO hinsichtlich seiner elektrischen Eigenschaften sich wie eine metallische Verbindung verhält. Es wurde gefunden, dass im Gebiet der Hoch-TiO-Phase bei einem stöchiometrischen Verhältnis $TiO_{<1.0}$ ein metallisches Verhalten auftritt, während bei einem stöchiometrischen Verhältnis $TiO_{>1.0}$ die Leitfähigkeit wie bei einem Halbleiter ist. Alle Proben wurden durch Sintern im Heliumstrom hergestellt. Sieben Sinterbehandlungen wurden angewandt und in allen Fällen zeigte das $TiO_{1.0}$ Kurven mit niedrigerem Widerstand als $TiO_{0.8}$, $TiO_{0.9}$, $TiO_{1.1}$ and $TiO_{1.2}$. Ein Einkristall von $TiO_{1.19}$ wurde ebenfalls untersucht. Es wurde versucht, an einer Reihe von Proben den Hall-Effekt zu messen.

1. INTRODUCTION

Since TiO has an electrical conductivity which approaches that of metals, its general electrical properties have become increasingly interesting for special applications. In the past, TiO had been considered as an ionic material, but recent investigators have classed it with the metals because of its electrical behaviour—i.e. with increasing temperature its conductivity decreases. Most of the electrical measurements that have been made were on TiO samples that had been produced either by melting or by sintering, crushing, and resintering. In contrast to these data it was observed that, with certain sintered samples of TiO, conductivity increased with temperature and the resistivity values were higher than those previously reported, which would seem to indicate some semi-conductor behaviour.*

Since the difference in conductivity of the various samples might have come from the sinter *vs* melting techniques of preparation, it was felt that an isoplethal study of compositions within the TiO phase field, with subsequent electrical measurements, should be made.

The original investigation of the Ti–O system was made by EHRLICH.[1, 2] In this work he determined the phases which exist in this system from 0 to 40 wt % of oxygen, and the approximate extent of the phase fields.

BUMPS, KESSLER, and HANSEN[3] determined the portion of the Ti–O system between 0 and 30 wt % of oxygen. A summary of their work showed that the Ti–O system had:

(1) A peritectic reaction, where melt $+ \alpha \Longleftrightarrow \beta$, in the limits of 1 to 5% oxygen at approximately 1,740°C.;

(2) Another peritectic reaction, where melt $+ \alpha \Longleftrightarrow$ TiO, in the limits of 14·5 to 20·5% oxygen at approximately 1,770°C.;

(3) A peritectoid reaction, where $\alpha +$ TiO $\Longleftrightarrow \delta$, within the limits of 14·4 to 23·5% oxygen at approximately 925°C.;

(4) The α-Ti phase showed a maximum melting temperature of 1,900°C. at 10% oxygen;

(5) With increasing oxygen content the lattice parameters of α solid solution get larger;

(6) TiO exhibits an NaCl-type structure the parameter constants of which decrease as the oxygen content goes up;

(7) The new phase δ was tentatively shown to be tetragonal.

SCHOFIELD and BACON re-evaluated the range of 0–35% oxygen and agreed largely with the findings of Bumps *et al,* the only differences being in the limits of the phase fields.

* This paper was taken from a thesis submitted to Rutgers, The State University, as a partial requirement for the degree of Doctor of Philosophy in November 1961 by M. G. McLaren.

BUMPS, KESSLER, and HANSEN,[3] SCHOFIELD and BACON,[4] NAYLOR,[5] WANG and GRANT,[6] and PEARSON [7] have all indicated the presence of a transition in TiO at approximately 950°C. NAYLOR [5] reported a break in the heat content curve at about 990°C. Pearson, by annealing and quenching samples over the range of 1,100° to 850°C., found that the powder patterns showed sharp NaCl structures down to 950°C. and that, for specimens quenched below this temperature, there were deviations from this pattern. Attempts to establish the exact structure of TiO below 950°C. have not been successful.[7]

A summary of the work on the Ti–O system up to TiO_2 has been consolidated into a phase diagram by DEVRIES and ROY.[8] This was compiled before Schofield and Bacon's work was completed, but it serves as a good indication of the limits of the phase fields that have been reported to exist.

In particular they summarize the compound TiO as having a very wide range of existence—i.e. from $TiO_{0.6}$ to $TiO_{1.25}$. They cite Bumps, Kessler, and Hansen for determining that about 1,760°C. TiO melts incongruently into the field of metal solid solution and liquid. They also cite DAWIHL and SCHROTER [2] as showing the melting point to be 1,750°C. The basis of their diagram up to TiO is largely taken from the work of Bumps, Kessler, and Hansen. A portion of this diagram is used here to illustrate the isoplethal study made in this experiment (Fig. 1).

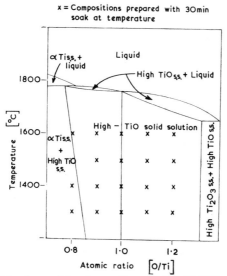

FIG. 1.—Portion of possible phase diagram for Ti–TiO_2 from data in literature. (After DEVRIES and ROY.[8])

It is also interesting that TiO has been found to form a defect structure with approximately 15% of its lattice spaces unoccupied.[1, 7] Pearson showed by density measurements that 14·6% of the lattice positions in his samples were unoccupied. Ehrlich showed that the density of TiO was much less than the X-ray density.

The resistivity of TiO has been determined by various investigators. ROSTAKER[9] has reported that TiO has a resistivity in the order of 300 $\mu\Omega$-cm at room temperature and that it exhibits metallic bonding. PEARSON[7] reports a resistivity of approximately 280 $\mu\Omega$-cm for TiO at room temperature on samples quenched at 1,100°C. with a 3-h soak. SCHWARTZ[10] in his investigation found that TiO behaved as a metal up to 500°C. and from there it behaved as a semi-conductor.

PEARSON'S[7] work has been the most extensive on the electrical properties of TiO. A summary of his results shows that:

(1) The phase of TiO which exists above 950°C. (α-TiO) has at room temperature a resistance of 281 $\mu\Omega$-cm.

(2) With increasing temperature from -162°C. to 362°C. the electrical resistivity increases (on melted samples).

(3) The conductivity of the melted sample plotted vs $1/T$ yields a straight line, which indicates its thermal conductivity is a constant, which is again characteristic of metals.

(4) The thermoelectric e.m.f. varies linearly with temperature. Also the sign of the e.m.f. was the same for oxygen-rich as oxygen-deficient samples, larger in magnitude for $TiO_{1·2}$ than $TiO_{0·8}$.

(5) With increasing oxygen content from $TiO_{0·7}$ to $TiO_{1·2}$ the conductivity decreases.

(6) Annealing-temperature/conductivity revealed that the phases present below 950°C. have higher conductivities than the cubic TiO.

(7) Conduction does not take place by cation migration.

A theory for the mechanism of conduction in TiO was proposed by F. J. MORIN[15] in his treatment of the " Oxides of the 3d Transition Metals ". He proposed a model for the arrangement of the type bonding expected in TiO on the basis of data in the literature. He proposed that the non-bonding 3d orbitals of neighbouring cations for the oxides of Sc, Ti, and V overlap enough to form a 3d conduction band.

In a later paper by MORIN[16] investigating oxides which show a metal-to-insulator transition at a Néel temperature, TiO and VO were compared with the other oxides.

In this work, TiO electrical conductivity was measured on a sample supplied by Pearson over the temperature range 300° to

1·5°K. and was found to behave like a metal with a conduction of approximately 3,500 ohm^{-1} cm^{-1}.

At the time that this investigation was being made, DENKER [11] also found that, at low temperatures, single crystals of oxygen-rich TiO and also polycrystalline TiO$_{1.15}$ showed weakly semi-conducting effects. In general, the resistivity values obtained were in agreement with those measured in this work.

2. METHOD OF PROCEDURE

As previously mentioned, in attempting to measure the resistivity of TiO, data were accumulated that were in opposition to the results of other investigations. It was found that, in what was thought to be TiO$_{1.0}$, the resistivity/temperature curve had a negative slope. Since most of the apparent difference between this material and the materials of other investigators was in the method of preparation (sintering-temperature and soaking-time), these effects were studied in conjunction with the changes produced by the variation of the amount of oxygen in TiO.

In general, the method of procedure was to investigate the upper TiO phase field along five different isopleths, which corresponded to the five stoicheiometric ratios TiO$_{0.8}$, TiO$_{0.9}$, TiO$_{1.0}$ TiO$_{1.1}$, and TiO$_{1.2}$. By sintering each of these compositions at different temperatures and varying the soaking-periods, a representative picture of the electrical properties of the TiO phase fields was determined.

The samples were prepared by: (1) blending the proper ratios of the purest available Ti powder and the purest available TiO$_2$ powder, (2) pressing them into bars, and (3) firing them in very accurately controlled atmospheres to the desired sintering-temperatures.

Photo-micrographs were taken to indicate the degree of sintering and the shape and the volume of the pores. X-ray patterns were obtained on all of the samples, for even small amounts of phases other than TiO would have influenced electrical properties greatly. In this respect it has been shown that, in the reaction between titanium and oxygen, other sub-oxides such as Ti$_2$O$_3$ are formed before TiO. Therefore if the reaction between Ti and TiO$_2$ had not proceeded to the point where Ti$_2$O$_3$ was eliminated, amounts of Ti$_2$O$_3$ might have been present at the grain-boundary sites.

3. SAMPLE PREPARATION

The titania used in this investigation was procured from National Lead Co., Titanium Division, South Amboy, New Jersey; it was designated "High-purity titanium dioxide", and was produced in a special batch by their Research Division Laboratories.

The titanium used was procured from the Clevite Corporation, 540 East 105th Street, Cleveland 8, Ohio. It was produced as -200-mesh in a special run by the Product Development Section of the above company and was designated as BHN 152-CPT 5007.

Since the very purest titanium has a Brinell hardness near 70, and since the oxygen content and other impurities influence the hardness of titanium so greatly, the figure of 150 Brinell units given for the titanium is considered especially good for powdered material.[12] In addition, in the analysis supplied, the only contaminating element present in quantity was oxygen, which could be dealt with in the compounding of the samples. For analysis and grain size, this was by far the best powdered titanium available.

The proper stoicheiometric ratios of the titania and titanium required to produce $TiO_{0.8}$, $TiO_{0.9}$, $TiO_{1.0}$, $TiO_{1.1}$, and $Tio_{1.2}$ were calculated. Care was taken to include the amount of oxygen carried into the reaction by the titanium as well as by the titania. Approximately 500 g of each ratio was prepared with careful weighing on a Fisher precision balance and then dry blending the batches in a Patterson-Kelly V blender for $1\frac{1}{2}$ h. Approximately 8% distilled water was added to the mix to improve the pressability. The mix was then V-blended again for 45 min in order to distribute the moisture evenly. Thirty-three grams of material were weighed out for each pressing, to help ensure uniform thickness of the bars. These batches were then pressed into bars $4 \times 1 \times \frac{3}{16}$ in. in a steel die on a Watts and Stillman hydraulic press with 12,500 p.s.i. pressure. The bars were air-dried for 4 days before firing.

The vacuum furnace in which these samples were fired was National Research Corporation's model 2904B with tungsten resistance heating-elements and molybdenum radiation shields.

The standard procedure for the firing of the test samples was as follows:

(1) The furnace was pumped down to 0.4×10^{-4} mm Hg.

(2) At this pressure the power was turned on and the variac set at a reading of five.

(3) The variac was increased to 10 after 5 min and thereafter increased 5 units every 15 min.

(4) This was kept up until a temperature of 1,000°C. was achieved (generally at a setting of 25).

(5) This temperature was maintained until the end of the outgassing period was indicated by the vacuum readings. The end was considered to be 0.1×10^{-4} mm Hg.

(6) The variac was then lowered 10 units every 5 min.

(7) The furnace was allowed to cool for 10 min and then the vacuum pumps were turned off and purified helium was allowed to pass into the chamber.

(8) When the chamber had reached atmospheric pressure and the helium was bubbling through the escape bottle, the power was turned on.

(9) The variac was raised 5 units every 8 min, which corresponded to approximately 150°C. rise per every 5 units.

(10) When the temperature to which the samples were to be fired was reached, a soaking-period of $\frac{1}{2}$ h was begun.

(11) After the soaking-period, the variac was reduced 10 divisions every 5 min. This was effectively a cooling rate of approximately 200°C. for every 10 variac units.

(12) After the furnace had cooled, it was opened and the test pieces were removed.

In each firing, one bar of each of the five stoicheiometric ratios was placed in the furnace in a zirconia crucible. The following firings were made:

(1) 1,300°C. with a $\frac{1}{2}$-h soak,
(2) 1,400°C. with a $\frac{1}{2}$-h soak,
(3) 1,500°C. with a $\frac{1}{2}$-h soak,
(4) 1,600°C. with a $\frac{1}{2}$-h soak,
(5) 1,600°C. with a 2-h soak,
(6) 1,300°C. with a 4-h soak,
(7) 1,000°C. in vacuum, no soak.

In all, 25 different points on the isopleths $TiO_{0.8}$, $TiO_{0.9}$, $TiO_{1.0}$, $TiO_{1.1}$, and $TiO_{1.2}$ were produced. In addition to these points, several variations of soaking at some of the temperatures were tried to determine the effect of soaking-time. The purpose of the 1,000°C. firing was to show the condition of the bars at the end of the out-gassing treatment.

After preparation, the samples were analysed by X-ray diffraction techniques to identify phases present. Summarizing the X-ray results showed that only in the 1,300°C. (30-min soak) firings were there phases other than TiO. In this firing the $TiO_{0.8}$ sample exhibited a slight excess of Ti, whereas the oxygen-rich samples ($TiO_{1.1}$ and $TiO_{1.2}$) showed minor amounts of Ti_2O_3, and in the case of $TiO_{1.2}$ also minor amounts of TiO_2. It was observed that there was gradual shifting of the major peaks with increased oxygen content. In all firing groups but the 1,500°C. (30-min soak) the angles of the major peaks seemed to increase to a maximum from $TiO_{0.8}$ to $TiO_{1.0}$ and then decrease again to $TiO_{1.2}$. The variations were small but measurable, being in the range of 0·3 to 0·4 deg.

The Ti_2O_3 present in $TiO_{1.1}$ and $TiO_{1.2}$ fired to 1,300°C. (30-min soak) probably helps account for the unusually high resistivities found in these samples. Since the only phase present in the higher-fired groups is TiO (NaCl type), differences in resistivity/temperature behaviour between the oxygen-rich and titanium-rich samples cannot be explained by the presence of different phases.

By means of a metallographic microscope it was determined that a magnification of 300 times gave the best picture of densification and pore structure. Photomicrographs of all the fired samples were then taken with a Zeiss Ultraphot metallograph, model II.*

Comparing the photomicrographs for the effect of increasing the sintering-temperature in each of the stoicheiometric ratios shows that as temperature is increased, there is greater densification (Fig. 2).

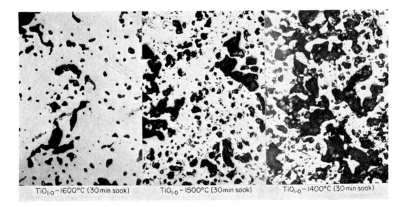

FIG. 2.—Effect of increased sintering-temperature on the densification of $TiO_{1.0}$

From the five stoicheiometric ratios fired at any given temperature it is evident that, as oxygen is added, the pattern of densification changes. $TiO_{0.8}$ has much larger individual voids than $TiO_{1.0}$ or $TiO_{1.2}$, and the total volume of void in $TiO_{1.2}$ and $TiO_{1.0}$ seems to be less than $TiO_{0.8}$—i.e. density increases through the stoicheiometric series.

The photomicrograph of $TiO_{1.0}$ fired to 1,300°C. with a 4-h soak seems to fit in between $TiO_{1.0}$ fired to 1,500°C. with a 30-min soak, and $TiO_{1.0}$ fired to 1,600°C. with a 30-min soak in relation to densification.

* Photographs were taken by the Camera Branch, Tech. Photo. Div. of WADC, WPAFB.

4. RESISTIVITY MEASUREMENTS

A four-point probe null method was used to eliminate the necessity for measuring and computing the contact resistance. The resistance read was that between the middle probes of the bridge, and this in turn was readily calculated into the resistivity of the material. The measuring circuit consisted only of the sample and a Queen's Kelvin bridge.

The resistivity of the test bars was measured from liquid-nitrogen temperature up to approximately 370°C. The furnace used for heating the samples was a horizontal platinum-wound resistance type with a variable resistance. Argon was passed slowly through the furnace to ensure a non-corrosive atmosphere when measuring the resistance. The temperature of the sample was measured by placing a copper/constantan thermocouple very close to the centre of the sample.

4.1 Calculations for Resistivity

In order to convert the resistance readings into the resistivities at the various temperatures, the following calculation was made:

$$R_m = \rho \, \frac{l}{s}$$

where R_m = reading in ohms
ρ = resistivity
l = probe distance
s = cross-sectional area

The resistivity of the first series of the five stoicheiometric ratios from $TiO_{0.8}$ to $TiO_{1.2}$ fired to 1,300°C. with a 30-min soak showed that $TiO_{0.8}$, $TiO_{0.9}$, and $TiO_{1.0}$ all have metallic behaviour—i.e. their resistivities increase with increasing temperature. In addition, the resistivity of the $TiO_{0.8}$ curve was higher than that of either the $TiO_{0.9}$ or $TiO_{1.0}$ curves. In fact, $TiO_{1.0}$ had the lowest resistivity curve of the group. $TiO_{1.1}$ and $TiO_{1.2}$ both exhibited the opposite type of curve—with increasing temperatures, resistivity decreased. Both of these curves were considerably higher in their resistivity values than the others.

Figure 3 shows the resistivity/temperature curves for $TiO_{0.9}$, $TiO_{1.0}$ and $TiO_{1.1}$ all fired to 1,400°C. with a 30-min soak. Here again it shows that $TiO_{0.9}$ and $TiO_{1.0}$ conducted as a metal whereas the $TiO_{1.1}$ behaved as a semi-conductor.

Figure 4 shows the resistivity/temperature curves of $TiO_{0.8}$, $TiO_{0.9}$, $TiO_{1.0}$, and $TiO_{1.2}$ fired to 1,500°C. with a 30-min. soak. $TiO_{0.8}$, $TiO_{0.9}$, and $TiO_{1.0}$ all behaved metallically, whereas the $TiO_{1.2}$ had decreasing resistivity with increasing temperature. $TiO_{1.0}$ had the lowest resistivity of the group. In fact, each of the curves fell in the same relative position as the 1,300° and 1,400°C. firings.

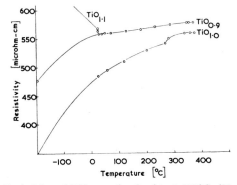

FIG. 3.—Resistivity of TiO samples fired to 1,400°C. (30-min soak)

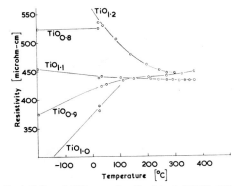

FIG. 4.—Resistivity of TiO samples fired to 1,500°C. (30-min soak)

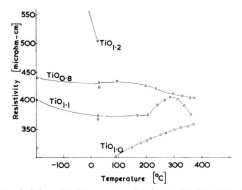

FIG. 5.—Resistivity of TiO samples fired to 1,600°C. (30-min soak)

Figure 5 shows the resistivity/temperature curves of $TiO_{0.8}$, $TiO_{0.9}$, $TiO_{1.0}$, $TiO_{1.1}$, and $TiO_{1.2}$ fired to 1,600°C. with a 30-min soak. $TiO_{0.9}$ and $TiO_{1.0}$ behaved metallically but the $TiO_{0.8}$, although in the same relative position as the other sets of curves, exhibited a very slight semi-conductor character. $TiO_{1.1}$ and $TiO_{1.2}$ again showed decreasing resistivity with increasing temperature. Again the $TiO_{1.0}$ had the lowest resistivity values. The $TiO_{0.9}$ and $TiO_{1.1}$ showed a hysteresis between the heating- and cooling-curves of the resistivity. No explanation of this is immediately apparent, although similar occurrences have been noted in the literature.

Figure 6 shows the resistivity/temperature curves of $TiO_{0.8}$, $TiO_{0.9}$, $TiO_{1.0}$, $TiO_{1.1}$, and $TiO_{1.2}$ fired to 1,600°C. with a 120-min soak. $TiO_{0.9}$ and $TiO_{1.0}$ behaved metallically. $TiO_{0.8}$ behaved metallically from liquid-nitrogen temperatures to room temperature and then behaved slightly like a semi-conductor. $TiO_{1.1}$ and $TiO_{1.2}$ exhibited decreasing resistivity with increasing temperature. However, the $TiO_{1.1}$ had an almost flat curve from room temperature to 370°C. This verified the speculation that there would be some composition and sintering-temperature which would yield a relatively straight line over the temperature range measured. The stoicheiometric compositions are in the same graphic position as the other firing series, and the $TiO_{1.0}$ has the lowest resistivity at room temperature of the group but crosses the other curves at higher temperatures.

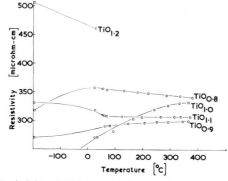

FIG. 6.—Resistivity of TiO samples fired to 1,600°C. (120-min soak)

Single crystals of $TiO_{1.19}$, produced by the arc-fusion process by Linde Company Division of Union Carbide Corporation, were purchased. This offered the opportunity of measuring the resistivity without grain-boundary interference. Measurement showed a higher resistivity at liquid-nitrogen temperature than at room temperature.

Figure 7 shows the resistivity/temperature curves for the single crystal of $TiO_{1.19}$ and $TiO_{1.0}$ sintered at 1,300°C. with a 240-min soak. The single crystal was measured only from liquid-nitrogen temperature to room temperature; it exhibited a semi-conductor behaviour. The $TiO_{1.0}$ fired at 1,300°C. with a 240-min soak behaved metallically and was intermediate between the 1,500°C., 30-min soak and the 1,600°C., 30-min soak $TiO_{1.0}$ samples in its resistivity curve.

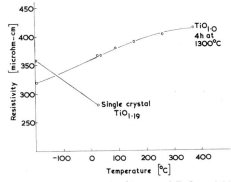

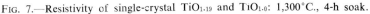

FIG. 7.—Resistivity of single-crystal $TiO_{1.19}$ and $TiO_{1.0}$: 1,300°C., 4-h soak.

Figure 8 shows the resistivity/temperature curves for the various degrees of sintering on $TiO_{1.0}$. In general, this series shows that, as sintering-temperature is increased while the same soaking-time is maintained, a lower resistivity curve is produced, and that as more soaking-time is given, the curves become flatter. As was noted before, the 4-h soak at 1,300°C. fell between the 1,500° and 1,600°C. firings with a 30-min soak, both in pore structure and resistivity values.

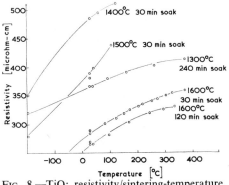

FIG. 8.—TiO: resistivity/sintering-temperature

It should also be noted that the type of conductivity was checked and that all samples exhibited P-type conductivity.

5. DISCUSSION

Several factors tend to promote the suspicion that TiO is not entirely metal-like in its electrical conductivity properties. First of all, the fact that TiO has a metallic structure hardly seems to be a fair assumption when the size and electro-negativities of the titanium and oxygen ions are taken into consideration. Metals in general are described as close-packed atomic arrangements, usually either hexagonal or cubic in structure and whose metal atoms are in a sea of free electrons. This is in general the type of structure favoured by some who feel that, in TiO, oxygen ions are forced interstitially but ordered in a close-packed titanium network, and that the same conductivity process exists in TiO as in titanium that has some oxygen dissolved in it.

On the basis of differences in the size of ionic radii and the difference in electronegativities between the titanium and oxygen ions, it would be difficult to force oxygen into the network without affecting some ionic character to the bond.

From PAULING's [13] work there appears to be a difference of approximately 1·9 electronegativity units between titanium and oxygen ions. Projecting this difference to his further work on predicting the fractional character of a bond A–B related to its difference in electronegativity X_A-X_B of the atoms shows that the bond between titanium and oxygen could have 50% ionic character.

A model is proposed in which the structure is that of an ionic lattice of titanium and oxygen whose bonding is partially ionic and partially covalent with charges being balanced by the 15% defect structure.

In this model the resistivity properties of TiO would probably favour those of a metal when there is an excess of titanium, and probably favour the properties of semi-conductors when there is an excess of oxygen. These materials might also have some ionic conductivity at higher temperatures.

Remembering that TiO has 15% defects in its structure, would make it possible to assume that, as temperature increases, the portion of conductivity due to defect concentration would increase as well.

An important consideration in the electrical properties is the effect of sintering on the TiO mass. Since the material studied had been formed by sintering, a polycrystalline mass of TiO grains was produced in which there might have been considerable difference in the electrical properties between the interior of the TiO grain and the grain boundary. KINGERY[14] points out this effect in semi-conductors where the grain boundary has a higher resistance than the grain. The resultant structure would tend to have a resistance which corresponded most closely to thin layers of the higher-resistance grain-boundary material.

In the formation of TiO from the sintering of TiO_2 and Ti together, the reaction will probably never proceed to the point where the grains and the grain boundaries have the same identical composition. It is likely that a higher concentration of oxygen atoms will occur at the grain interface. If this structure follows the mechanisms as outlined by KINGERY,[14] where the material will behave electrically as if it were thin layers of the boundary material, it will help to show the effect of sintering on the basic electrical properties. As the sintering-temperature is increased, it is suspected that the difference in oxygen content between grain and grain boundary is minimized and presents a lower resistivity. The effect of increasing soaking-time on the electrical properties probably produces the same general effect as increased sintering temperature.

Another consideration related to sintering-treatment which plays a role in the conductivity is the amount of porosity in the material. As KINGERY'S[14] discussion indicates, the distribution of pores through a good conducting-material would be the same as dispersing a higher-resistance phase throughout the material. This tends to increase the resistivity of the material.

PEARSON[7] minimized this effect by crushing the sintered TiO and then resintering the mass.

6. SUMMARY AND CONCLUSIONS

The results obtained during this investigation show that the amount of oxygen in the TiO lattice and the total effect of sintering-temperature and soaking-time influence the electrical properties of TiO.

It was shown that as oxygen was added from $TiO_{0.8}$ to $TiO_{1.0}$, the resistivity at room temperature decreased. Adding more oxygen to the lattice from $TiO_{1.0}$ to $TiO_{1.2}$ increased the room-temperature resistivity. The sign of the slope of the resistivity/temperature curve changed from $TiO_{0.8}$ to $TiO_{1.0}$ as compared with the curves from $TiO_{1.0}$ to $TiO_{1.2}$, the former exhibiting increasing resistivities with increasing temperatures and the latter showing decreasing resistivities with increasing temperatures. All of the resistivity/temperature curves at each sintering-temperature indicate that the lowest room-temperature resistivity of the various stoicheiometric ratios is $TiO_{1 \cdot 0}$.

The photomicrographs of the various compositions with different sintering-treatments proved a reliable guide as to the type and value of the resistivity curves. Specifically the greater the densification, the lower the resistivity. It was observed that the total effect between sintering-temperature and soaking-time played a large role in the electrical properties. An example of this was $TiO_{1 \cdot 0}$ fired at 1,300 °C. with a 4-h soak, the electrical properties of which fell intermediate between the $TiO_{1 \cdot 0}$ sintered at 1,500 °C. with a 30-min soak and $TiO_{1 \cdot 0}$ fired at 1,600 °C. with a 30-min soak. The densification patterns shown in the corresponding photomicrographs would have placed this in the same relative position.

Although the single crystals of $TiO_{1 \cdot 19}$ were only checked at room- and at liquid-nitrogen temperatures, the resistivity/temperature properties were much the same as sintered samples with the similar oxygen content. However, as might have been expected, the resistivity values of the single-crystal material were considerably lower than those of the sintered samples, probably due to the absence of grain boundaries.

The attempt to measure the Hall effect on the sintered and single-crystal samples was unsuccessful in establishing a numerical value, but the upper limits of the Hall voltages were determined within reasonable error. It was seen that the maximum Hall voltage was 0·5 mV under the conditions of this experiment, which corresponded to a minimum number of carriers in the range of 4×10^{21} carriers per cm^3. Using this value and the resistivity values obtained with the Kelvin bridge, the mobility of the carriers was calculated as not more than 5 cm^2/V sec. The carrier concentration and the mobility of these carriers obtained by these calculations places the electrical properties of the samples in between those of semi-conductors and metals. The figures indicate that the samples are closer to metals than semi-conductors.

The accumulated results indicate that specific electrical properties, within the limits of the measured values, could be obtained by manipulating the stoicheiometric ratios of titanium and oxygen in TiO and by varying the sintering-temperature and soaking-period. In fact, it was possible to produce a sample which, with proper oxygen content, proper sintering-temperature and soaking-treatment, exhibited an almost constant resistivity over a 500 °C. range.

In conclusion then, the bulk of the evidence indicates that the resistivity properties of the TiO field from $TiO_{0 \cdot 8}$ to $TiO_{1 \cdot 2}$ are controllable by the stoicheiometric ratio, the sintering-temperature and the soaking-time, and that, by varying these three, almost any resistivity value can be obtained within the limits of the lowest and highest resistivity found in this investigation. Admittedly, trace impurities are an important factor in the electrical properties of conductors, and the relatively high impurity level in the TiO samples compared to the extremely pure semi-conducting materials now available is large, but it is considered that the basic properties measured in this investigation still have validity.

ACKNOWLEDGMENTS

The author wishes to extend his gratitude to the following: Dr. John H. Koenig, Dr. H. T. Smyth, and Dr. R. B. Sosman of The Rutgers School of Ceramics for their council and guidance; Dr. Robert Ruh and Dr. B. C. Weber of the Aeronautical Research Laboratories at Wright Patterson Air Force Base; Paper Makers Importing Co., Inc., and Mr. S. D. Brian for sponsoring this work.

REFERENCES

1. Ehrlich, P., "Phase Ratios and Magnetic Properties in the System Titanium–Oxygen," *Electrochem.*, **45**, 362, 1939.
2. Ehrlich, P., "The Solubility of Oxygen in Metallic Titanium," *Z. Anorg. Chem.*, **247**, 54, 1941.
3. Bumps, E. S., Kessler, H. D., and Hansen, M., "The Titanium–Oxygen System," *Trans. Amer. Soc. Metals*, **45**, 1008, 1953.
4. Schoefield, T. H., and Bacon, A. E., "The Constitution of the Titanium Oxygen Alloys in the Range 0 to 35 Weight Per Cent Oxygen," *J. Inst. Metals*, **84**, 47, 1955.
5. Naylor, B. F., "Transition Temperature of TiO at 991°C.," *J. Amer. Chem. Soc.*, **68**, 1077, 1946.
6. Wang, C. C., and Grant, N. J., "Transformation of the TiO Phase," *J. Metals*, **8**, 184, 1956.
7. Pearson, A. D., "Studies on the Lower Oxides of Titanium," Ph.D. Thesis, Massachusetts Institute of Technology, Lab. for Insulation Research.
8. DeVries, R. C., and Roy, Rustum, "A Phase Diagram for the System Ti–TiO₂ Constructed from Data in the Literature," *Bull. Amer. Ceram. Soc.*, **33**, 370, 1954.
9. Rostaker, W., "Observation of the Lattice Parameters of the Alpha and TiO Phases in the Titanium–Oxygen Systems," *Trans. Amer. Inst. Mining Met. Engrs.*, (1941), 981, 1952.
10. Swartz, D. L., "Resistivity Measurements of the Sub-oxides of Titania," Master's Thesis, Alfred University. June 1953.
11. Denker, S. P., "Low Temperature Resistivity of Titanium Monoxide," Progress Report No. XXIX, Laboratory for Insulation Research, Massachusetts Institute of Technology.
12. Discussion with Mr. Edward P. Weber, Head of the Pilot Manufacturing Section, Clevite Corporation, Cleveland, Ohio.

13. Linus, Pauling, " The Nature of the Chemical Bond " (Cornell University Press, Ithaca, New York, 1948), pp. 58 ff, 69 ff, 346.
14. Kingery, W. D., " Introduction to Ceramics " (John Wiley & Sons, Inc., New York, 1960), pp. 719, 729.
15. Morin, F. J., " Oxides of the 3d Transition Metals," *Bell Systems Techn. J.*, **37,** 1047, 1958.
16. Morin, F. J., " Oxides which show a Metal-to-Insulator Transition at the Neél Temperature," *Phys. Rev. Letters,* **3,** 34, 1959.

28—Glass-Ceramics

By J. M. STEVELS

Philips Research Laboratories,
N.V. Philips' Gloeilampenfabrieken,
Eindhoven, Netherlands

ABSTRACT   V382

A survey is given of glass-ceramics—what they are, how they are manufactured and their typical features. Special compositions show a high resistance to thermal shock and other compositions high mechanical strength. Other recent developments in the improvement of the mechanical strength of glass are discussed.

Verre-céramique

La composition, la méthode de fabrication et les caractéristiques typiques du verre-céramique sont décrites. Des compositions spéciales manifestent une résistance élevée au choc thermique et d'autres compositions présentent une résistance mécanique élevée. D'autres développements relatifs à l'amélioration de la résistance mécanique du verre sont étudiés.

Vitrokeramik

Eine Übersicht der Literatur über keramikähnliche glasig-kristallinen Gegenstände aus Glas (Vitrokeramik) wird gegeben. Näher eingegangen wird auf die Herstellungsweise und speziellen Eigenschaften. Bestimmte Zusammensetzungen geben eine hohe Widerstandsfähigkeit gegen schnelle Temperaturwechslungen und andere Zusammensetzungen eine hohe mechanische Festigkeit. Weiter werden neue Methoden zur Erhöhung der mechanischen Festigkeit von Glas besprochen.

1. INTRODUCTION

In recent years the border between traditional ceramics on the one hand and glass technology on the other hand has become more and more vague. In the past the highest ideal of the glassmaker and the glass technologist has been to compound and to manufacture transparent glass, if possible without heterogeneities (crystallizations, stones, bubbles) and without inhomogeneities (striae) and a great deal of effort has been spent in the course of centuries by many people to try to realize this ideal.

However, it has been found in the last ten years or so that partially crystallized vitreous systems have quite interesting properties. Once the glass scientist had succeeded in controlling the crystallization of vitreous systems as far as grain size and chemical composition of the crystals are concerned, materials with very interesting properties were obtained, and these materials are known nowadays as glass-ceramics.

The development of this group of materials with its outstanding properties will affect the ceramic industry, and especially the traditional ceramic industry, to a great extent, which will become evident in this paper. In the literature[1] very recent, good and broad surveys on the subject exist, and they will inform the reader more fully than can be done in this short paper.

Let us first describe very briefly how a glass-ceramic is made. A glass with a certain composition, to which a very small amount of a nucleation agent has been added, is melted. Then the object is formed by one of the processes well known in glass technology such as rolling, blowing (either free or in a mould), drawing, pressing, etc. The nucleation agent at this stage of the process is homogeneously dissolved in the vitreous system, and it remains so when the system is cooled down at the usual rate.

The object is then kept at a certain temperature (usually for between a few seconds and a few hours) so that the growth of nuclei for crystallization can take place. The optimum temperature for this nucleation is usually some $100°C.$ *above* the annealing temperature of the glass. At this temperature, a sufficient number of stable nuclei are formed, although these nuclei do not necessarily have the same composition as the nucleation agent.

The object is then kept at a temperature roughly some $100°C.$ *below* the softening point of the glass-ceramic to be formed. This temperature is usually the optimum one for the formation of a major crystalline phase throughout the object. During this process the small crystals of the nuclei act as "germs". The first known catalysts used were Au, Ag, Cu, and Pt, with the help of which the controlled formation of crystals of, for instance, NaF, Li_2SiO_3, $BaSi_2O_5$, could be achieved. With the help of TiO_2 as nucleation agent (which was also discovered as such at an early stage) other crystals, which will be discussed presently, may be formed in certain glass compositions. Since then a wealth of phenomena has come to light in the literature. Other nucleation agents, such as ZrO_2, Cr_2O_3, V_2O_5, NiO, P_2O_5, and ZnO, are mentioned. These give rise to different major crystalline phases, depending on the original glass composition.

Generally speaking, one can say that glass-ceramics look like densely opaque glasses, and therefore at first sight they very much resemble porcelain. Thanks to their microstructure of very small grains, and thanks to the absence of porosity, glass-ceramics are much more resistant to tensile load than the great majority of glasses and traditional ceramic materials. They usually have higher moduli of elasticity than the two other groups, their indentation hardness and abrasion hardness are much better—in other words, their overall mechanical properties are better than those of the traditional ceramic products and also of the traditional glasses.

The surface of glass-ceramic objects is usually much smoother than that of traditional ceramics (one can even bake an egg in a skillet of certain glass-ceramics without using butter). Moreover, the object can be formed with the rather easy techniques of glass technology, so that such difficult problems as grinding and sintering can be avoided and shrinkage does not play an important role.

2. SOME TYPES OF GLASS-CERAMICS

Two commercial products, manufactured by Corning Glass Works, have been known for some time under the name of Pyroceram. In Pyroceram 9606 the nucleation agent is TiO_2 and the major crystalline phase is cordierite ($2MgO.2Al_2O_3.5SiO_2$). Its main feature is that its dielectric properties, like those of pure cordierite, are very good (low power factor, especially at microwave frequencies —for instance, tan $\delta = 3 \times 10^{-4}$ at $100°C$. for a frequency $f = 2.4 \times 10^{10}$ c/s). The original glass in this case, however, has a short working-range of temperature, i.e. a high temperature coefficient of viscosity, so that it is somewhat difficult to manufacture objects, at least with the traditional methods, but products are readily obtainable with special methods. Applications are mainly in the electronics field.

A product with quite another field of application is Pyroceram 9608. Again the nucleation agent is TiO_2; the major crystalline phases are β-spodumene ($Li_2O.Al_2O_3.4SiO_2$), or β-eucryptite ($Li_2O.Al_2O_3.2SiO_2$) or a mixture of both. This type is manufactured easily in a continuous process. It lends itself to easy forming by high-speed automatic glass-forming methods; the glass in question can be drawn, pressed, blown and rolled. Its largest application is as cooking-ware, though there are other applications.

The coefficient of expansion for the type is very low indeed. Between the limits of $-75°C$. and $+60°C$. the mean coefficient is zero. In the temperature range between $0°$ and $500°C$. it is comparable with the very low expansion of used silica (11×10^{-7} $(°K)^{-1}$ for Pyroceram 9608 as compared to 5×10^{-7} $(°K)^{-1}$ for fused silica) and this is the reason for its outstanding resistance to thermal shock. Cooking-ware made of this material can be transferred from a refrigerator straight into an oven, without any warming-up period. It can also withstand thermal shock in the reverse direction.

Another development is Pyroceram 9609, less widely known at the moment.

Though, generally speaking, the types of Pyroceram mentioned so far can be made somewhat stronger than the traditional non-crystallized glasses, the latter type—albeit combined with an interesting artifice—excel in mechanical strength.

Of course, glass is the most ideal material of all, were it not for its low mechanical strength. However, for some years the slogan "glass stronger than steel" has inspired many glass scientists and glass technologists, and one can say that this aim has practically been reached at this moment. It is in this connection that Pyroceram 9609 plays a dominant role. Pyroceram is the bulk material of Centura Ware, another type of cooking ware. The feature of Pyroceram 9609 is that it contains a very homogeneous distribution of fine grains, resulting in a good mechanical strength. This strong material, which has a coefficient of expansion of 120×10^{-7} $(°K)^{-1}$, is covered with a glass having a coefficient of expansion of about 90×10^{-7} $(°K)^{-1}$. On cooling, the bulk material shrinks more rapidly than the glaze, and thus a surface layer strongly in compression is formed, and a product is obtained with very high strength. That a difference of 30×10^{-7} $(°K)^{-1}$ is admissible in this case is because the bulk itself is already strong.

3. IMPROVEMENT OF THE MECHANICAL STRENGTH
OF GLASS

Generally speaking, the mechanical strength of glass is rather poor. Though this property from a theoretical point of view is expected to be 3000 kg/mm², pristine glass shows tensile strengths only of the order of 300 kg/mm². By the simple fact of handling the glass the strength falls to some 5–10 kg/mm², owing to the formation of surface flaws. By acid polishing, a process in which the outer layer of the glass is removed, the original strength can be restored but, of course, only temporarily since the surface is vulnerable to new damage.

There are several processes by which the surface can be improved more permanently. Since glass owes its poor strength to flaws more or less perpendicular to the surface, it is specially vulnerable to tensile load, but not vulnerable to compressive load. The proposed methods for the strengthening of glass have one feature in common—a surface layer in compression is formed. In this way the object can withstand a much higher tensile load caused by an impact from outside, since the critical strains (e.g. tensions) are more difficult to reach.

In practice the following processes are used.

3.1 Physical Strengthening

The glass object is heated above its annealing temperature, and the outside is cooled rapidly. The outer layer solidifies faster than the bulk and since, on decreasing temperatures, the inside continues to shrink while the outside layer has become solid, the latter is finally under compression. The best known application of this process is in the production of toughened windscreen for cars, in which the glass shows tensile strengths of the order of 15 to 20 kg/mm², an improvement by a factor of 3 over the usual values.

3.2 Strengthening by Glazing or Enamelling

The object is covered with a suitable glass, enamel, or glaze, with a coefficient of expansion lower than that of the bulk glass. On cooling the object after firing, the glass bulk shrinks more than the enamel, so that a surface layer in compression is obtained. Obviously, optimum results are obtained when the coefficients of expansion of the glass and the enamel differ as much as possible. Mechanical strengths (measured on rods of 3 mm diam.) of some 50 kg/mm² are possible, provided that a layer of the order of some 50μ is applied.

3.3 Strengthening by Surface Crystallization

A recent solution is to make use of a controlled crystallization process. By guiding this process in such a way that *above* the annealing-temperature crystals with a lower coefficient of expansion than the bulk glass are formed in a surface layer, the same result as described under (2) above is obtained.

For instance, if one thinks of compositions where β-eucryptite crystals are formed in the surface layer, giving rise to extremely low or even negative coefficients of expansion, it is obvious that very strong objects may be obtained. In practice, strengths of 50 kg/mm² are realized in this way for rods of 6 mm. diam. The minimum thickness of the crystallized layer should again be of the order of about 50μ in order to obtain sufficient scratch resistance.

This process was developed by Corning Glass Works and known as the Chemcor process. There are two different techniques. One employs surface nucleation of a suitable lithia–alumina–silica glass. Another begins with a soda–alumina–titania–silica glass, replaces the sodium ions in the surface with lithium ions by immersion in a high-temperature molten lithium sulphate bath, and finishes with titania-nucleated crystallization of β-eucryptite crystals in the glass.[2] In both these treatments the glass article ends up with its surface layer under compression.

In order to get a product that is practically transparent, the remaining vitreous matrix should have the same refractive index as the β-eucryptite crystals. This of course imposes limits on the composition of the mother glass. The refractive indices of the glass and the crystal can never be matched completely, since β-eucryptite is anisotropic; the resulting product therefore is somewhat cloudy.

The second method described is closely connected with a technique developed earlier by HOOD and STOOKEY.[3]

3.4 Strengthening by Ion Exchange

3.41 Exchange Above the Annealing Temperature

Some six years ago HOOD and STOOKEY published a method of strengthening a glass by replacing Na^+ ions in the surface layer by Li^+ ions from a bath of a molten lithium salt.[4] The ion exchange has to take place *above* the annealing temperature of the glass. On cooling, the bulk glass shrinks more than the surface layer, by which process the surface layer builds up a compressive stress.

For ordinary soda–lime–glasses a permanent strengthening up to 20 kg/mm² can be obtained, as measured on rods of 6 mm diam. The layer should again be of the order of some 50μ.

3.42 Exchange Below the Annealing Temperature

This is another method for the strengthening of glass, which was described independently for the first time by KISTLER[5] and by ACLOQUE and TOCHON,[6] and is based on somewhat different principles. Here the Na^+ ion is replaced by a K^+ ion in a molten potassium sulphate bath, but now some 100°C. *below* the annealing temperature. Since the K^+ ion is much bigger than the Na^+ ion, a compressive stress is developed in the surface layer. This compressive stress is maintained during the cooling process to room temperature, in spite of the effect of the difference in expansion, which now works in the opposite and thus in the wrong direction.

Ion exchange should take place at least some 75°C. below the annealing temperature, in order to prevent relaxation of the built-in compressive stress. On the other hand, the temperature should be as high as possible so as to help the diffusion of the sodium and the potassium ions.

Generally speaking the diffusion is rather slow: one can achieve some improvement of conventional soda–lime glasses in a reasonable time in this way. However, the strength is not maintained after damage—in other words, the layer is too thin. If the exchange has taken place for some months, however, the layer is sufficiently thick and then gives rise to permanent strengthening.

There is some real hope, as has been shown by CORNELISSEN,[7] that conditions can be found under which objects can be strengthened permanently in this manner within a reasonable time. In this way the objects can be formed with a strength of some 60 to 100 kg/mm². One thing is certain. The tensile strength of steel, according to official sources, is of the order of some 60 kg/mm². "Glass stronger than steel" is no longer a slogan, it is a reality. This achievement is due partly to the recent developments in glass-ceramics, though it cannot be denied that there seem to be other means of achieving this aim.

REFERENCES

1. Corning Glass Works, *Progr. Report No. 3*, " Pyroceram 9606-9608 "; Lillie, H. R., *Glass Technology*, **1**, 115, 1960; Sawai, I., *Glass Technology*, **2**, 243, 1961; Robredo, J., *Verres Réfractaires*, **16**, 225, 282, 1962; Reser, M. K., Symposium on Nucleation and Crystallization in Glasses and Melts, Columbus, Ohio, 1962; Maurer, R., and Stookey, S. D., " Progress in Ceramic Science " (Oxford, 1962), pp. 77-102.
2. Olcott, J. S., and Stookey, S. D., " Advances in Glass Technology " (Technical Papers, VIth International Congress on Glass) (New York, 1962), p. 397.
3. Hood, H. P., and Stookey, S. D., *U.S. Pat.* 2,779,136, 1957.
4. Cf. also Garfinkel, H. M., Rothermal, D. L., and Stookey, S. D., " Advances in Glass Technology " (Technical Papers, VIth International Congress on Glass) (New York, 1962), p. 404.
5. Kistler, S. S., *Bull. Amer. Ceram. Soc.*, **40**, 231, 1961; *J. Amer. Ceram. Soc.*, **45**, 59, 1962.
6. Acloque, P., and Tochon, J., " Symposium sur la résistance du verre et les moyens de l'améliorer " (Compte Rendu, Charleroi 1962). p. 687.
7. Cornelissen, J., *Klei en Keramiek*, **13**, 187, 1963.

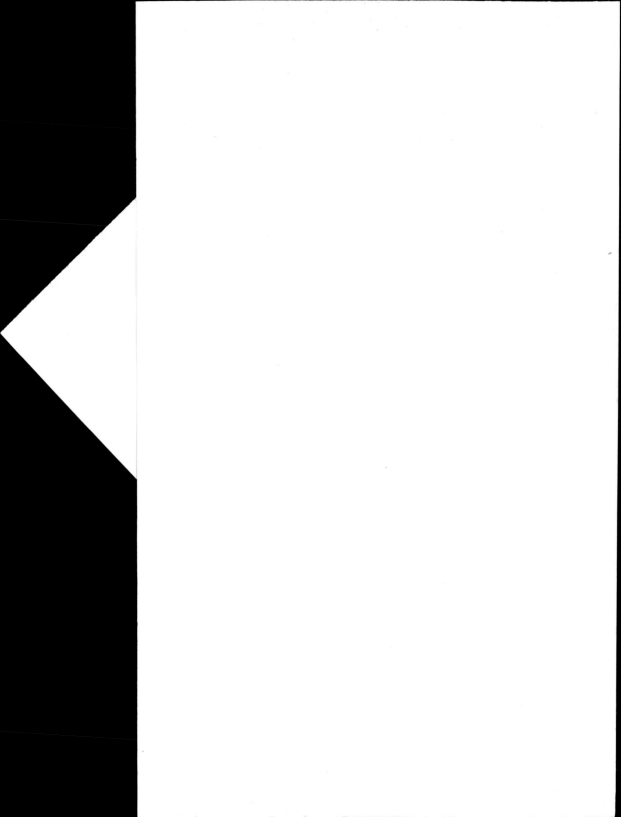

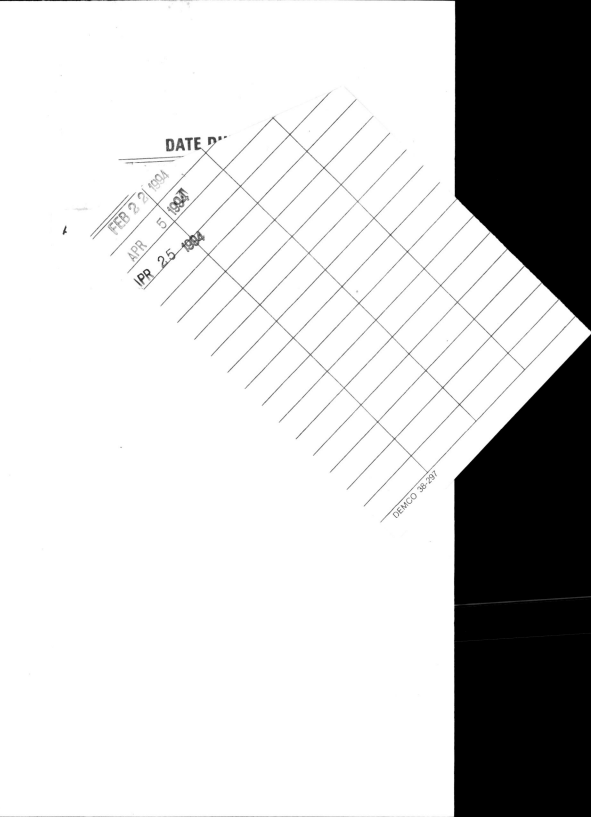

DATE DU...

FEB 2 2 1994

APR 5 1994

APR 2 5 1994

DEMCO 38-297